Synthetic Membranes:

Volume I

Desalination

Albin F. Turbak, EDITOR

ITT Rayonier Inc.

Based on the 20th Anniversary
Symposium honoring Drs. Loeb and
Sourirajan sponsored by the
Cellulose, Paper, and Textile
Division at the Second Chemical
Congress of the North American
Continent, Las Vegas, Nevada,
August 25–29, 1980.

ACS SYMPOSIUM SERIES 153

AMERICAN CHEMICAL SOCIETY
WASHINGTON, D. C.   1981

Library of Congress CIP Data

Synthetic membranes.
  (ACS symposium series, ISSN 0097–6156; 153–154)

  Includes bibliographies and index.

  Contents: v. 1. Desalination—v. 2. Hyper- and ultrafiltration uses.
  1. Membranes (Technology)—Congresses. I. Loeb,
Sidney. II. Sourirajan, S. III. Turbak, Albin F.,
1929–   . IV. American Chemical Society. Cellulose,
Paper, and Textile Division. V. Series.

TP159.M4S95   660.2'8424   81–1259
ISBN 0–8412–0622–8 (v. 1)   AACR2
ISBN 0–8412–0625–2 (set) ACSMC8 153 1–469 1981

ACS Symposium Series

M. Joan Comstock, *Series Editor*

FOREWORD

The ACS Sʏᴍᴘᴏsɪᴜᴍ Sᴇʀɪᴇs was founded in 1974 to provide
a medium for publishing symposia quickly in book form. The
format of the Series parallels that of the continuing Aᴅᴠᴀɴᴄᴇs
ɪɴ Cʜᴇᴍɪsᴛʀʏ Sᴇʀɪᴇs except that in order to save time the
papers are not typeset but are reproduced as they are sub-
mitted by the authors in camera-ready form. Papers are reviewed under the supervision of the Editors with the assistance
of the Series Advisory Board and are selected to maintain the
integrity of the symposia; however, verbatim reproductions of
previously published papers are not accepted. Both reviews
and reports of research are acceptable since symposia may
embrace both types of presentation.

CONTENTS

PREFACE

This volume is the result of a symposium honoring Drs. Sidney Loeb and S. Sourirajan on the 20th anniversary of their discovery of the first functionally useful reverse osmosis membrane. Both of these esteemed gentlemen participated as plenary speakers and described not only how their membrane originated but also reviewed membrane theory and put the membrane field into present and future perspective.

During this four-day symposium membrane experts from 13 countries participated in paying tribute to these fine scientists and 55 papers were presented covering a vast spectrum of current membrane uses. All but four of these papers are included in this symposium series. The large number of papers necessitated publication in two volumes. This first volume, covering 27 papers, is dedicated to desalination in the areas of (1) membrane genesis and theory, (2) commercial use, (3) modified and composite membranes, and (4) noncellulosic membranes. The second volume covers membrane usage in food, medical, and biopolymer fields and in the separation of gases and organic solutes from waste streams.

The commercial and growth potential of reverse osmosis can be appreciated best by realizing that there are presently over 300 membrane plants in operation economically supplying millions of gallons of potable water throughout the world. Japan alone now is producing over 21 MGD (80,000 m³/d) with the largest single reverse osmosis plant delivering over 3.5 MGD. Similar situations exist in Israel and Saudi Arabia. This past May the Florida Aqueduct Authority broke ground for a 3 MGD facility.

When technology such as this exists it is difficult to understand why, for example, many cities throughout the world suffer drought alerts and water-rationing fears while mighty rivers nearby daily spew untold billions of gallons of water into the ocean. As politics begins to catch up with technology, reverse osmosis will be one area that justifiably will expand.

With each such expansion our debt to and appreciation of the pioneering contributions of Drs. Loeb and Sourirajan will develop even deeper meaning. It was a real pleasure to have been part of this tribute and I would like to take this opportunity to thank all of the participants for their wonderful spirit of cooperation in making this occasion such a great success.

ALBIN F. TURBAK
I.T.T. Rayonier Inc.
Eastern Research Division
Whippany, NJ 07981
December 24, 1980.

S. Sourirajan, Albin Turbak, and Sidney Loeb

DEDICATION

Twenty years ago two researchers laboring diligently at the University of California at Los Angeles developed the first modified asymmetric membranes which seemed to have commercial potential for what was to become the exciting field that today is known as hyperfiltration or reverse osmosis. Since that time, these dedicated scientists have given freely of themselves and their talents not only to further contribute technically, but also to help guide, teach, and train others to grow in this frontier area.

It is little wonder then that so many contributors from so many countries throughout the world responded so enthusiastically to the initial announcement regarding the organization of a symposium to recognize, honor, and pay tribute to Drs. Sidney Loeb and S. Sourirajan on the 20th anniversary of their initial contribution.

From the beginning it was apparent that this four-day symposium covering a seeming myriad of membrane information and uses would be one of the major events of the Fall 1980 Las Vegas A.C.S. National Meeting. This symposium, highlighted by plenary lectures from Drs. Loeb and Sourirajan, had an outstanding attendance. Even on the fourth day there were still more people attending this symposium than normally are present for the initial phases of most other sessions. This in itself says more than anyone could say regarding the universal interest in membranes and the high esteem in which Sid Loeb and S. Sourirajan are held by their peers throughout the world.

Today their initial work on the preparation of suitable asymmetric membranes has touched nearly every aspect of life including uses in water purification, food technology, biological separations, waste treatment, medical applications, and bioengineering, and this appears to be just the beginning.

I know that I speak for all of their many friends when I take this opportunity to wish Drs. Loeb and Sourirajan continued good health and, if possible, even more success in their future research and development efforts.

ALBIN F. TURBAK

The Loeb–Sourirajan Membrane:
How It Came About

SIDNEY LOEB

Chemical Engineering Department, Ben-Gurion University of the Negev, Beersheva, Israel

In the early 1950's Professor Samuel Yuster at the University of California, Los Angeles (UCLA) conceived the idea of using the Gibbs adsorption equation as a guideline to find techniques for producing fresh water from brines (1,2). The Gibbs equation is given by:

$$U = -(1/\nu RT)(\partial\sigma/\partial\ln a)_{T,Ar} \tag{1}$$

where U is the adsorption of solute per unit area of surface, ν is the number of ions into which the electrolyte can dissociate, R is the gas constant, T is the absolute temperature, σ is the surface tension of the solution, a is the activity of the solute, and Ar is the area of the surface of the solution. According to this equation, brines in contact with air or other hydrophobic surfaces, will have a layer of relatively pure water, 3 or 4 Angstroms thick, adjacent to the interface. Therefore it should be possible to 'skim off' this fresh water, and in fact the project was called "Sea Water Demineralization by the 'Surface-Skimming' Process" until 1960.

After funding by the State of California began in the mid-50s, efforts were made to skim fresh water, first with fine capillary tubes and second with bubble generation to transport the (hopefully) water-enriched solution surrounding the bubbles. Both efforts failed.

I. Shift to Reverse Osmosis - Discovery of the Semipermeability of Cellulose Acetate.

The first success at UCLA was reported in 1958 (1,2). A flat plastic film, supported by a porous plate, was used. The film was pressurized by a salt solution such that water permeation could occur by virtue of the pressure drop across the film and a more concentrated brine could be left behind. This was

0097–6156/81/0153–0001$05.00/0

reverse osmosis to all intents and purposes. Pressure was obtained by a hand-operated hydraulic pump, and this was adequate
considering the permeation rates that were obtained.

A commercially available cellulose acetate film which we
would now describe as homogeneous or isotropic, gave the results
shown in Row 2 of Table I. The volumetric permeation rate of
water per unit membrane area, called the water permeation flux
J_1,m^3/m^2day, and the water permeation constant, A, m^3/m^2 day atm
were both very low, but a salt rejection of 94 percent was obtained. We define:

$$J_1 = A(\Delta P - \Delta \Pi) \tag{2}$$

but say that for our purposes:

$$J_1 = A(P - \Pi) \tag{3}$$

where ΔP and $\Delta \Pi$ are the hydraulic and osmotic pressure differences across the wall of the membrane, P and Π are the hydraulic
and osmotic pressures on the feed brine. Also:

$$\text{Salt rejection, \%} = (100)(1 - \frac{\text{solute conc.permeate}}{\text{solute conc.feed brine}}) \tag{4}$$

Sourirajan took a few milliliters of desalinized water
(collected over a period of a few days in the 15.5 cm^2 cell), to
the home of Professor Yuster, by then terminally ill. Nevertheless he excitedly got out of bed and predicted (correctly) that
if it could be done with a few milliliters it could be done with
a million gallons. (This anecdote was told to me by someone who
was present, a relative of Shuster's).

Unbeknownst to Sourirajan, Breton and Reid working at the
University of Florida under Office of Saline Water sponsorship,
also found that cellulose acetate is semipermeable to sea water
electrolytes (3, 4). Comparative results of Breton and Reid are
shown in Row 1 of Table I. It can be seen that the water permeation constant is considerably higher than that of Sourirajan.
This difference is largely accounted for by the difference in
thickness of the homogeneous membranes involved, such that the
product of water permeation constant and membrane thickness is
about the same for both membranes. The constant arises from the
diffusion model of permeation in which:

$$A \sim D_1/(\text{Effective membrane thickness}) \tag{5}$$

where D_1 is diffusivity of the permeate in the membrane. We see
then that with homogeneous membranes, for which the effective
membrane thickness is also λ, the total thickness, $A\lambda$ is proportional to membrane diffusivity.

TABLE I

PERFORMANCE OF HOMOGENEOUS AND ASYMMETRIC CELLULOSE ACETATE MEMBRANES

Investigator legend:
B – Breton, R – Reid, Y – Yuster, S – Sourirajan, Be – Bernstein, L – Loeb

Fabricator legend:
B – Breton, DP – Du Pont, S and S – Schleicher and Schuell, L-S – Loeb and Sourirajan

Investigator	Morphology Fabricator	% acetylation / Total thickness λ microns	Type of feed brine solute concentration %	Pressures, Hydraulic, P Osmotic Net driving $(P - \pi)$, atmospheres	Water permeation flux, J_1 (Note 1) $\dfrac{m^3}{m^2\,day}$	Water permeation constant, A (Note 2) $\dfrac{m^3}{m^2\,day\,atm}$	Constant times total thickness A $\dfrac{m^3\ micron}{m^2\,day\,atm}$	Solute rejection %
B – Ref.3, p.21	Homogeneous B	43% $\lambda = 6$	not given	not given	not given	$(1.2)(10)^{-4}$	$(7.2)(10)^{-4}$	99+
Y, S & B Ref.1, p.45	Homogeneous DP	% not known $\lambda = 30$	NaCl 3.7%	P = 85, π = 30, $P-\pi$ = 55	0.0013	$(0.24)(10)^{-4}$	$(7.2)(10)^{-4}$	94
L & S – Ref.11 p.125	Asymmetric S & S heated to? °C	% not known $\lambda = 100$	Sea water 3.5%	P = 102, π = 25	0.073	$(9.5)(10)^{-4}$	$(950)(10)^{-4}$	92
L & S–Ref.11 p.127	Asymmetric L-S heated to 80 °C	39.8% $\lambda = 100$	Sea water 4%	P = 102, π = 29, $P-\pi$ = 73	0.35	$(48)(10)^{-4}$	$(4800)(10)^{-4}$	99

(1) To convert to gal/ft²day multiply by 24.5

(2) To convert to gal/ft²day psi multiply by 5/3

It was recognized by both the Florida and UCLA groups that economic utilization of reverse osmosis depended on obtaining a great increase in flux(and water permeation constant) without serious loss in electrolyte rejection properties. It was also recognized that one path to increased flux lay in decreased membrane thickness.

II. Testing of Materials Other than Cellulose Acetate.

In the summer of 1958 Sourirajan accepted me as a partner. In the next six months a number of plastic films were tested(5,6) but none were equal to cellulose acetate. Among other negative results was an attempt to increase flux by heating of the membrane.The hope was that some permanent expansion could be induced and that such expansion would enlarge pores thus increasing flux. Unfortunately it was found that heating contracted the membrane.

A number of tests were made with porous Teflon sheet. Teflon was chosen for its hydrophobic nature as required by the Gibbs equation. A series of sintering experiments were made to find just the right combination of heat and pressure which would reduce the pores to the proper dimension as required by the Gibbs equation. No such combination was found except two which gave a low level desalination for a short period. As a result of these tests my own enthusiasm waned for further use of the Gibbs adsorption equation as a primary guideline to membrane development.

III. Tests With Schleicher and Schuell Cellulose Acetate Membranes.

Cellulose acetate membranes were then reconsidered with emphasis on porosity to increase flux. In 1959 we tested such porous membranes extensively(7,8,9,10). These membranes, made in Germany and marketed by the Schleicher and Schuell(S & S) Co. of Keene,N.H.,were actually ultrafiltration membranes and only the "Ultrafine, Superdense" grade was useful for us. This grade allegedly contains pores of 50 Angstroms or less. Nevertheless, as received, the S & S membrane gave a very high flux and no desalination,as expected from an ultrafiltration membrane.

The S & S membranes were immersed in dilute alcohol solutions during shipment and storage. The alcohol could be replaced by water, but the membrane could not be allowed to dry or it would shrink in an irreversible manner to become a useless membrane. Recalling the unsuccessful tests of Section II we heated the S & S membranes under water to temperatures in the order of 80° - $90^{\circ}C$. By this means the desalinizing capability of the membrane could be increased proportionately to the increase in heating temperatures, i.e., the membrane could be "tailored" to the desalinizing job at hand. The water permeation flux was an inverse function of the heating temperature.

A curious problem arose in the testing of the S & S membrane.

The results with the same membrane were sometimes good and sometimes very bad, i.e., rejection might be quite good the first time
a membrane would be mounted in the test cell, bad the next time,
good the next two times, etc. Naturally a leak was suspected and
naturally it was attempted to fix the blame on Ed Selover, who
made the cell. However, it was finally realized that the incidence
of failures about equalled the incidence of successes with the
randomness of results obtained when a coin is flipped, and from
there it was correctly postulated that when one side of the membrane faced the brine,results would be different from those when
the other side was against the brine. The membrane did indeed
have a "rough" side and a "smooth" side and it was the rough side
which had to face the brine. This was our first encounter with
membrane asymmetry or anisotropy.

Comparative results with the Schleicher and Schuell membrane
are shown in the third row of Table I(11). The flux and the water
permeation constant increased by a factor of 40 over the previous
results. Furthermore Aλ, the product of water permeation constant
and total membrane thickness increased by a factor of 130. The
most obvious explanation for these results is that the effective
membrane thickness was much less than the total membrane thickness.
Thus the concept of membrane asymmetry was also supported by a
comparison of Schleicher and Schuell membrane performance with
that of homogeneous membranes.

The study of the S & S membrane provided several important
steps in the development of the technique for fabrication of the
Loeb- Sourirajan membrane, viz.,storage under water, heating under
water to an appropriate temperature to tailor membrane performance
properties, and finally recognition that membrane asymmetry may
play an important role in the obtainment of a sufficiently large
flux for economic operations. Such recognition was thrust upon us
by the experimental results. It would be nice to say that we made
analytical calculations which indicated a priori the necessity
for a very thin skin surmounting a porous substructure, but that
isn't the way it happened.

IV. The Work of Dobry.

The S & S film represented a quantum jump in membrane performance. However,it still wasn't good enough to meet our goal. Specifically we could not produce potable water, less than 500 ppm
salt, from sea water in one pass through the S & S film,no matter
how high we heated the film. Therefore we undertook to make our
own membranes, with the following guidelines(11):
1) cellulose acetate would be used as the film matrix;
2) acetone or other solvent would be used in the casting solution;
3) some means for making the film permeable to water would be
employed.

As a result of a literature search it appeared that a technique described in 1936 by Dobry(12), a French investigator,might

meet all three of the above guidelines. She dissolved incompletely
acetylated cellulose acetate (i.e., not all hydroxyl groups had
been replaced by acetyl groups) in an aqueous solution of a perchlorate such as magnesium perchlorate, $Mg(ClO_4)_2$. She then
spread the solution in a thin film on a glass plate and plunged
it under water. The $Mg(ClO_4)_2$ diffused into the water leaving a
porous film of cellulose acetate. (Mme Ducleaux, nee Dobry, has
been informed of this symposium. She conveys felicitations and
also her best wishes to all the participants in the symposium(13)).

V. Fabrication Technique for the Loeb-Sourirajan Membrane.

We followed the instructions of Dobry, making up solutions
containing 4,8, and 10 percent of cellulose acetate (Eastman) in
saturated aqueous magnesium perchlorate solutions(14). Membranes
made by immersion of such solutions in water were far too porous
for our purposes; i.e. no desalination was obtained. It was believed that the ratio of cellulose acetate to $Mg(ClO_4)_2$ had to be
increased, but above 10% of cellulose acetate in the saturated
solution the casting solution viscosity was too high. As an alternative the $Mg(ClO_4)_2$ could be reduced by using an undersaturated
perchlorate solution, but then the cellulose acetate was not
soluble. The solution to this problem, suggested by Lloyd Graham,
a graduate student on the project, was partially to replace the
$Mg(ClO_4)_2$ solution with acetone, a solvent for cellulose acetate.
The resulting 4-component solution was just what was needed.
Since the $Mg(ClO_4)_2$ need no longer play a solvent role, its concentration could be optimized for its role as "pore-producing
agent" or "flux-enhancer" depending upon whether one thought of
it from the standpoint of cause or effect. A typically good casting solution contained cellulose acetate, acetone, water, and magnesium perchlorate in the weight percentages 22.2, 66.7, 10.0 and 1·1
(15). Thus finally the magnesium perchlorate was only a small
part of the total casting mix, but neither it nor water could be
eliminated without a disastrous reduction in membrane performance.
Membranes could now be cast with appropriate porous properties such that the previously mentioned "tailoring" operation
could be carried out, i.e., the underwater heating of the membrane to a temperature which would provide adequate desalination.
For best results two other features were found to be useful, as
discussed in the detailed fabrication instructions of Reference
15. First, the casting was carried out with all components, chemical and mechanical, at a low temperature, 0° to $-10^\circ C$; Second,
the as-cast film had to be immersed in ice water within a short
time after casting.
As with the modified S & S membrane, the L-S membrane was
found to be asymmetric. The side of the membrane away from the
casting surface had to be in contact with the feed brine during
service.
The performance of an L-S membrane heated to $80^\circ C$ is shown

in the last row of Table I. The improvement in water permeation
constant over the modified S and S membrane is by a factor of
five and would be considerably more if the L-S membrane were fabricated to give the same rejection, 92%, as stated for the S and
S membrane. For the stated rejection of 99 percent it is also
instructive to compare the L - S membrane with the previously
discussed membranes by examining the last column of Table I. The
further dramatic increase of $\Lambda\lambda$, the product of water permeation
constant and total membrane thickness, again supports the asymmetry postulate (See Section III), and can be explained by a ratio
of effective to total membrane thickness considerably lower even
than that with the S and S membrane.

VI. Summary.

In retrospect, (a vantage point from which accomplished
research frequently appears as a marvel of logically sequential
steps) the development of the Loeb-Sourirajan membrane can be
attributed to: a determination to apply the Gibbs adsorption
equation to desalination; the discovery of the semipermeability
of cellulose acetate; the prior existence of a cellulose acetate
ultrafilter which, by a novel heat treatment could be made into
an asymmetric reverse osmosis membrane; the recognition of this
asymmetry and its importance in obtaining a flux greatly increased over that of previously-tested membranes, which were
homogeneous; the discovery by an earlier investigator of the
special properties of aqueous perchlorate solutions vis-a-vis
incompletely acetylated cellulose acetate; and finally utilization
of all this hard-won material, together with further novel modifications, to produce a working reverse osmosis membrane.

VII. Acknowledgements

To the people and legislators of the State of California who
have had the patience and foresight to support this and other
desalination projects at the University from the middle 1950's
until now.
    To Emeritus Professor Everett Howe of the Berkeley Campus.
Professor Howe was a very effective statewide coordinator of
University Desalination Research, a job which required skillful
liaison between the legislature and the research workers, in
addition to a technological purview of the various projects.
    To Professor Llewellyn Boelter, deceased, who had overall
cognizance of the UCLA effort, as Dean of Engineering, and who
also contributed, in my opinion, by virtue of his qualities as a
real human being.
    To Edward Selover who has been involved with mechanical
component design and fabrication at UCLA since the beginning of
the project. It is only after I have been deprived of his work
that I have realized how much he contributed to the project. He
still does.

The above acknowledgements cover the period from the inception of the project until 1960. Thus subsequent important contributions from UCLA such as that of Manjikian, and the leadership of McCutchan after 1966 are not discussed nor the tremendous body of knowledge later contributed by the ever-widening reverse osmosis community, the United States part of which was largely established by the Office of Saline Water, U.S. Dept. of the Interior.

VIII. Literature Cited

1. Yuster,S.T., Sourirajan,S., Bernstein,K., "Sea Water Demineralization by the 'Surface Skimming' Process", University of California (UCLA), Dept. of Engineering,March,1958,Rept.58-26.

2. Sourirajan, S., "Sea Water Demineralization by the 'Surface Skimming' Process",UCLA Dept. of Engineering, May,1958, Sea Water Research Quarterly Progress Repts. 58-46, 48, 50, 51 (Collected in one report).

3. Breton,E.J.Jr., "Water and Ion Flow Through Imperfect Osmotic Membranes", Office of Saline Water,U.S.Dept. of the Interior, April,1957,Res.&Dev.Prog.Rept.16.

4. Reid,C.E.,Breton.E.J.,"Water and Ion Flow Across Cellulosic Membranes", J. Appl.Polymer Sci., 1959, I (Issue No.2),133-143.

5. Sourirajan,S., "Sea Water Demineralization by the 'Surface Skimming' Process", UCLA Dept. of Engineering,June-Aug,1958, Sea Water Research Quarterly Progress Rept. 58-65.

6. Loeb,S., Sourirajan,S., "Sea Water Demineralization by the 'Surface Skimming'Process", UCLA,Dept.of Engineering,Nov,1958, Sea Water Research Quarterly Progress Rept. 59-3.

Loeb,S.,"Sea Water Demineralization by the 'Surface Skimming' Process, UCLA Dept. of Engineering, Sea Water Research, Quarterly Progress Repts. (OPR):

7. Dec. 1958 - Feb,1959 OPR 59-28.

8. March-May,1959, OPR 59-46 .

9. July-Sept, 1959, QPR 60-5.

10. Loeb,S., "Characteristics of Porous Acetyl Cellulose Membranes for Pressure Desalination of Dilute Sodium Chloride Solutions", Master of Science Thesis,UCLA Dept. of Engineering,May,1959.

11. Loeb,S., Sourirajan,S., "Sea Water Demineralization by Means of an Osmotic Membrane", American Chemical Society,Advances in Chemistry Series, ACS 38, 1963, 117-132 .

12. Dobry, A., "Les Perchlorates Comme Solvants de la Cellulose et de ses Derives",Bull. de la Societe Chim. de France, 1936, 5^e Serie,t.3,312-318.

13. Private Communication from Mme Ducleaux, 27 June, 1980 .

14. Loeb,S., Graham,L., "Sea Water Demineralization by Means of a Semipermeable Membrane", UCLA Dept. of Engineering,Oct-Dec , 1959, Sea Water Research Quarterly Progress Report 60-26.

15. Loeb,S., Sourirajan,S., "Sea Water Demineralization by Means of a Semipermeable Membrane", UCLA Dept. of Engineering, July, 1960, Sea Water Research Rept. 60-60.

RECEIVED December 4, 1980.

Reverse Osmosis: A New Field of Applied Chemistry and Chemical Engineering

S. SOURIRAJAN

Division of Chemistry, National Research Council of Canada, Ottawa, Canada, K1A 0R9

First I wish to thank the American Chemical Society and the officers of the Cellulose Division for organizing this symposium. I deeply appreciate this honor, and I would like to share this honor equally with every one of my past and present associates who have together contributed the most in all work on reverse osmosis with which I am associated.

In this lecture, I wish to call attention to some of the fundamental aspects of reverse osmosis, and point out that what we are commemorating today (1) is truly the emergence of a *new* field of applied chemistry and chemical engineering, immensely relevant to the welfare of mankind.

Reverse Osmosis and Reverse Osmosis Membranes

"Reverse osmosis" is the popular *name* of a general process for the separation of substances in solution. The process consists in letting the solution flow under pressure through an *appropriate* porous membrane (called the "reverse osmosis membrane") and withdrawing the membrane permeated product generally at atmospheric pressure and surrounding temperature. The product is enriched in one or more constituents of the mixture, leaving a solution of higher or lower concentration on the high pressure side of the membrane. No heating of the membrane is necessary, and no phase change in product recovery is involved in this separation process.

Reverse osmosis is applicable for the separation, concentration, and/or fractionation of inorganic or organic substances in aqueous or nonaqueous solutions in the liquid or the gaseous phase, and hence it opens a new and versatile field of separation technology in chemical process engineering. Many reverse osmosis processes are also popularly called "ultra-filtration", and many reverse osmosis membranes are also practically useful as ultrafilters.

Object of This Lecture

The emergence of reverse osmosis is a major *scientific*
event in the field of applied chemistry and chemical engineering;
all applications and technology of reverse osmosis arise from the
science of reverse osmosis; a fundamental approach to the science
of reverse osmosis, and the development of this science in all
its aspects based on such approach are absolutely necessary for
the effective utilization of reverse osmosis for any application
whatsoever. To present this point of view is the object of this
lecture.

Reverse osmosis is commonly recognized as a technological
accomplishment, and indeed, it is; however, it is seldom
recognized as an accomplishment in applied science. Such lack
of recognition and its consequences retard the scientific and
industrial progress of reverse osmosis; therefore, this situation
must change.

Fundamental Question on Reverse Osmosis

From the point of view of the science of reverse osmosis,
the fundamental question is "what governs reverse osmosis
separations?". This is an intensely practical question; because,
to the extent this question is answered correctly, precisely,
and completely, to that extent - and, to that extent only - the
applications and technology of reverse osmosis can be made
effective. Further, this overriding question becomes specially
significant when one considers the obvious potential applications
of reverse osmosis, and their immense social relevance in the
context of today.

Reverse osmosis touches many vital areas of everyday life -
such as water, air, food, medicine and energy. The most well
known application of reverse osmosis is of course in the broad
area of water treatment including water desalination, water
purification, water pollution control, water reuse, and waste
recovery. This application is currently under growing industrial
utilization in many parts of the world. That reverse osmosis is
equally applicable for gas separations is much less well-known,
but no less significant. Applications such as oxygen enrichment
in air, helium recovery from natural gas, air pollution control,
separation and purification of industrial gases, and treatment
of gases arising in coal, petroleum and biomass conversion
processes, though industrially very important, are far less
developed today. From an economic stand point, potentially the
most profitable use of reverse osmosis is in its applications in
the area of food processing involving separation, concentration
and/or fractionation of proteins, food sugars and flavor
components, and treatment of milk, whey, fruit juices, instant
foods and beverages. Similar operations in the pharmaceutical
industry, and the applications of reverse osmosis membranes in

medical and biomedical areas such as kidney machines, medical
implantations and controlled drug release devices illustrate the
relevance of reverse osmosis and reverse osmosis membranes in
the area of medicine. The relevance of reverse osmosis to the
field of energy is of far reaching significance. The use of
reverse osmosis membranes for direct production of energy is
still a virgin field, but the potential is easy to recognize.
When a river of relatively pure water joins a sea of salt water,
we have in effect a naturally occurring chemical waterfall in
terms of chemical potential gradient; using a reverse osmosis
membrane at the river water-sea water junction, the difference
in chemical potential of water can be converted directly into
mechanical or electrical energy. Indirectly, the relevance of
reverse osmosis to the area of energy production and conservation
is even far greater, by virtue of the applicability of reverse
osmosis for the separation, concentration, and fractionation of
constituents in nonaqueous solutions, and also in aqueous
solutions containing high concentrations of organic solutes;
consequently, a large part of distillation operations in
petroleum refining, synthetic fuel, and fermentation industries
can be replaced by reverse osmosis operations.

Key to Industrial Progress of Reverse Osmosis

The terms "osmosis" and "semipermeable", which are popularly
associated with reverse osmosis processes and reverse osmosis
membranes respectively, have absolutely no science-content in
them, and they contributed nothing to the emergence of reverse
osmosis. Explaining reverse osmosis as the reverse *of* osmosis is
just incorrect. Under isothermal operating conditions, the
tendency for material transport is always in the direction of
lower chemical potential in *both* osmosis and reverse osmosis;
hence reverse osmosis is *not* the reverse of osmosis. Further,
simply calling a reverse osmosis membrane as a "semipermeable"
membrane does not, and cannot, *explain* why the membrane is
semipermeable in the first place. Therefore, in spite of enormous
amount of published literature on the subject, a comprehensive
answer to the fundamental question raised earlier has not yet
emerged. When this is realized, it should be clear that the key
to industrial progress of reverse osmosis lies in understanding
fully the fundamental basis of reverse osmosis separations and
assiduously developing the overall science of reverse osmosis
(based on such understanding) suitable for its effective practical
utilization in all its applications; that of course is not
enough; it is indeed absolutely important that the necessary
technology of reverse osmosis is developed fully and brought into
the market place to serve the society. For such industrial
progress, the primary problem of reverse osmosis today is not
technology; it is *understanding* which is the basis of technology.

Emergence of Reverse Osmosis Processes and Reverse Osmosis Membranes

The origin of the development of the first practical cellulose acetate reverse osmosis membrane for sea water desalination, announced in 1960 (1), was the conception of reverse osmosis itself in 1956 based on an *appreciation* of the already well-known chemistry at interfaces, of which the Gibbs adsorption equation (2) is just one expression. This equation indicates that surface forces can give rise to steep concentration gradients at interfaces. Such concentration gradient at an interface in effect constitutes positive or negative adsorption, or *preferential sorption*, of one of the constituents of the solution at the interface. The details of such preferential sorption must necessarily depend on the nature of the interface involved. This means that, for a given membrane-solution system, the details of preferential sorption at the membrane-solution interface depend on the chemical nature of the *surface* of the membrane material in contact with the solution. Since surface forces are natural and ever-present, preferential sorption at a membrane-solution interface is also natural and inevitable, and the concentration profile of the solution in the interfacial region is different from that of the bulk solution that is sufficiently away from the membrane surface. By letting the preferentially sorbed interfacial fluid under the influence of surface forces, flow out under pressure through suitably created pores (i.e., interstices or void spaces) in the membrane material, a new physicochemical separation process unfolds itself. That was how reverse osmosis was conceived in 1956. In retrospect, looking back into the literature (3,4,5), even that conception was not fundamentally new. What was indeed new, is the fact that the above conception arose, independently, direct from a true appreciation of chemistry at interfaces, and such appreciation naturally generated a program of dedicated work to translate that conception into practice to achieve a desired objective resulting in the development in 1960 of the now well-known asymmetric porous cellulose acetate reverse osmosis membranes (6a,6b) for water desalination applications. This approach to reverse osmosis is designated in the literature as the "preferential sorption-capillary flow mechanism" for reverse osmosis, schematically illustrated in Figure 1. The various scientific consequences of this mechanism are discussed in the literature (6a,7,8). It needs only to be pointed out here that the above mechanism was not proposed as an explanation of reverse osmosis after its accomplishment; on the other hand, reverse osmosis processes *and* reverse osmosis membranes emerged from that mechanism, and the above 1960-development itself was just the first, and indeed a very befitting, practical expression of the approach represented by that mechanism.

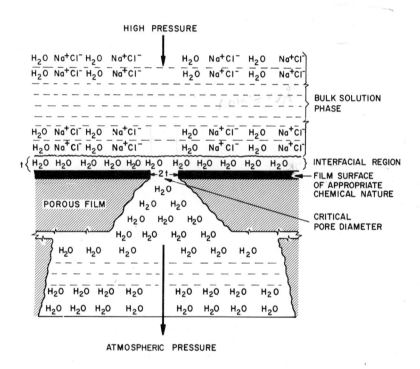

Figure 1. Schematic of preferential sorption–capillary flow mechanism for reverse-osmosis separations of sodium chloride from aqueous solutions

The Approach and The Science

According to the above mechanism, reverse osmosis separation
is governed by two distinct factors, namely (i) an equilibrium
effect which is concerned with the details of preferential
sorption in the vicinity of the membrane surface, and (ii) a
kinetic effect which is concerned with the mobilities of solute
and solvent through membrane pores. While the former
(equilibrium effect) is governed by repulsive and attractive
potential gradients in the vicinity of the membrane surface, the
latter (mobility effect) is governed both by the potential
gradients (equilibrium effect) *and* the steric effects associated
with the structure and size of molecules relative to those of
pores on the membrane surface.

Consequently, an appropriate chemical nature of the membrane
surface in contact with the solution *and* the existence of pores
of appropriate size and number on the area of the membrane at the
interface *together* consitutute the indispensable twin-requirement
for the practical success of this separation process. For
reverse osmosis separation to take place, at least one of the
constituents of the feed solution must be preferentially sorbed
at the membrane-solution interface; this means that a
concentration gradient, arising from the influence of surface
forces, must exist in the vicinity of the membrane surface in
contact with the feed solution. Further, to be practically
useful, the reverse osmosis membrane must have a microporous and
heterogeneous surface layer at all levels of solute separation,
its entire porous structure must be asymmetric, and there should
be no chemical reaction between the constituents of the feed
solution and the material of the membrane surface. There is no
one particular level of solute separation or solvent flux
uniquely specific to any given *material* of the membrane surface.
With an appropriate chemical nature for the material of the
membrane surface, a wide range of solute separations in reverse
osmosis is possible by simply changing the average pore size on
the membrane surface and the operating conditions of the
experiment. Aside from the process requirements indicated above,
reverse osmosis is fundamentally *not limited* to any particular
solvent, solute, membrane material, level of solute separation,
level of solvent flux, or operating conditions of the experiment.
Consequently, the overall science of reverse osmosis arising from
the above approach unfolds itself through proper integration of
the physicochemical parameters governing preferential sorption of
solvent or solute at membrane-solution interfaces, materials
science of reverse osmosis membranes, and the engineering science
of reverse osmosis transport and process design. While there is
still a long way to go towards the full development of the
science of reverse osmosis in all its aspects, considerable
progress has already been made (8,9); that this progress offers
a firm basis for a fuller understanding of reverse osmosis is
the theme of the rest of this paper.

For purposes of illustration, the following discussion, unless otherwise specified, is limited to single-solute aqueous feed solutions, cellulose acetate membranes, and reverse osmosis systems for which osmotic pressure effects are essentially negligible.

Surface Forces and Reverse Osmosis

Following the foregoing approach, if surface forces govern details of preferential sorption at membrane-solution interfaces and transport of solute and solvent through membrane pores in reverse osmosis, then, under otherwise identical experimental conditions, membrane performance (fraction solute separation, f, and membrane permeated product rate for a given area of membrane surface (PR)) must change, if there is any change in one or more of the following variables, namely, chemical nature of solute, that of solvent, that of the surface of the membrane material, and the porous structure of the membrane surface. That such change in membrane performance *always* takes place is common experience in all experimental work on reverse osmosis.

Further, the effects of surface forces on the concentration gradient at the membrane-solution interface, and the transport of solute and solvent through membrane pores during reverse osmosis must also account for the different types of changes in membrane performance experimentally observed as a result of changes in operating pressure or average pore size on the membrane surface, even when the chemical nature of solvent and that of the surface of the membrane material remain the same. For example, with cellulose acetate membranes and aqueous feed solution systems, at least four different types of changes in membrane performance data have been observed experimentally (10,11,12) depending on the chemical nature of the solute and the operating pressure involved, as illustrated in Figures 2(a) to 2(d).

Figure 2(a) shows experimental reverse osmosis data obtained with 0.5 molal NaCl-H_2O feed solutions (10); in this system, the osmotic pressure effects are significant because of the fairly high concentration of the feed solution. The results show that both solute separation and product rate increase with increase in operating pressure, while, at any given pressure, solute separation increases and product rate decreases with decrease in average pore size on the membrane surface. The reverse osmosis data given in Figures 2(b), 2(c), and 2(d) are for very dilute aqueous feed solutions for which osmotic pressures are practically negligible. Figure 2(b) shows that for the p-chlorophenol-water system (11), solute separation can be positive or negative depending on experimental conditions; solute separation can pass through a minimum with decrease in average pore size on membrane surface; further, at a sufficiently low operating pressure, solute separation is positive, and it

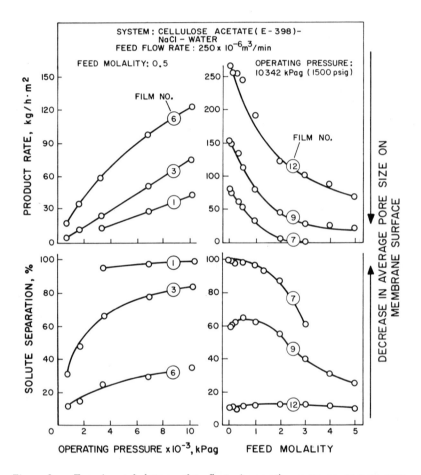

Figure 2a.   Experimental data on the effect of operating pressure, average pore size on membrane surface, and feed concentration on solute separation and product rate for the reverse osmosis system cellulose acetate membrane–sodium chloride–water (10)

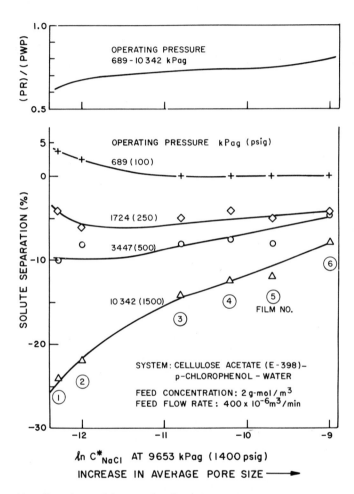

Figure 2b.   *Experimental data on the effect of operating pressure and average pore size on membrane surface on solute separation and (PR)/(PWP) ratio for the reverse osmosis system cellulose acetate membrane–p-chlorophenol–water (11)*

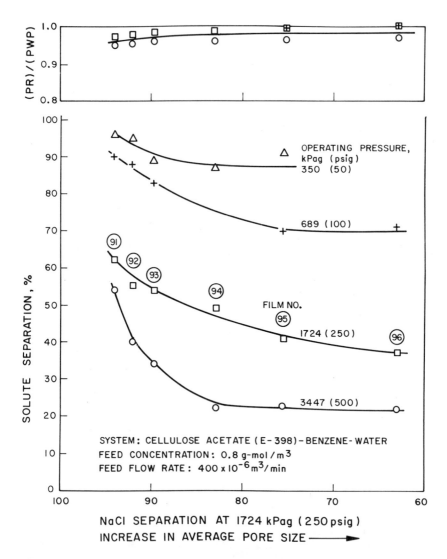

Figure 2c.   Experimental data on the effect of operating pressure and average pore size on membrane surface on solute separation and (PR)/(PWP) ratio for the reverse osmosis system cellulose acetate membrane–benzene–water (12)

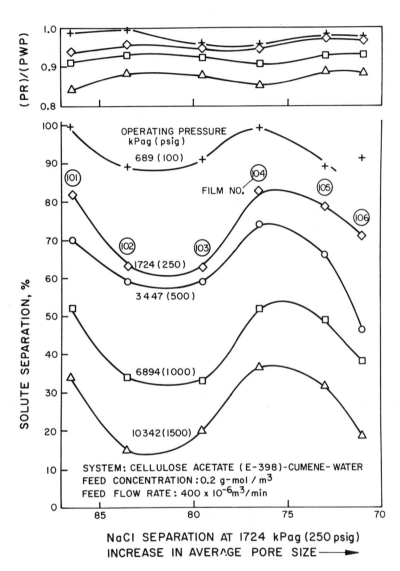

Figure 2d.   Experimental data on the effect of operating pressure and average pore size on membrane surface on solute separation and (PR)/(PWP) ratio for the reverse osmosis system cellulose acetate membrane–cumene–water (12)

increases with decrease in average pore size on the membrane
surface; at a sufficiently high operating pressure, solute
separation is negative, and it decreases with decrease in average
pore size on the membrane surface; and at all operating pressures,
the (PR)/(PWP) (product rate/pure water permeation rate) ratio is
less than unity, and it decreases with decrease in average pore
size on the membrane surface. Figures 2(c) and 2(d) show
experimental reverse osmosis data for the systems benzene-water
and cumene-water respectively (12). For both these systems,
solute separation is positive, and (PR)/(PWP) ratio is less than
unity under the indicated experimental conditions. Further, for
the system benzene-water, solute separation tends to decrease
with increase in operating pressure, and it tends to increase
with decrease in average pore size on the membrane surface; for
the system cumene-water, solute separation again tends to
decrease with increase in operating pressure, but it passes
through maxima and minima with decrease in average pore size on
the membrane surface.

The above results are significant. They show that reverse
osmosis is not limited to 100%, near 100%, or any particular
level of solute separation. Depending upon membrane-solution-
operating systems and other experimental conditions, reverse
osmosis can give rise to wide variations, and also different
types of variations, in solute separations. Reverse osmosis can
give rise to high separations or low separations, positive
separations, negative separations and all separations in-between,
increase in separation or decrease in separation with increase in
operating pressure, increase in separation or decrease in
separation with decrease in average pore size on the membrane
surface, and solute separations which pass through maxima and
minima with decrease in average pore size on the membrane
surface. Reverse osmosis *includes* all such variations in solute
separations; in particular, reverse osmosis is *not limited* to one
or any set of such variations. Consequently, any valid mechanism
of reverse osmosis must show that all such variations in solute
separations are indeed natural.

The preferential sorption-capillary flow mechanism of
reverse osmosis does that. In the NaCl-H$_2$O-cellulose acetate
membrane system, water is preferentially sorbed at the membrane-
solution interface due to electrostatic repulsion of ions in the
vicinity of materials of low dielectric constant (13) and *also*
due to the polar character of the cellulose acetate membrane
material. In the p-chlorophenol-water-cellulose acetate
membrane system, solute is preferentially sorbed at the interface
due to higher acidity (proton donating ability) of p-chlorophenol
compared to that of water and the net proton acceptor (basic)
character of the polar part of cellulose acetate membrane
material. In the benzene-water-cellulose acetate membrane, and
cumene-water-cellulose acetate membrane systems, again solute is
preferentially sorbed at the interface due to nonpolar

(hydrophobic) character of solutes and that of the membrane
material; further, cumene is relatively more nonpolar than
benzene. How these physicochemical characteristics naturally
give rise to the types of variations in reverse osmosis
separations shown in Figures 2(a) to 2(d) is discussed in detail
in the literature (11-18).

On the basis of the preferential sorption-capillary flow
mechanism, the types of variations in reverse osmosis separations
shown in Figures 2(a) to 2(d) should also be *predictable* from an
analysis of mass transport through capillary pores under the
influence of surface forces expressed explicitly; that this is
indeed so has been demonstrated recently (19). In this analysis
(19), the relative solute-membrane material interactions at the
membrane-solution interface are expressed in terms of electrostatic or Lennard-Jones-type surface potential functions (Φ) and
the transport of solute and solvent through the membrane under
the influence of such forces is expressed through appropriate
mass transport equations applicable for an individual circular
cylindrical pore. The potential function representing electrostatic repulsion of ions at the interface due to relatively long-
range coulombic forces is expressed as

$$\Phi = \frac{A}{d} \tag{1}$$

and the Lennard-Jones-type potential function for nonionic
solutes (representing the sum of the relatively short-range van
der Waals attractive force and the still shorter-range repulsive
force due to overlap of electron clouds at the interface
respectively) is expressed as

$$\Phi = -\frac{B}{d^3} + \frac{C}{d^{12}}$$

$$\text{or} \quad \Phi = \begin{cases} 10 & \text{when } d \leqq D \\ -\dfrac{B}{d^3} & \text{when } d > D \end{cases} \tag{2}$$

and, the potential function Ψ representing friction force against
the movement of solute (under the influence of the above surface
forces) through the membrane pore is expressed as

$$\Psi = \frac{E}{d} \tag{3}$$

where A, B, C, and E are the respective force constants
characteristic of the interface, d is the distance between the
membrane surface or pore wall and the solute molecule, and D is

the value of d at which Φ becomes very large. Assigning
appropriate values for the above quantitities, one can obtain
the above potential functions for the membrane material-solution
systems discussed above, as shown in Figures 3(a) and 3(d).
Using these potential functions, one can then calculate (19)
solute separation, product rate, and (PR)/(PWP) ratio obtainable
for the reverse osmosis systems corresponding to data given in
Figures 2(a) to 2(d). The results of such calculations are
given in Figures 4(a) to 4(d) where the indicated values of pore
radius R represent only relative values.

Figure 4(a) shows that for 0.2 molal NaCl-H$_2$O feed
solutions, both solute separation and product rate increase with
increase in operating pressure, and at any given operating
pressure, solute separation increases and product rate decreases
with decrease in R. Figure 4(b) shows that for dilute p-chlorophenol-water feed solutions, solute separation can be positive,
or negative, or zero depending on experimental conditions, solute
separation decreases with increase in operating pressure and
passes through a minimum with decrease in R, and (PR)/(PWP) ratio
is less than unity. Figures 4(c) and 4(d) show that for dilute
benzene-water and cumene-water feed solutions, solute separation
is positive, and (PR)/(PWP) ratio is less than unity; further,
for the benzene-water system, solute separation tends to decrease
with increase in operating pressure, and it tends to increase
with decrease in R; for the cumene-water system, solute separation
again tends to decrease with increase in operating pressure, and
it passes through maxima and minima with progressive decrease in
R. Thus the results presented in Figures 4(a) to 4(d) show that
an analysis of reverse osmosis transport through capillary pores
under the influence of surface forces correctly predicts all the
different types of variations in reverse osmosis separations
obtained experimentally as shown in Figures 2(a) and 2(d). Such
predictability offers decisive confirmation that an appreciation
of surface forces at membrane-solution interface and the effects
of such surface forces on solute and solvent transport through
capillary pores in the membrane, offers a valid means of
understanding reverse osmosis separations.

Preferential Sorption at Membrane-Solution Interfaces and Solute Separation in Reverse Osmosis

The solute-solvent-polymer (membrane material) interactions,
similar to those governing the effect of structure on reactivity
of molecules (20,21,22,23,24) arise in general from polar-,
steric-, nonpolar-, and/or ionic-character of each one of the
three components in the reverse osmosis system. The overall
result of such interactions determines whether solvent, or
solute, or neither is preferentially sorbed at the membrane-
solution interface.

While details of preferential sorption represent mainly the

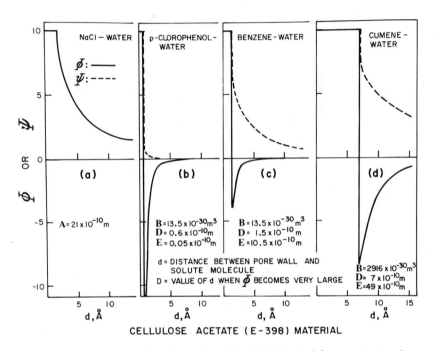

Figure 3. Potential functions for surface (Φ) and friction (Ψ) forces as a function of the distance d *from cellulose acetate membrane material for different solution systems (19)*

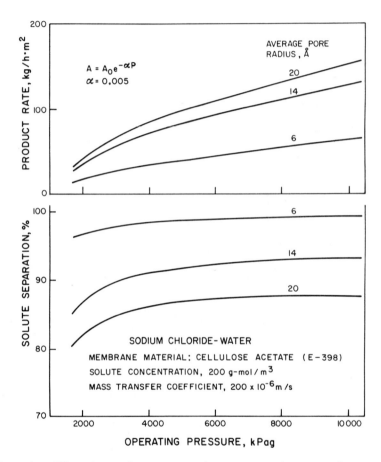

Figure 4a. Effect of operating pressure and average pore size on membrane surface on solute separation and product rate for the reverse osmosis system cellulose acetate membrane–sodium chloride–water calculated on the basis of data on potential functions given in Figure 3

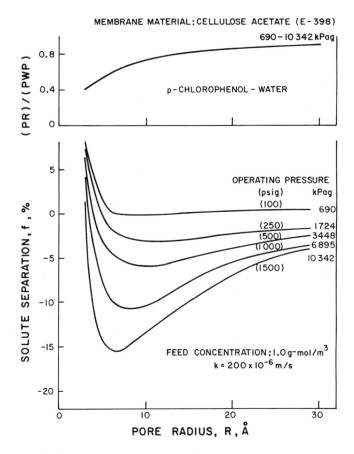

Figure 4b. Effect of operating pressure and average pore size on membrane surface on solute separation and (PR)/(PWP) ratio for the reverse osmosis system cellulose acetate membrane–p-chlorophenol–water calculated on the basis of data on potential functions given in Figure 3

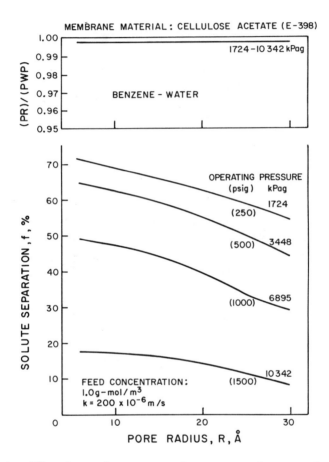

*Figure 4c. Effect of operating pressure and average pore size on membrane sur-
face on solute separation and (PR)/(PWP) ratio for the reverse osmosis system
cellulose acetate membrane–benzene–water, calculated on the basis of data on
potential functions given in Figure 3*

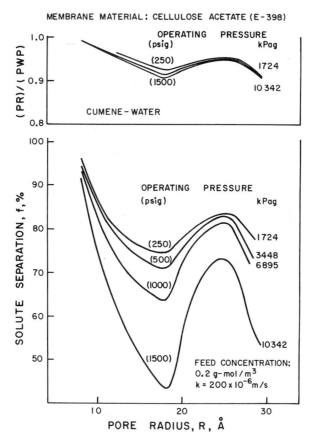

Figure 4d.   Effect of operating pressure and average pore size on membrane sur-face on solute separation and (PR)/(PWP) ratio for the reverse osmosis system cellulose acetate membrane–cumene–water calculated on the basis of data on potential functions given in Figure 3

equilibrium condition at the membrane-solution interface, solute
separation in reverse osmosis, as pointed out already, is a
function of both preferential sorption and the effect of surface
forces on relative mobilities of solute and solvent through
membrane pores, and also other experimental conditions. However,
in general, when solute is repelled sufficiently away from the
surface of the membrane material and the chemical nature of the
latter has appropriate hydrophillic/hydrophobic ratio, water is
preferentially sorbed at the membrane-solution interface, in
which case positive solute separations can be obtained in reverse
osmosis. On the other hand, when solute is attracted
sufficiently strongly towards the surface of the membrane
material, then solute is preferentially sorbed at the membrane-
solution interface, in which case, solute separation in reverse
osmosis can be positive, negative, or zero depending on operating
conditions; further, in this case, solute molecules tend to block
membrane pores and constrain fluid flow during process operation
so that (PR)/(PWP) ratio is always less than unity even when
osmotic pressure effects are excluded. The above two cases are
illustrated by the experimental data presented in Figures 2(a) to
2(d). In between the above two cases, many intermediate cases
exist, where both repulsive and attractive forces have varying
effects on equilibrium and transport, and hence on reverse
osmosis separations. Under certain conditions, the overall
effect of such forces on reverse osmosis could also be such that
no solute separation is possible whatever be the porous structure
of the membrane material. At least a few examples of such cases
appear to exist (25,26), which indicates that a detailed
investigation of this aspect of the subject is necessary for
developing precise and comprehensive practical criteria for
preferential sorption of solvent or solute at membrane-solution
interfaces.

Physicochemical Parameters Characterizing Solutes

With particular reference to reverse osmosis systems
involving cellulose acetate membranes and aqueous solutions, the
membrane material has both polar and nonpolar character, and the
solvent, of course, is polar. When these two components of the
reverse osmosis system are kept constant, preferential sorption
at the membrane-solution interface, and, in turn, solute
separation in reverse osmosis, may be expected to be controlled
by the chemical nature of the solute. If the latter can be
expressed by appropriate quantitative physicochemical parameters
representing polar-, steric-, nonpolar-, and/or ionic-character
of the solutes, then one can expect unique correlations to exist
between such parameters and reverse osmosis data on solute
separations for each membrane. Experimental results confirm
that such is indeed the case (18).

The Polar Parameters. The polar character of a solute
molecule can be expressed in quantitative terms by either one of
the following parameters: (i) the hydrogen bonding ability of
the solute as represented by its $\Delta\nu_s$ (acidity) (relative shift in
the OH band maximum in the IR spectra of the solute in CCl_4 and
ether solutions), or $\Delta\nu_s$ (basicity) (relative shift in the OD
band maximum in the IR spectra of CH_3OD in benzene and the proton
accepting solvent used as solute in reverse osmosis), or (ii)
dissociation constant of solute K_a or K_b expressed as pK_a, (iii)
the Taft (σ^* or $\Sigma\sigma^*$) or the Hammett (σ or $\Sigma\sigma$) number for the
substituent group in the solute molecule with reference to a
functional group, or (iv) the interfacial polar free energy
parameter $(-\Delta\Delta G/RT)$ for the nonionized solute molecule and/or the
dissociated ion in solution.

The basis for correlating data on $\Delta\nu_s$ (acidity) and $\Delta\nu_s$
(basicity) with the relative hydrogen bonding ability of proton-
donar and proton-acceptor molecules respectively stems from the
work of Barrow (27), Gordy and coworkers (28,29,30,31), and
several others (32,33,34,35). Since hydrogen bonding represents
the tendency for proton transfer from an acid to a base as
expressed by the stretching of the OH or OD bond corresponding to
the incipient ionization of the acid or the base concerned, a
higher hydrogen bonding ability represents a higher proton
donating power for an acid (such as an alcohol or phenol), and a
higher proton accepting power for a base (such as an ether or
ester). Thus, increase in $\Delta\nu_s$ (acidity) and that in $\Delta\nu_s$
(basicity) both represent an increase in hydrogen bonding ability
with respect to the molecules concerned; however, in terms of the
effect of structure on reactivity of molecules, the proton-
donating and proton-accepting powers represent mutually opposing
tendencies. Therefore, one would expect that the effect of
increase in $\Delta\nu_s$ (acidity) of alcohols and phenols and that of
decrease in $\Delta\nu_s$ (basicity) of ethers and esters on relative
change in solute separation in reverse osmosis should be similar.
This is indeed the case as illustrated by the experimental data
given in Figures 5(a) and 5(b) (15,16). These data also indicate
that phenols, whose $\Delta\nu_s$ (acidity) values are greater than $\Delta\nu_s$
(acidity) for water (≈ 250 cm^{-1}), are preferentially sorbed at the
membrane-solution interface, and the cellulose acetate membrane
material has a net proton acceptor character.

When the acidity or the basicity of the solute molecule is
high enough to stretch the OH or OD bond to the point of rupture,
then the molecule dissociates into ions in solution. Therefore
the dissociation constants also serve as a measure of acidity or
basicity of solute molecules, especially those which are subject
to significant ionization. Since the coulombic forces causing
repulsion of ions at membrane-solution interfaces extend to
distances farther than those involved in the polar hydrogen
bonding repulsions of nonionized solutes at such interfaces, one
would expect that a dissociated molecule to be repelled and, in

turn, separated to a greater extent than an undissociated molecule in reverse osmosis with a given membrane. Consequently, with respect to molecules which are ionized significantly, solute separation must increase with decrease in pK_a for acids and increase in pK_a for bases, and also with increase in degree of dissociation for both acids and bases. This is indeed the case as illustrated by the experimental data given in Figures 6(a) and 6(b) (15,16,17).

The correlations of Taft ($\Sigma\sigma^*$) and Hammett ($\Sigma\sigma$) numbers with data on reverse osmosis separations arise from the extensive discussions of Taft (36) on such parameters. The numerical value of $\Sigma\sigma^*$ or $\Sigma\sigma$ is a quantitative measure of the electron withdrawing power (or proton donating power or acidity) of the substituent group in a polar organic molecule. Since the values of $\Sigma\sigma^*$ or $\Sigma\sigma$ are independent of the nature of the reaction considered, they have general applicability in many areas of physical organic chemistry, and that should include reverse osmosis as well. On the basis of the foregoing discussion, one would expect that with respect to solute molecules having the same functional group, a decrease in $\Sigma\sigma^*$ or $\Sigma\sigma$ should correspond to an increase in solute separation in reverse osmosis for any given cellulose acetate membrane. This is indeed the case, as illustrated by the set of experimental data given in Figure 7(a) (15,37).

The parameters $\Delta\nu_s$ (acidity), $\Delta\nu_s$ (basicity), pK_a, and $\Sigma\sigma^*$ represent properties of solute in the bulk solution phase. If reverse osmosis separation is governed by the property of solute in the membrane-solution interface, the existence of unique correlations between data on reverse osmosis separations and those on the above parameters, means that the property of solute in the bulk solution phase and the corresponding property of solute in the membrane-solution interface are also uniquely related. This leads one to the development of interfacial free energy parameters ($-\Delta\Delta G/RT$) for both nonionized solute molecules and dissociated ions in solution for reverse osmosis systems where water is preferentially sorbed at the membrane-solution interface.

Polar Free Energy Parameters. When water is preferentially sorbed at the membrane-solution interface, $\Delta\Delta G/RT$ gives a quantitative measure of solute repulsion at the interface on a relative scale. This parameter was initially developed for inorganic ions, and later extended to nonionized polar organic solutes, organic ions, and inorganic ion-pairs (38-43). The basis for this parameter arises from (i) Born equation for ion-solvent interaction (free energy of hydration, ΔG) as applied to the bulk feed solution phase *and* the membrane-solution interface, (ii) the thermodynamic basis of Hammett and Taft equations representing the effect of structure on reaction rates and equilibria (36), (iii) the relationship between the parameters of

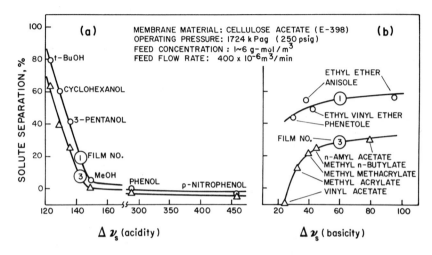

Figure 5.   Experimental data on the effect of (a) Δv_s(acidity) and (b) Δv_s(basicity) of solutes (in centimeters^{-1}) on their reverse osmosis separations in systems involving dilute aqueous solutions and cellulose acetate membranes (15, 16)

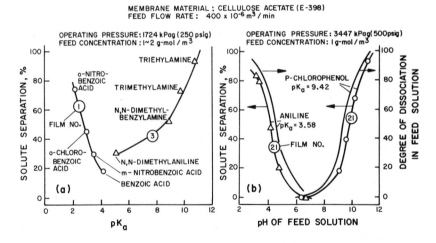

Figure 6.   Experimental data on the effect of pK_a and degree of dissociation of acids and bases on their reverse osmosis separations in systems involving dilute aqueous solutions and cellulose acetate membranes (15, 16, 17)

Taft equation (eq 16 in reference (36)) and reverse osmosis data
on solute transport parameter $D_{AM}/K\delta$ (defined by eq 12 later in
this discussion) for different solutes and membranes (44,45,46),
and (iv) the functional similarity of the thermodynamic quantity
$\Delta\Delta F^{\ddagger}$ representing the transition state free energy change (36)
and the quantity $\Delta\Delta G$ defined as

$$\Delta\Delta G = \Delta G_I - \Delta G_B \tag{4}$$

which represents the energy needed to bring an ion, or the
nonionized solute molecule, from the bulk solution phase
(subscript B) to the membrane-solution interface (subscript I)
under reverse osmosis conditions. The quantity $-\Delta\Delta G/RT$, which
is an interfacial property, is a function of the chemical nature
of the solute, the solvent, and the membrane material; further,
the relative values of $-\Delta\Delta G/RT$ are independent of pore size on
the membrane surface when the solute molecules are predominantly
under the influence of surface forces. A lower value of
$\Sigma(-\Delta\Delta G/RT)$ for the ions involved in the solute molecule (for
completely ionized solutes) or for the nonionized solute
molecule yields a lower value for $D_{AM}/K\delta$ for the solute, and
hence higher solute separation in reverse osmosis as illustrated
in Figure 7(b). A considerable amount of data is now available
in the literature (9) for computing the values of $(-\Delta\Delta G/RT)$ for
different ionic and nonionic solutes applicable for reverse
osmosis systems involving aqueous solutions and cellulose
acetate membranes.

Steric Parameters. Steric hindrance to reactivity of
molecules arises from repulsions between nonbonded atoms and also
from interference of groups or atoms with each other's motions,
and such hindrance parallels also the effective size of the
molecules concerned. Steric hindrance is always a repulsive
force. The numerical values of the steric constants E_s given by
Taft (36) for the substituent groups in polar organic molecules
involving monofunctional groups offer a quantitative basis for
studying the steric effects in reverse osmosis separations of
such solutes. Even though polar and steric effects cannot be
entirely separated (36,47), on the basis of their definitions
(36), the parameters $\Sigma\sigma^*$ and ΣE_s may be treated as mutually
exclusive for practical purposes of analysis of experimental
reverse osmosis data if only unique relationships exist between
data on $\Sigma\sigma^*$ and solute separations in reverse osmosis for solutes
whose polar character is the most, and similar relationships also
exist between data on ΣE_s and solute separations in reverse
osmosis for solutes whose polar character is the least. On the
basis of experimental data on heats of vaporization, and Florry-
Huggins polymer interaction parameter as measured by swelling
equilibrium, Pinsky (48) gives the following order for the
polarity of functional groups: $-COOH > -OH > C=O > C-O-C$. This

order is confirmed by the numerical data given by Diamond and
Wright (49) on the effect of polar group on the change in partial
molar free energy of solution in water. That unique correlations
exist between data on reverse osmosis separations of alcohols and
their $\Sigma\sigma^*$ values has already been illustrated (Figure 7(a), (37))
on the basis of which one can expect similar correlations to
exist between data on reverse osmosis separations of ethers and
their ΣE_s values. This is indeed the case as illustrated by the
experimental data given in Figure 8(a) (45).

Nonpolar Parameters. In a reverse osmosis system involving
cellulose acetate membranes and aqueous solutions of hydrocarbon
solutes, the adsorption of water and that of solute on the polar
and nonpolar sites of the membrane surface respectively may be
expected to take place essentially independently. Further, since
the polymer-solute interaction forces are attractive in nature
for the above case, the mobility of the solute molecules through
the membrane pore is retarded, and they also tend to agglomerate
(50) at the membrane-solution interface. Consequently, one may
expect positive solute separations for such solutes in the above
reverse osmosis systems; that this is indeed the case is confirmed
by extensive experimental data reported in the literature ((12),
and Figures 2(c) and 2(d)).

A direct measure of nonpolar character of a hydrocarbon
molecule is given either by its molar solubility in water or by
its molar attraction constant (Small's number) as given by Small
(51). Unique correlations exist between data on reverse osmosis
separations and the above physicochemical properties (12), which
indicates that the latter two properties, and hence also single-
quantities combining the above two properties, should be
appropriate parameters for representing the nonpolar character of
solutes in reverse osmosis. The Small's number versus logarithm
of solubility is a straight line which is different for different
reactive series of compounds of similar chemical nature including
paraffins, cycloparaffins, olefins, cycloolefins, diolefins,
acetylenes and aromatics. By adjusting the data on Small's
number for various structural groups such that the correlation of
Small's number for the paraffin hydrocarbon (taken as reference)
versus logarithm of its molar solubility in water is valid for
hydrocarbons in all the above reactive series, a new nonpolar
parameter called "modified Small's number", represented by the
symbol s*, has been generated for different structural groups
(12). The nonpolar parameter Σs^* for a hydrocarbon molecule, or
the hydrocarbon backbone of a polar organic molecule is obtained
from its chemical structure using the additive property of s* for
different structural groups. The scale of Σs^* is consistent
within each of the groups of aromatic, cyclic and noncyclic
hydrocarbon structure. Just as $\Sigma\sigma^*$ and ΣE_s, Σs^* represents the
property of the solute in the bulk solution phase. The numerical
values of Σs^* (9) give a quantitative measure of the relative

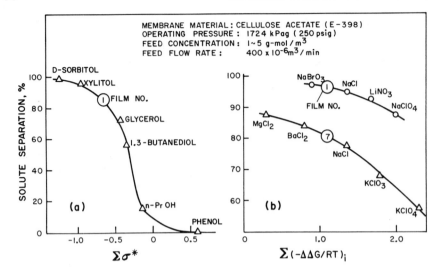

Figure 7.   Experimental data on the effect of (a) Taft's number for alcohols and (b) interfacial free energy parameter for ionized inorganic solutes on their reverse osmosis separations in systems involving dilute aqueous solutions and cellulose acetate membranes (9, 15, 37, 38)

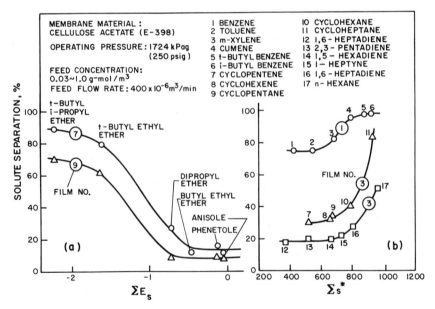

Figure 8.   Experimental data on the effect of (a) Taft's steric parameter for ethers and (b) modified Small's number for hydrocarbons on their reverse osmosis separations in systems involving dilute aqueous solutions and cellulose acetate membranes (12, 45)

mutual attraction of organic molecules to one another as a result of dispersion forces. Consequently, one would expect unique correlations to exist between data on reverse osmosis separations of each of the above classes of solutes and the corresponding data on their Σs^* values. That this is indeed the case is illustrated by the experimental data given in Figure 8(b) (12).

Liquid-Solid Chromatography (LSC) Data and Reverse Osmosis

The relevance of LSC data to reverse osmosis stems from the physicochemical basis (adsorption equilibrium considerations) of liquid-solid chromatography (52), and the principle that the solute-solvent-membrane material (column material) interactions governing the relative retention times of solutes in LSC are analogous to the interactions prevailing at the membrane-solution interface under reverse osmosis conditions. The work already reported in several papers on the subject (53-58) indicate that the foregoing principle is valid, and hence LSC data offer an appropriate means of characterizing interfacial properties of membrane materials, and understanding solute separations in reverse osmosis.

Materials Science of Reverse Osmosis Membranes - Characterization of Polymeric Membrane Materials

Using different polymeric materials in the chromatographic columns and LSC data on retention times (t) of suitably chosen reference solutes, three interfacial parameters (α_p, α_n, and β), defined below, have been generated for characterizing polymeric membrane materials (53,56)

$$\alpha_p = 0.812 \, (\ln r_1 - \ln r_2) \tag{5}$$

$$\text{and} \quad \alpha_n = 0.188 \, \ln r_1 + 0.812 \, \ln r_2 \tag{6}$$

$$\text{where} \quad r_1 = (t_{\text{benzyl alcohol}} - t_{uc})/(t_{\text{phenol}} - t_{uc}) \tag{7}$$

$$\text{and} \quad r_2 = (t_{\text{phenethyl alcohol}} - t_{uc})/(t_{\text{benzyl alcohol}} - t_{uc}) \tag{8}$$

$$\text{and} \quad \beta = \ln \left[\frac{\sqrt{(t_{t-\text{BuOH}} - t_{\text{raffinose}})(t_{s-\text{BuOH}} - t_{\text{raffinose}})}}{t_{\text{NaSCN}} - t_{\text{raffinose}}} \right] \tag{9}$$

In eq 7, 8, and 9, the values of t are at constant solvent flow rate. The quantities $\ln r_1$ and $\ln r_2$ represent the differences in free energy changes in the adsorption equilibrium for the solutes involved. The dimensionless parameters α_p and α_n represent the polar (hydrogen bonding) and nonpolar (hydrophobic) properties respectively characterizing the polymer material. The constants in eq 5 and 6 arise from the choice of the reference

solutes and the arbitrary units chosen to represent the polar-
and nonpolar-character for the solute molecules involved. The
dimensionless quantity β, defined by eq 9, is a measure of the
affinity of the polymer material for nonionized polar organic
solutes relative to that for an ionized inorganic solute. The
experimental values of α_p, α_n and β for several polymeric
membrane materials are given in Table I.

Table I. Characteristics of Different Polymers as Reverse
          Osmosis Membrane Materials (53,56)

Polymer	α_p	α_n	β	$-\Delta\Delta G/RT$ at 25°C Na+	Cl-
Cellulose acetate	-1.00	-0.017	1.37	5.79	-4.42
Cellulose acetate propionate	-1.33	0.143	0.74	4.00	-3.40
Cellulose acetate butyrate	-1.28	-0.377	1.26	2.80	-2.30
Ethyl cellulose phthalate	–	–	1.16	-1.20	1.20
Aromatic copolyamide	-0.43	0.259	0.46	-1.35	1.35
Aromatic copolyamidohydrazide (PPPH1115)	-0.22	0.149	0.20	-1.40	1.40
Aromatic copolyamidohydrazide (PPPH8273)	-0.31	0.144	0.17	-1.50	1.50
Aromatic copolyhydrazide	-0.54	0.041	0.67	-1.50	1.50

Experimental data on α_p and α_n for different polymer
materials exhibit unique correlations with δ_h (hydrogen bonding)
and δ_d (dispersion) components respectively of solubility
parameter δ_{sp} of polymer (53,60) which can be calculated from
data on structural group contributions to δ_h and δ_d available in
the literature (61). The existence of such correlations (Figures
9(a) and 9(b)) indicate that LSC data can be used to characterize
the chemical nature of polymeric membrane materials.

A higher value of α_p (or δ_h) indicates stronger hydrogen
bonding capacity of polymer material and hence its potential for
higher sorption capacity for water. A higher value of α_n (or δ_d)
for the polymer material results in greater mobility of
preferentially sorbed water through the membrane pores when water
is preferentially sorbed, and lower mobility of solute through
the membrane pores when solute is preferentially sorbed at the
membrane-solution interface; both these effects tend to
contribute to higher solute separation in reverse osmosis. It
may be noted that many presently well-known newer membrane
materials such as aromatic polyamides, polyurea (NS-100),
sulfonated polyfuran (NS-200), poly(ether/amide) (PA-300) and
polybenzimidazolone (PBIL) have values of α_p (or δ_h) and α_n (or
δ_d) higher than the corresponding values for cellulose acetate

material. The usefulness of the above polymers as membrane
materials for sea water desalination applications indicate that
the numerical values of α_p (or δ_h) and α_n (or δ_d) can offer
useful guidelines for the choice of membrane materials for
different reverse osmosis applications.

The definition of the β-parameter, which includes nonionized
polar organic solutes and an inorganic electrolytic solute as
reference solutes in LSC, makes it possible to compare the
relative affinities of different polymer materials for the above
classes of organic and inorganic solutes in aqueous solutions.
Since retention time in LSC is a direct measure of polymer
affinity for the solute, a larger value of β denotes stronger
affinity of the polymer for the organic solutes relative to
ionized inorganic solutes. Since stronger affinity between the
polymer and solute results in lesser preferential sorption for
water at the membrane-solution interface, a larger value of β for
the polymer material tends to give lower solute separations for
nonionized polar organic solutes in reverse osmosis at any given
level of solute separation for a reference electrolytic solute
such as sodium chloride. This tendency is consistent with the
common experience that, at a given level of NaCl separation, the
corresponding reverse osmosis separations for nonionized polar
organic solutes are generally lower with membranes made from
cellulose acetate material whose β-parameter is 1.37, compared
with membranes made from different aromatic polyamide materials
whose β-parameters are considerably lower ($< \sim 0.5$).

A plot of δ_{sp} vs β for several cellulosic and noncellulosic
polymers is shown in Figure 10(b); and, for the same polymers, a
plot of δ_{sp} vs $\delta_h/\delta_d\delta_{sp}$ is shown in Figure 10(a). The results
show that unique correlations exist between the parameters
plotted, both correlations are exactly similar and pass through
a maximum at δ_{sp} value of ~ 25 $J^{\frac{1}{2}}cm^{-3/2}$ and the cellulose acetate
material is close to the maximum in these correlations. These
correlations are significant. It is known (62) that dielectric
constants of different polymeric materials are directly
proportional to their solubility parameters; it is also known
(13,14), that ionic repulsion is less in the vicinity of a
material whose dielectric constant is less than, but closer to
that of water. Consequently, one can draw several conclusions
from the correlations shown in Figures 10(a) and 10(b). Some of
them are the following. As reverse osmosis membrane materials,
the cellulosic and noncellulosic polymers are not mutually
exclusive; the decrease in β and $\delta_h/\delta_d\delta_{sp}$ with decrease in δ_{sp}
on the left sides of the maximum in Figures 10(a) and 10(b) is
primarily due to the increased hydrophobic character of the
polymer material; for a given level of NaCl separation in reverse
osmosis (under otherwise identical experimental conditions), the
average pore diameters (d_{av}) needed on the membrane surface are
in the order: d_{av}(cellulose esters) > d_{av}(aromatic polyamides) >
d_{av}(cellulose); and by progressive hydrolysis of a cellulose

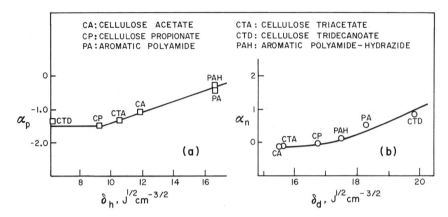

Figure 9.   Correlations of (a) α_p and δ_h and (b) α_n and δ_d for different polymeric membrane materials (53)

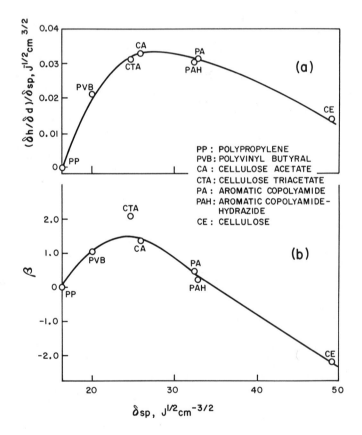

Figure 10.   Correlations of solubility parameter with (a) $\delta_h/\delta_d\delta_{sp}$ ratio and (b) β-parameter for different polymeric membrane materials (56)

acetate polymer, its δ_{sp} value can be increased and its β-
parameter can be decreased approaching the corresponding values
of pure cellulose, which indicates the possibility of obtaining
a cellulosic polymer whose δ_{sp} and β values are identical to
those of an aromatic polyamide polymer, by controlled hydrolysis
of a cellulose ester polymer. These conclusions have important
consequences in reverse osmosis (some of which have already been
verified (54,56), and they contribute to a fuller understanding
of interfacial properties of membrane materials and solute
separations in reverse osmosis.

Materials Science of Reverse Osmosis Membranes – Factors Governing Porous Structure of Membranes

Having chosen an appropriate membrane material, one still
has to create a useful membrane out of that material suitable for
the specific application on hand. A direction for accomplishing
the latter objective is shown by the preferential sorption-
capillary flow mechanism for reverse osmosis. According to this
mechanism, as already pointed out, the entire membrane must be
porous; only the layer of the membrane surface which comes into
contact with the feed solution needs to have pores of appropriate
size and number suited for the specific application; the material
of the membrane underneath the surface layer can be and, for
practical advantage, must be grossly porous with big inter-
connected pores. This means that the surface layer of a useful
membrane must be as thin as possible, and the entire porous
structure of the membrane must be asymmetric. This direction
has been the basis of numerous successful studies on the
development of flat and tubular cellulose acetate membranes for
practical reverse osmosis applications (6b,10,57,63–85). These
studies involve an appreciation of surface chemistry, colloid
chemistry, and physical chemistry of polymer solutions as they
relate to film casting solutions, film casting conditions, film
casting techniques, and the mechanism of pore formation and
development of asymmetric porous structure in resulting membranes.
In view of the different requirements of reverse osmosis
membranes for different applications and the large number of
variables involved in the film making process, such studies may
be expected to continue forever, building steadily the
foundations of a new and ever-expanding area of applied chemistry
and reverse osmosis membrane technology. Even though this area
of materials science of reverse osmosis membranes is still in its
early stages of development, the work referred above has already
provided certain broad guidelines in terms of cause and effect
relationships governing the porous structure of such membranes.
    The film casting solution is usually a mixture of the
polymer (e.g., cellulose acetate), a solvent (e.g., acetone), and
an essentially nonsolvent swelling agent (e.g., aqueous solution
of magnesium perchlorate, or formamide). The film making

procedure involves generally the following steps: (i) casting
the polymer solution as a thin film on a surface; (ii) evaporation
(or removal by other means) of solvent from the surface; (iii)
immersion of the film in an appropriate gelation medium such as
cold water or an aqueous ethanol solution; and finally (iv)
thermal shrinking, pressurization and/or other membrane pretreatment techniques. Each one of the above steps affects the
ultimate porous structure of the entire membrane, and hence its
subsequent performance in reverse osmosis. Further the solute
separation versus shrinkage temperature correlation, called the
shrinkage temperature profile, expresses pore size distribution
on the membrane surface, and hence it is an important guide for
quality control in membrane research and development.

The state or the structure of the casting solution and the
rate of solvent evaporation (or solvent removal) from the surface
during film formation together constitute an important inter-
connected variable governing the ultimate porous structure and
hence the performance of the resulting membrane in reverse
osmosis. The structure of the casting solution (i.e., the state
of supermolecular polymer aggregation in the casting solution)
is a function of its composition and temperature; no precise
quantitative parameter has yet been developed to specify that
structure. Solvent evaporation rate during film formation is a
function of solution temperature, temperature of the casting
atmosphere and the ambient nature of the casting atmosphere.
With reference to a given casting solution, its temperature and
that of the casting atmosphere (together with the ambient nature
of the casting atmosphere) are two separate variables in the
specification of film casting conditions; by appropriate choice
of these two variables alone, the productivity of resulting
membranes can be changed and improved as illustrated in Figure
11(a).

The size of the supermolecular polymer aggregate in the
casting solution can be decreased by increasing solvent/polymer
ratio, decreasing nonsolvent/solvent ratio, and/or increasing the
temperature of the casting solution (Figures 11(a) and 11(b)).
Smaller size of polymer aggregates tends to create a larger
number of smaller size nonsolvent droplets in the interdispersed
phase during film formation, resulting ultimately in larger
number of smaller size pores on the membrane surface. Since
higher droplet density favors droplet-coalescence, there is an
optimum size of polymer aggregate in the casting solution for
maximum productivity of resulting membranes. High solvent
evaporation rate favors both droplet formation and droplet
coalescence. The solvent evaporation rate should be high enough
to generate the largest number of interdispersed droplets, and
low enough to prevent excessive droplet coalescence during film
formation. For each casting solution structure, there exists an
optimum solvent evaporation rate for maximum membrane
productivity. A given solution structure-evaporation rate

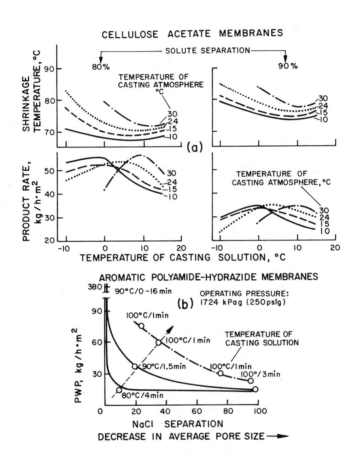

Figure 11. Effect of film casting conditions on the performance of resulting (a) cellulose acetate (72) and (b) aromatic polyamide–hydrazide membranes. The latter data are those of O. Kutowy and S. Sourirajan (not yet published).

combination (howsoever it is achieved) results in membranes of
identical productivity provided their shrinkage temperature
profiles are the same. Gelation control can be an effective
means of changing pore size, and pore size distribution, on the
membrane surface; this technique is particularly relevant for
making ultrafiltration membranes.

The foregoing conclusions arising from earlier work (6b,10,
57,63-85) offer fruitful directions for a continuing program of
research and development involving a wide variety of membrane
materials, and reverse osmosis and ultrafiltration systems.

Engineering Science of Reverse Osmosis Transport and Process Design

This discussion is concerned with reverse osmosis systems
where water is preferentially sorbed at the membrane-solution
interface, and where the solute does not block membrane pores
constraining fluid flow during process operation. Under such
conditions, solute separation in reverse osmosis is always
positive; further, at any point in the system, the (PR)/(PWP)
ratio is unity when osmotic pressure effects are excluded. The
latter is practically the case when the net polymer (membrane
material)-solute interaction is either repulsive or only weakly
attractive. A large number of reverse osmosis systems including
many of those involved in water desalting, water pollution
control, and water purification applications satisfy the two
criteria mentioned above. For such systems, the engineering
science of reverse osmosis transport is currently well developed
in a manner suitable for its practical utilization for specifying
and predicting the performance of membranes and systems from a
minimum of experimental data (6c,6d,8,9,38,39,40,41,42,44,56,
86-113). This is indicated by the following brief review of
transport equations for reverse osmosis.

Basic Transport Equations. At any given operating
temperature and pressure, the experimental reverse osmosis data
on pure water permeation rate (PWP), product rate (PR) and
fraction solute separation f at any point in the reverse osmosis
system can be analyzed on the basis that (PWP) is directly
proportional to the operating pressure, the solvent water
transport (N_B) through the membrane is proportional to the
effective pressure, the solute transport (N_A) through the
membrane is due to pore diffusion through the membrane
capillaries and hence proportional to the concentration
difference across the membrane, and the mass transfer coefficient k on the high pressure side of the membrane is given
by the "film" theory on mass transport. This analysis which is
applicable to all membrane materials and membranes at all levels
of solute separation, gives rise to the following basic transport
equations for reverse osmosis where the viscosity of the membrane

permeated product solution is assumed to be practically the same
as that of pure water.

$$A = (PWP)/(M_B \times S \times 3600 \times P) \tag{10}$$

$$N_B = A \left[P - \pi(X_{A2}) + \pi(X_{A3}) \right] \tag{11}$$

$$= \left(\frac{D_{AM}}{K\delta}\right)\left(\frac{1-X_{A3}}{X_{A3}}\right)(c_2 X_{A2} - c_3 X_{A3}) \tag{12}$$

$$= kc_1(1-X_{A3})\ln\left(\frac{X_{A2}-X_{A3}}{X_{A1}-X_{A3}}\right) \tag{13}$$

All symbols are defined at the end of the paper. Equation 10
defines the pure water permeability constant A for the membrane
which is a measure of its overall porosity; eq 12 defines the
solute transport parameter $D_{AM}/K\delta$ for the membrane, which is also
a measure of the average pore size on the membrane surface on a
relative scale. The important feature of the above set of
equations is that neither any one equation in the set of
equations 10 to 13, nor any part of this set of equations is
adequate representation of reverse osmosis transport; *the latter
is governed simultaneously by the entire set of eq 10 to 13.*
Further, under steady state operating conditions, a single set
of experimental data on (PWP), (PR), and f enables one to
calculate the quantities A, X_{A2}, $D_{AM}/K\delta$ and k at any point
(position or time) in the reverse osmosis system using eq 10 to
13.

For the purpose of this review, it is assumed that for a
given membrane at any specified operating temperature and
pressure, the value of $D_{AM}/K\delta$ for a given solute is independent
of X_{A2}; this assumption is not, and need not be, valid in *all*
cases, but it is valid with respect to cellulose acetate
membranes and many organic and inorganic solutes, including
sodium chloride, in aqueous solutions. In any case, the above
assumption does not restrict the practical scope of this analysis
(113).

Membrane Specifications. At a specified operating
temperature and pressure, a cellulose acetate membrane is
completely specified in terms of its pure water permeability
constant A and solute transport parameter $D_{AM}/K\delta$ for a convenient
reference solute such as sodium chloride. A *single* set of
experimental data on (PWP), (PR), and f at known operating
conditions is enough to obtain data on the specifying parameters
A and $(D_{AM}/K\delta)_{NaCl}$ at any given temperature and pressure.

Predictability of Membrane Performance. Combining eq 11, 12
and 13,

$$A[P-\pi(X_{A2})+\pi(X_{A3})] = \left(\frac{D_{AM}}{K\delta}\right)\left(\frac{1-X_{A3}}{X_{A3}}\right)(c_2 X_{A2}-c_3 X_{A3}) \tag{14}$$

$$\frac{(c_2 X_{A2}-c_3 X_{A3})}{X_{A3}} = \frac{k}{(D_{AM}/K\delta)} \; c_1 \ln\left(\frac{X_{A2}-X_{A3}}{X_{A1}-X_{A3}}\right) \tag{15}$$

For a membrane specified in terms of A and $D_{AM}/K\delta$, eq 14 and 15, together with eq 11, enable one to predict membrane performance (X_{A3} and N_B, and hence f and (PR)) for any feed concentration X_{A1} and any chosen feed flow condition as specified in terms of k. Several theoretical and experimental methods of specifying k for different solutes under different conditions are available in the literature (6c,6d,18b,90,100). The quantities f and (PR) are related to X_{A3} and N_B through the following equations:

$$f = \frac{m_1-m_3}{m_1} = 1-\left(\frac{X_{A3}}{1-X_{A3}}\right)\left(\frac{1-X_{A1}}{X_{A1}}\right) \approx 1-\frac{X_{A3}}{X_{A1}} \tag{16}$$

$$(PR) = \frac{N_B \times M_B \times S \times 3600}{\left[1-\cfrac{1}{\left(1+\cfrac{1000}{m_1(1-f)M_A}\right)}\right]} \tag{17}$$

Using eq 11, 14, 15, 16 and 17, one can for example calculate the effect of feed concentration and feed flow rate on f and (PR) for $NaCl-H_2O$ feed solutions obtainable with a cellulose acetate membrane specified in terms of A and $(D_{AM}/K\delta)_{NaCl}$.

Relationships Between $(D_{AM}/K\delta)_{NaCl}$ and $(D_{AM}/K\delta)$ for Other Solutes. For completely ionized inorganic and simple (i.e., where steric and nonpolar effects are negligible) organic solutes,

$$(D_{AM}/K\delta)_{solute} \propto \exp\left\{n_c\left(-\frac{\Delta\Delta G}{RT}\right)_{cation} + n_a\left(-\frac{\Delta\Delta G}{RT}\right)_{anion}\right\} \tag{18}$$

where n_c and n_a represent the number of moles of cation and anion respectively in one mole of ionized solute. Applying eq 18 to $(D_{AM}/K\delta)_{NaCl}$,

$$\ln (D_{AM}/K\delta)_{NaCl} = \ln C^*_{NaCl} + \left\{\left(-\frac{\Delta\Delta G}{RT}\right)_{Na^+} + \left(-\frac{\Delta\Delta G}{RT}\right)_{Cl^-}\right\} \tag{19}$$

where $\ln C^*_{NaCl}$ is a constant representing the porous structure of the membrane surface expressed in terms of $(D_{AM}/K\delta)_{NaCl}$.

Using the data on $(-\Delta\Delta G/\underset{\sim}{R}T)$ for Na^+ and Cl^- ions for the membrane
material involved (Table I), the value of $\ln C^*_{NaCl}$ for the
particular membrane used can be calculated from the specified
value of $(D_{AM}/K\delta)_{NaCl}$. Using the value of $\ln C^*_{NaCl}$ so obtained,
the corresponding value of $D_{AM}/K\delta$ for any completely ionized
inorganic or simple organic solute can be obtained from the
relation:

$$\ln (D_{AM}/K\delta)_{solute} = \ln C^*_{NaCl} + \left\{ n_c \left(-\frac{\Delta\Delta G}{\underset{\sim}{R}T} \right)_{cation} \right.$$

$$\left. + n_a \left(-\frac{\Delta\Delta G}{\underset{\sim}{R}T} \right)_{anion} \right\} \qquad (20)$$

Thus, for any specified value of $(D_{AM}/K\delta)_{NaCl}$, the corresponding
values of $(D_{AM}/K\delta)$ for a large number of completely ionized
solutes can be obtained from eq 20 using data on $(-\Delta\Delta G/\underset{\sim}{R}T)$ for
different ions available in the literature (8,9).

With respect to electrolytic inorganic solutes, a few
special cases arise. For a solution system involving ions and
ion-pairs, eq 20 can be written as

$$\ln (D_{AM}/K\delta)_{solute} = \ln C^*_{NaCl} + \alpha_D \left\{ n_c \left(-\frac{\Delta\Delta G}{\underset{\sim}{R}T} \right)_{cation} \right.$$

$$\left. + n_a \left(-\frac{\Delta\Delta G}{\underset{\sim}{R}T} \right)_{anion} \right\} + (1-\alpha_D) \left(-\frac{\Delta\Delta G}{\underset{\sim}{R}T} \right)_{ip} \qquad (21)$$

where α_D represents the degree of dissociation, and the subscript
ip refers to the ion-pair formed; for the particular case where
the ion-pair itself is an ion, eq 20 assumes the more general
form

$$\ln (D_{AM}/K\delta)_{solute} = \ln C^*_{NaCl}$$

$$+ \alpha_D \left\{ n_c \left(-\frac{\Delta\Delta G}{\underset{\sim}{R}T} \right)_{cation} + n_a \left(-\frac{\Delta\Delta G}{\underset{\sim}{R}T} \right)_{anion} \right\}$$

$$+ (1-\alpha_D) \left(-\frac{\Delta\Delta G}{\underset{\sim}{R}T} \right)_{ip} + (1-\alpha_D)(n_c - n_{ipc}) \left(-\frac{\Delta\Delta G}{\underset{\sim}{R}T} \right)_{cation}$$

$$+ (1-\alpha_D)(n_a - n_{ipc}) \left(-\frac{\Delta\Delta G}{\underset{\sim}{R}T} \right)_{anion} \qquad (22)$$

where n_{ipc} and n_{ipa} represent number of moles of cation and
anion respectively involved in one mole of ion-pair. For the
case of a feed solution which is subject to partial hydrolysis,
eq 20 becomes

$$\ln (D_{AM}/K\delta)_{solute} = \ln C^*_{NaCl}$$

$$+ (1-\alpha_H) \left\{ n_c \left(- \frac{\Delta\Delta G}{RT}\right)_{cation} + n_a \left(- \frac{\Delta\Delta G}{RT}\right)_{anion} \right\}$$

$$+ \alpha_H \left\{ n_{hy} \left(- \frac{\Delta\Delta G}{RT}\right)_{hy} + \left(- \frac{\Delta\Delta G}{RT}\right)_{OH^- \text{ or } H^+} \right\} \qquad (23)$$

where α_H represents the degree of hydrolysis and the subscript hy refers to the hydrolyzed species resulting from the hydrolysis reaction and the subscripts OH^- and H^+ represent the hydroxyl and hydrogen ions respectively. In eq 21, 22, and 23, the applicable values of α_D and α_H are those corresponding to the boundary concentration X_{A2}.

For a completely nonionized polar organic solute,

$$\ln (D_{AM}/K\delta)_{solute} = \ln C^*_{NaCl} + \ln \Delta^* + \left(- \frac{\Delta\Delta G}{RT}\right)$$

$$+ \delta^* \Sigma E_s + \omega^* \Sigma s^* \qquad (24)$$

Referring to the quantities on the right side of eq 24, the quantity $\ln C^*_{NaCl}$ is obtained from eq 19; the quantity $\ln \Delta^*$ is a scale factor setting a scale for $\ln (D_{AM}/K\delta)_{solute}$ in terms of $\ln C^*_{NaCl}$ when the polar $(-\Delta\Delta G/RT)$, steric $(\delta^*\Sigma E_s)$ and nonpolar $(\omega^*\Sigma s^*)$ parameters applicable for the system are each set equal to zero. The methods of computing the latter three parameters for different solutes, membrane materials and membranes are illustrated in detail in the literature (8,9,56). The quantity $\ln \Delta^*$ is a function of the chemical nature of the membrane material (such as that represented by the β-parameter) and the porous structure of the membrane surface (such as that represented by the quantity $\ln (C^*_{NaCl}/A)$. The steric coefficient δ^* is also a function of the chemical nature of the membrane material and the porous structure of the membrane surface; in addition, it is also a function of the chemical nature of the solute. Figure 12 gives a set of correlations of $\ln \Delta^*$ and δ^* (obtained experimentally) (56) expressing their above properties; the data given in Figure 12 can be used in conjunction with eq 24 for obtaining the values of $\ln (D_{AM}/K\delta)$ for different solutes.

The object of the foregoing discussion is two-fold: eq 19 to 24, together with Figure 12, show how one can obtain the values of $D_{AM}/K\delta$ of solutes for a very large number of membrane-solution systems from $D_{AM}/K\delta$ data for a single reference solute such as sodium chloride; they also show how the physicochemical parameters characterizing solutes, membrane-materials and membrane-porosities are integrated into the transport equations in the overall development of the science of reverse osmosis.

Predictability of Membrane Performance for Aqueous Feed
Solution Systems Involving Mixed Solutes. This subject is
obviously of great practical interest. Even though a full
development of the subject is yet to come, considerable progress
has been made at least with respect to certain kinds of mixed
solute systems (6e,44,101,102,103,104). The latter include (i)
mixtures of any number of electrolytic solutes involving a common
ion, (ii) mixtures of any number of nonionized organic solutes
with no solute-solute interactions, and (iii) mixtures of two
electrolytic solutes involving four *different* ions (either all
of them univalent, or one of them divalent and the rest
univalent). The prediction techniques involved for the mixed-
solute systems (i) and (ii) use the basic transport equations
given above, treating each solute independently, so that the net
result is simply the additive effect of each individual component
in the mixed-solute system. In the prediction technique for the
mixed solute system (iii), the basic transport equations are
written for each ion along with the necessary additional equations
for overall electroneutrality for the system; these equations,
together with eq 20 written for each possible electrolytic solute
combining the cations and the anions present in the system yield
a set of equations which can be solved to give the necessary data
on ion separations and product rates from data on membrane
specifications only. Even though these techniques require
considerable effort in solving the computational complexities
involved, they are simple in principle, fundamental in approach,
and offer a firm basis for the analytical treatment of more
complex systems.

Analysis of Reverse Osmosis Modules. The basic transport
eq 10 to 13 apply to any point (position or time) in a reverse
osmosis module, where the fraction recovery (Δ) of product water
is assumed infinitely small for purposes of analysis. A
practical reverse osmosis module involves a finite and often a
high value of Δ, which means solute concentrations and membrane
fluxes change continuously from the entrance to the exit of the
module (or time t=0 to t=t of module operation). Thus the
product water leaving the module as a whole has an average
concentration corresponding to a specified Δ value. The
performance of the module as a whole can then be predicted by
applying the basic transport equations to the entire reverse
osmosis system and analyzing the various relationships applicable
to the entire system which can be represented as shown in Figure
13. The technique for such analysis has been developed in detail
with particular reference to water treatment applications of
reverse osmosis (6d,8,9,105-113). The essential features of this
analysis are as follows.

System Specification. Any reverse osmosis system may be
specified in terms of three nondimensional parameters γ, θ, and

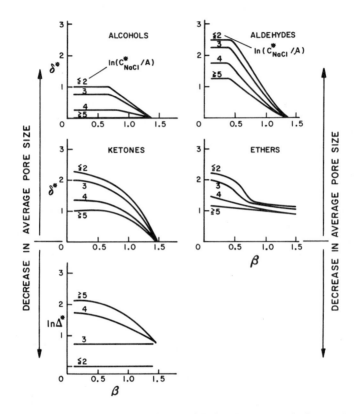

Figure 12.   Variations of δ* for alcohols, aldehydes, ketones, and ethers and ln Δ* for nonionized polar organic solutes with β-parameter for the polymeric membrane material as a function of surface porosity (correlations with C* in centimeters/second and A in gram-moles H₂O centimeters²/second atm) (56)

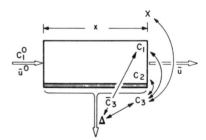

Figure 13.   Schematic of a reverse osmosis system for process design

λ defined as follows:

$$\gamma = \frac{\pi(x_{A1}^o)}{P} = \frac{\text{osmotic pressure of initial feed solution}}{\text{operating pressure}} \tag{25}$$

$$\theta = \frac{(D_{AM}/K\delta)}{v_w^*} = \frac{\text{solute transport parameter}}{\text{pure water permeation velocity}} \tag{26}$$

$$\lambda = \frac{k}{(D_{AM}/K\delta)} = \frac{\begin{array}{c}\text{mass transfer coefficient on the high}\\ \text{pressure side of membrane}\end{array}}{\text{solute transport parameter}} \tag{27}$$

where $v_w^* = \dfrac{AP}{c}$ \hfill (28)

and the quantity $\pi(x_{A1}^o)$ refers to the osmotic pressure of the feed solution at membrane entrance in a flow process or start of operation in a batch process. The quantities γ, θ and $\lambda\theta(=k/v_w^*)$ may be described as the osmotic pressure characteristic, membrane characteristic, and the mass transfer coefficient characteristic respectively of the system under consideration. The significance of system specification is that a single set of numerical parameters can represent an infinite number of membrane-solution-operating systems; conversely, any two membrane-solution-operating systems can be simply and precisely differentiated in terms of unique combinations of numerical parameters.

<u>System Analysis and Predictability of System Performance.</u>
For the purpose of this analysis, the following assumptions and definition are made.
<u>Assumptions:</u> $c_1 = c_2 = c_3 = c$; $\pi(X_A) \propto X_A$, $X_{A3} \ll 1$; $D_{AM}/K\delta$ is independent of X_{A2} for the Δ value considered; and longitudinal diffusion is negligible; these assumptions are practically valid for many reverse osmosis systems in water treatment applications.
<u>Definitions:</u>

$$C = X_A/X_{A1}^o \tag{29}$$

so that $C_1 = X_{A1}/X_{A1}^o$, $C_1^o = 1$, $C_2 = X_{A2}/X_{A1}^o$, $C_2^o = X_{A2}^o/X_{A1}^o$,

$C_3 = X_{A3}/X_{A1}^o$, $C_3^o = X_{A3}^o/X_{A1}^o$, and $\bar{C}_3 = \bar{X}_{A3}/X_{A1}^o$. Further, for a reverse osmosis system involving longitudinal feed flow pattern in the module (such as in spiral wound or tubular modules), let

$$X = v_w^* \, x/\bar{u}^o h \tag{30}$$

and, for a reverse osmosis system involving radial feed flow pattern in the module (such as in DuPont hollow fiber module), let

$$X' = \frac{\alpha}{2}\left\{\left(\frac{r_o}{r_i}\right)^2 - 1\right\} \tag{31}$$

where

$$\alpha = r_i\, v_w^*/\bar{u}^o h \tag{32}$$

and for a reverse osmosis system involving a batch process, let

$$T = Sv_w^* t/V_1^o \tag{33}$$

On the basis of the above assumptions and definitions, for a reverse osmosis system illustrated in Figure 13, the following relationships have been derived (112,113).

$$c_1^o = 1 = c_3^o\left[1 + \frac{1}{(\gamma c_3^o + \theta)}\ \exp\left\{-\frac{1}{\lambda(\gamma c_3^o + \theta)}\right\}\right] \tag{34}$$

$$c_2^o = c_3^o\left[1 + \frac{1}{(\gamma c_3^o + \theta)}\right] \tag{35}$$

$$C_1 = C_3\left[1 + \frac{1}{(\gamma C_3 + \theta)}\ \exp\left\{-\frac{1}{\lambda(\gamma C_3 + \theta)}\right\}\right] \tag{36}$$

$$C_2 = C_3\left[1 + \frac{1}{(\gamma C_3 + \theta\ )}\right] \tag{37}$$

$$Z = \int_{c_3^o}^{C_3}\left[\frac{\gamma}{\lambda(\gamma C_3 + \theta)^2} - \frac{\gamma}{(\gamma C_3 + \theta)} + \left\{\frac{(\gamma C_3 + \theta)}{C_3}\ \exp\frac{1}{\lambda(\gamma C_3 + \theta)}\right\}\right.$$
$$\left. + \frac{1}{C_3}\right]dC_3 \tag{38}$$

$$\left.\begin{array}{c}X\\ \text{or}\\ X'\\ \text{or}\\ T\end{array}\right\} = \int_{c_3^o}^{C_3}\left[\frac{\gamma}{\lambda(\gamma C_3 + \theta)} - \gamma + \frac{(\gamma C_3 + \theta)}{C_3}\left\{1 + (\gamma C_3 + \theta)\right.\right.$$
$$\left.\left. \times \exp\frac{1}{\lambda(\gamma C_3 + \theta)}\right\}\right]\frac{\exp\ (-Z)}{\theta}\ dC_3 \tag{39}$$

$$\Delta = 1 - \exp\ (-Z) \tag{40}$$

$$C_1(1 - \Delta) + \bar{C}_3\Delta = 1 \tag{41}$$

The above equations show that for a reverse osmosis system specified in terms of γ, θ, and λ, any one of the six quantities (performance parameters) C_1, C_2, C_3, $\bar{C}_3$, X or X' or T, and Δ uniquely fixes all the other five quantities ([112]). Further, since the relationships represented by the set of eq 34 to 41 involve 8 equations with 12 unknowns, namely, γ, θ, λ, Z, Δ, C_1, C_2, C_2^o, C_3, C_3^o, $\bar{C}_3$ and X or X' or T, by fixing any four independent quantities included in the above unknowns, eq 34 to 41 can be solved simultaneously to obtain the remaining 8 quantities. The utility of this approach to system analysis for reverse osmosis process design and predicting the performance of reverse osmosis modules is illustrated in detail in the literature ([6d,105,107,108,111,112,113]).

In all the foregoing discussion on reverse osmosis transport, system analysis and process design, no new chemical engineering principle is involved. But the manner in which the known principles are combined and expressed is new; the kind of results arising from such expressions is new; and the direction such approach sets for future work on the subject is also new, all of which open a new area of chemical engineering.

Ultrafiltration and Reverse Osmosis

The emergence of reverse osmosis accounts for the current resurgence of ultrafiltration. In the light of the foregoing discussion, a new approach to ultrafiltration presents itself. *That an ultrafiltration membrane is also a reverse osmosis membrane is the essence of this approach.* This means that, just as in reverse osmosis, in ultrafiltration also, both the chemical nature and the porous structure of the membrane surface in contact with the feed solution govern the separation and permeability characteristics of the membrane under the operating conditions of the process. At the membrane-solution interface, whatever solute-solvent-membrane material interactions can prevail, they do prevail whether the solute is small or big, the solvent is aqueous or nonaqueous, the average pore size on the membrane surface is small or big, the osmotic pressure of the feed solution is significant or insignificant, or the operating pressure used for the process is high or low. This means that all the factors governing solute and solvent transport through reverse osmosis membranes also govern such transport through ultrafiltration membranes. Consequently, the science of reverse osmosis offers a natural basis for the scientific and technical development of ultrafiltration ([57,114,115,116]). In addition, when ultrafiltration membranes are used in conjunction with macromolecular solutes or with colloidal or particulate matter suspended in feed solutions, several additional considerations on membrane transport necessarily arise due to the chemistry of the systems involved, which makes ultrafiltration even a newer area of applied science than reverse osmosis. From this point of

view, a comprehensive science of reverse osmosis including all
aspects of ultrafiltration is yet to emerge.

Conclusion

In all the foregoing discussion, the chemistry is not new;
but the appreciation of chemistry is new. This appreciation is
essentially one of understanding, dedication and development.
From such appreciation, a *new* field of applied chemistry and
chemical engineering has been emerging. This new field of
applied science, which is now called popularly as "reverse
osmosis", is of enormous practical significance to society,
industry, and science itself. The event which we commemorate
today has amply justified itself to be a befitting representation
of the unfoldment of this new field of applied science. What we
know about this field is still very little; but that is enough to
show that the development of the science and technology of
reverse osmosis is vital to the health and well-being, and the
industrial and material prosperity of every community. Further,
the inherent potential of reverse osmosis processes, and reverse
osmosis membranes to contribute significantly to the health and
welfare of all beings, and also to the progress of many fields of
science, engineering, biology and medicine, is far more than what
one can comprehend at any time. Thus the social relevance of
reverse osmosis is an abiding one, and second to none. Therefore,
the science and technology of reverse osmosis must grow. For
this to happen, appropriate institutions must be created. I
hence suggest the establishment of research institutes where work
on reverse osmosis - work on the science, engineering and
technology of the broad area of synthetic membranes and their
applications - can take roots, grow, and unfold itself in all its
aspects. I also suggest that the American Chemical Society, and
all similar scientific societies concerned with the applications
of chemistry and chemical engineering for the welfare of mankind,
take further steps to recognize reverse osmosis as a new field of
applied chemistry and chemical engineering, and promote the
growth of reverse osmosis in all its aspects in every part of the
world.

In conclusion, I wish to take this opportunity to express my
deep appreciation and gratitude to the University of California,
Los Angeles, and the National Research Council of Canada, Ottawa,
for giving me the opportunity to be associated with the
conception, unfoldment, and the continuing emergence of a new,
and extraordinarily significant, field of applied chemistry and
chemical engineering during the past twenty-four years.

Nomenclature

A	= pure water permeability constant, kg-mol H_2O/m^2 s kPa
$\underset{\sim}{A}$	= constant defined by eq 1, m
$\underset{\sim}{B}$	= constant defined by eq 2, m^3
c	= molar density of solution, kg-mol/m^3
C	= concentration ratio defined by eq 29
$\underset{\sim}{C}$	= constant defined by eq 2, m^{12}
$\ln C^{*}_{NaCl}$	= quantity defined by eq 19
d	= distance between pore wall (membrane surface) and solute molecule, m
d_{av}	= average pore diameter needed on the membrane surface for a given level of NaCl separation, m
$\underset{\sim}{D}$	= distance between pore wall (membrane surface) and solute molecule at which Φ becomes very large, m
$D_{AM}/K\delta$	= solute transport parameter (treated as a single quantity), m/s
$E_s, \Sigma E_s$	= Taft's steric constant for the substituent group in the organic molecule
$\underset{\sim}{E}$	= constant defined by eq 3, m
f	= fraction solute separation defined by eq 16
$\Delta\Delta F^{\ddagger}$	= transition state free energy change, J/kg-mol
ΔG	= free energy of hydration, J/kg-mol
$\Delta\Delta G$	= quantity defined by eq 4
$(-\Delta\Delta G/\underset{\sim}{R}T)$	= free energy parameter
h^{-1}	= membrane area per unit volume of fluid space, m^{-1}
k	= mass transfer coefficient for the solute on the high pressure side of the membrane, m/s
K_a, K_b	= dissociation constant of solute (acid or base respectively)
m	= solute molality
M_A, M_B	= molecular weights of solute and water respectively
n_a, n_c	= number of moles of anion and cation respectively in one mole of ionized solute
n_{hy}	= number of moles of hydrolyzed species resulting from the hydrolysis of one mole solute
n_{ipa}, n_{ipc}	= number of moles of anion and cation respectively involved in one mole of ion-pair
N_A, N_B	= solute flux and solvent flux respectively through membrane, kg-mol/m^2 s
P	= operating pressure, kPag
(PR)	= membrane permeated product rate through given area of membrane surface, kg/h
(PWP)	= pure water permeation rate through given area of membrane surface, kg/h
r_i, r_o	= radii of the distributor tube and hollow fiber bundle respectively in DuPont B-9 module, m
r_1, r_2	= retention time ratios in LSC for solutes 1 and 2 respectively, defined by eq 7 and eq 8 respectively
R	= relative pore radius, Å

$\underset{\sim}{R}$ = gas constant, J/kg-mol K

$\underset{\sim}{s}^*, \Sigma s^*$ = modified Small's number for the organic molecule, $J^{1/2} m^{3/2} kg$-mol^{-1}

S = effective area of membrane surface, m^2

t = time, s

T = absolute temperature, K

$\bar{u}^o$ = average fluid velocity at membrane entrance, m/s

v_w^* = pure water permeation velocity through membrane, m/s

V_1^o = initial fluid volume, m^3

x = longitudinal length of feed flow in a reverse osmosis module, m

X = quantity defined by eq 30

X' = quantity defined by eq 31

X_A = mole fraction of solute

Z = quantity defined by eq 38

Greek Letters

α = quantity defined by eq 32

α_D = degree of dissociation

α_H = degree of hydrolysis

α_n = nonpolar parameter defined by eq 6

α_p = polar (hydrogen bonding) parameter defined by eq 5

β = quantity defined by eq 9

γ = quantity defined by eq 25

δ = effective membrane thickness

δ^* = coefficient associated with steric constant ΣE_s

δ_d = dispersion component of solubility parameter, $J^{1/2} cm^{-3/2}$

δ_h = hydrogen bonding component of solubility parameter, $J^{1/2} cm^{-3/2}$

δ_{sp} = overall solubility parameter, $J^{1/2} cm^{-3/2}$

Δ = fraction product water recovery

$\ln \Delta^*$ = quantity defined by eq 24 when polar, steric, and nonpolar parameters are each set equal to zero

θ = quantity defined by eq 26

λ = quantity defined by eq 27

$\Delta \nu_s$(acidity) = relative shift in the OH band maximum in the IR spectra of solute in CCl_4 and ether solutions, cm^{-1}

$\Delta \nu_s$(basicity) = relative shift in the OD band maximum in the IR spectra of CH_3OD in benzene and the proton accepting solvent used as solute in reverse osmosis, cm^{-1}

$\pi(X_A)$ = osmotic pressure of solution corresponding to mole fraction X_A of solute, kPa

$\pi(X_{A1}^o)$ = osmotic pressure of feed solution at membrane entrance, kPa

$\sigma, \Sigma \sigma$ = Hammett number for the substituent group in the organic molecule

$\sigma^*, \Sigma \sigma^*$ = Taft number for the substituent group in the organic molecule

T	= quantity defined by eq 33
Φ	= potential function of force exerted on solute molecule by pore wall (membrane surface)
Ψ	= potential function of frictional force restricting the movement of solute through pore
ω^*	= coefficient associated with modified Small's number Σs^*, $J^{-1/2}$ $m^{-3/2}$ kg-mol

Subscripts

B	= bulk solution phase
I	= interfacial solution phase
1	= bulk feed solution on the high pressure side of the membrane
2	= concentrated boundary solution on the high pressure side of the membrane
3	= membrane permeated product solution on the atmospheric pressure side of the membrane

Abstract

    Gibbs adsorption equation is an expression of the natural
phenomenon that surface forces can give rise to concentration
gradients at interfaces. Such concentration gradient at a
membrane-solution interface constitutes preferential sorption of
one of the constituents of the solution at the interface. By
letting the preferentially sorbed interfacial fluid under the
influence of surface forces, flow out under pressure through
suitably created pores in an appropriate membrane material, a
new and versatile physicochemical separation process unfolds
itself. That was how "reverse osmosis" was conceived in 1956.
An appreciation of that conception was the origin of the
development of the first practical cellulose acetate membrane
for sea water desalination announced in 1960. Understanding
reverse osmosis in all its aspects is the key to its fullest
practical utilization. A detailed appreciation of chemistry at
interfaces offers a firm basis for a fuller understanding of
reverse osmosis. An overall science of reverse osmosis arising
from such appreciation unfolds itself through proper integration
of the physicochemical parameters governing preferential sorption
at membrane-solution interfaces, materials science of reverse
osmosis membranes, and engineering science of reverse osmosis
transport and process design. The progress in the development of
this science is reviewed briefly to show that reverse osmosis is
a new field of applied chemistry and chemical engineering
immensely relevant to the welfare of mankind.

Literature Cited

1. University of California, Office of Public Information, Press Release, "New Water Desalting Process Developed at UCLA", August 23, 1960.
2. Sourirajan, S. Ind. Eng. Chem. Fundam. 1963, 2, 51.
3. Tinker, F. Proc. Roy. Soc. 1916, 92A, 357.
4. Brown, A.J.; Tinker, F. Proc. Roy. Soc. 1916, 89B, 373.
5. Tinker, F. Proc. Roy. Soc. 1917, 93A, 268.
6. Sourirajan, S. "Reverse Osmosis"; Academic Press: New York, 1970; (a) Chap. 1; (b) Chap. 2; (c) Chap. 3; (d) Chap. 4; (e) Chap. 6.
7. Sourirajan, S. In "Reverse Osmosis and Synthetic Membranes"; Sourirajan, S., Ed.; National Research Council Canada: Ottawa, 1977; Chap. 1.
8. Sourirajan, S. Pure Appl. Chem. 1978, 50, 593.
9. Sourirajan, S.; Matsuura, T. Proc. EPA Symp. on Textile Industry Technology, 1979, EPA-600/2-79-104; pp. 73-106.
10. Sourirajan, S.; Govindan, T.S. Proc. First International Symp. on Water Desalination, Washington, D.C. 1965 (Pub. U.S. Dept. Interior, Office of Saline Water, Washington, D.C., Vol. 1, pp. 251-74).
11. Dickson, J.M.; Matsuura, T.; Sourirajan, S. Ind. Eng. Chem. Process Des. Dev. 1979, 18, 641.
12. Matsuura, T.; Sourirajan, S. J. Appl. Polym. Sci. 1973, 17, 3683.
13. Onsager, L.; Samaras, N.N.T. J. Chem. Phys. 1934, 2, 528.
14. Bean, C.P. Research and Development Progress Report No. 465, Office of Saline Water, U.S. Dept. Interior, Washington, D.C. 1969.
15. Matsuura, T.; Sourirajan, S. J. Appl. Polym. Sci. 1971, 15, 2905.
16. Matsuura, T.; Sourirajan, S. J. Appl. Polym. Sci. 1972, 16, 1663.
17. Matsuura, T.; Sourirajan, S. J. Appl. Polym. Sci. 1972, 16, 2531.
18. Sourirajan, S.; Matsuura, T. In "Reverse Osmosis and Synthetic Membranes"; Sourirajan, S., Ed.; National Research Council Canada: Ottawa, 1977; (a) Chap.2; (b) Chap. 3.
19. Matsuura, T.; Sourirajan, S. Ind. Eng. Chem. Process Des. Dev. (in press).
20. Newman, M.S., Ed. "Steric Effects in Organic Chemistry"; Wiley: New York, 1956.
21. Wong, K.W.; Eckert, C.A. Ind. Eng. Chem. 1970, 62(9), 16.
22. Hansch, C.; Deutsch, E.W.; Smith, R.W. J. Am. Chem. Soc. 1965, 87, 2783.
23. Hansch, C.; Kiehs, K.; Lawrence, G.L. J. Am. Chem. Soc. 1965, 87, 5770.

24. Kiehs, K.; Hansch, C.; Moore, L. Biochemistry, 1966, 5, 2602.
25. Matsuura, T.; Sourirajan, S. J. Appl. Polym. Sci. 1973, 17, 3661.
26. Kopecek, J.; Sourirajan, S. Can. J. Chem. 1969, 47, 3467.
27. Barrow, G.M. J. Phys. Chem. 1955, 59, 1129.
28. Gordy, W. J. Chem. Phys. 1939, 7, 93.
29. Gordy, W.; Stanford, S.C. J. Chem. Phys. 1940, 8, 170.
30. Gordy, W.; Stanford, S.C. J. Chem. Phys. 1941, 9, 204.
31. Gordy, W. J. Chem. Phys. 1941, 9, 215.
32. Kuhn, L.P. J. Am. Chem. Soc. 1952, 74, 2492.
33. Pimentel, G.C.; McClellan, A.L. "The Hydrogen Bond"; W.F. Freeman: San Francisco, 1960; Chap. 8.
34. Pauling, L. "The Chemical Bond"; Cornell University Press: Ithaca, N.Y., 1967; p. 221.
35. Kagiya, T.; Sumida, Y.; Inoue, T. Bull. Chem. Soc. Jpn. 1968, 41, 767.
36. Taft, R.W., Jr. In "Steric Effects in Organic Chemistry"; Newman, M.S., Ed.; Wiley: New York, 1956; pp. 556-675.
37. Matsuura, T.; Sourirajan, S. J. Appl. Polym. Sci. 1973, 17, 1043.
38. Matsuura, T.; Pageau, L.; Sourirajan, S. J. Appl. Polym. Sci. 1975, 19, 179.
39. Matsuura, T.; Dickson, J.M.; Sourirajan, S. Ind. Eng. Chem. Process Des. Dev. 1976, 15, 149.
40. Matsuura, T.; Dickson, J.M.; Sourirajan, S. Ind. Eng. Chem. Process Des. Dev. 1976, 15, 350.
41. Rangarajan, R.; Matsuura, T.; Goodhue, E.C.; Sourirajan, S. Ind. Eng. Chem. Process Des. Dev. 1976, 15, 529.
42. Matsuura, T.; Blais, P.; Pageau, L.; Sourirajan, S. Ind. Eng. Chem. Process Des. Dev. 1977, 16, 510.
43. Rangarajan, R.; Matsuura, T.; Goodhue, E.C.; Sourirajan, S. Ind. Eng. Chem. Process Des. Dev. 1978, 17, 71.
44. Matsuura, T.; Bednas, M.E.; Sourirajan, S. J. Appl. Polym. Sci. 1974, 18, 567.
45. Matsuura, T.; Bednas, M.E.; Dickson, J.M.; Sourirajan, S. J. Appl. Polym. Sci. 1974, 18, 2829.
46. Matsuura, T.; Bednas, M.E.; Dickson, J.M.; Sourirajan, S. J. Appl. Polym. Sci. 1975, 19, 2473.
47. Shorter, J. In "Advances in Linear Free Energy Relationships"; Chapman, N.B., Shorter, J., Eds.; Plenum: New York, 1972; pp. 72-117.
48. Pinsky, J. Mod. Plast. 1957, 34(4), 145.
49. Diamond, J.M.; Wright, E.N. In "Annual Review of Physiology"; Hall, V.E., Ed.; Annual Review Inc.: Palo Alto, Calif., 1969; p. 632.
50. Green, W.J.; Frank, H.S. J. Solution Chem. 1979, 8, 187.
51. Small, P.A. J. Appl. Chem. 1953, 3, 71.
52. Baumann, F. In "Basic Liquid Chromatography"; Hadden, N., Baumann, F., MacDonald, F., Munk, M., Stevenson, R., Gere, D., Zamaroni, F., Majors, R., Eds.; Varian Aerograph: Walnut Creek, Calif., 1971; pp. 3-9.

53. Matsuura, T.; Blais, P.; Sourirajan, S. J. Appl. Polym. Sci.
    1976, 20, 1515.
54. Matsuura, T.; Sourirajan, S. Proc. 6th Intern. Symp. on
    Fresh Water from the Sea, Las Palmas, 1978, 3, 227.
    (Delyannis, A., Delyannis, E., Eds.; Tsaldari St., 34,
    Athens-Amaroussion, Greece).
55. Matsuura, T.; Sourirajan, S. J. Coll. Interface Sci. 1978,
    66, 589.
56. Matsuura, T.; Sourirajan, S. Ind. Eng. Chem. Process Des.
    Dev. 1978, 17, 419.
57. Sourirajan, S.; Matsuura, T.; Hsieh, F.H.; Gildert, G.R.
    Paper presented at the ACS Symp. on Ultrafiltration
    Membranes and Applications, Washington, D.C., September
    9-14, 1979.
58. Matsuura, T.; Taketani, Y.; Sourirajan, S. Paper presented
    at the ACS Symp. on Synthetic Membranes and Their
    Applications, San Francisco, August 25-28, 1980.
59. Rohrschneider, L. In "Advances in Chromatography"; Giddings,
    J.C., Keller, R.A., Eds.; Marcel Dekker: New York, 1967;
    pp. 333-363.
60. Hansen, C.M. Ind. Eng. Chem. Prod. Res. Dev. 1969, 8, 2.
61. Van Krevelen, D.W. "Properties of Polymers"; Elsevier:
    Amsterdam, 1976.
62. Darby, J.R.; Touchette, N.W.; Sears, K. Polym. Eng. Sci.
    1967, 7(10), 295.
63. Loeb, S.; Sourirajan, S. Dept. of Engineering, University of
    California, Los Angeles, Report No. 60-60, July 1960.
    (Report released, June 1961).
64. Loeb, S.; Sourirajan, S. Adv. Chem. Ser. 1963, 38, 117.
65. Kopecek, J.; Sourirajan, S. J. Appl. Polym. Sci. 1969, 13,
    637.
66. Kunst, B.; Sourirajan, S. J. Appl. Polym. Sci. 1970, 14, 723.
67. Kunst, B.; Sourirajan, S. Desalination, 1970, 8, 139.
68. Kunst, B.; Sourirajan, S. J. Appl. Polym. Sci. 1970, 14,
    1983.
69. Kunst, B.; Sourirajan, S. J. Appl. Polym. Sci. 1970, 14,
    2559.
70. Ohya, H.; Sourirajan, S. J. Appl. Polym. Sci. 1971, 15, 705.
71. Pilon, R.; Kunst, B.; Sourirajan, S. J. Appl. Polym. Sci.
    1971, 15, 1371.
72. Pageau, L.; Sourirajan, S. J. Appl. Polym. Sci. 1972, 16,
    3185.
73. Johnston, H.K.; Sourirajan, S. J. Appl. Polym. Sci. 1972,
    16, 3375.
74. Johnston, H.K.; Sourirajan, S. J. Appl. Polym. Sci. 1973,
    17, 2485.
75. Johnston, H.K.; Sourirajan, S. J. Appl. Polym. Sci. 1973,
    17, 3717.

76. Thayer, W.L.; Pageau, L.; Sourirajan, S. J. Appl. Polym. Sci. 1974, 18, 1891.
77. Johnston, H.K.; Sourirajan, S. J. Appl. Polym. Sci. 1974, 18, 2327.
78. Kunst, B.; Sourirajan, S. J. Appl. Polym. Sci. 1974, 18, 3423.
79. Kutowy, O.; Sourirajan, S. J. Appl. Polym. Sci. 1975, 19, 1449.
80. Sourirajan, S.; Kunst, B. In "Reverse Osmosis and Synthetic Membranes"; Sourirajan, S., Ed.; National Research Council Canada: Ottawa, 1977; pp. 129-152.
81. Thayer, W.L.; Pageau, L.; Sourirajan, S. Desalination, 1977, 21, 209.
82. Tweddle, T.A.; Sourirajan, S. J. Appl. Polym. Sci. 1978, 22, 2265.
83. Kutowy, O.; Thayer, W.L.; Sourirajan, S. Desalination, 1978, 26, 195.
84. Gildert, G.R.; Matsuura, T.; Sourirajan, S. J. Appl. Polym. Sci. 1979, 24, 305.
85. Kutowy, O.; Thayer, W.L.; Capes, C.E.; Sourirajan, S. J. Sep. Process Technol. (in press).
86. Kimura, S.; Sourirajan, S. A.I.Ch.E.J. 1967, 13, 497.
87. Sourirajan, S.; Kimura, S. Ind. Eng. Chem. Process Des. Dev. 1967, 6, 504.
88. Kimura, S.; Sourirajan, S. Ind. Eng. Chem. Process Des. Dev. 1968, 7, 41.
89. Kimura, S.; Sourirajan, S. Ind. Eng. Chem. Process Des. Dev. 1968, 7, 197.
90. Kimura, S.; Sourirajan, S. Ind. Eng. Chem. Process Des. Dev. 1968, 7, 539.
91. Kimura, S.; Sourirajan, S. Ind. Eng. Chem. Process Des. Dev. 1968, 7, 548.
92. Agrawal, J.P.; Sourirajan, S. Ind. Eng. Chem. Process Des. Dev. 1969, 8, 439.
93. Sourirajan, S.; Agrawal, J.P. Ind. Eng. Chem. 1969, 61(11), 62.
94. Matsuura, T.; Blais, P.; Dickson, J.M.; Sourirajan, S. J. Appl. Polym. Sci. 1974, 18, 3671.
95. Dickson, J.M.; Matsuura, T.; Blais, P.; Sourirajan, S. J. Appl. Polym. Sci. 1975, 19, 801.
96. Thayer, W.L.; Pageau, L.; Sourirajan, S. Can. J. Chem. Eng. 1975, 53, 422.
97. Dickson, J.M.; Matsuura, T.; Blais, P.; Sourirajan, S. J. Appl. Polym. Sci. 1976, 20, 1491.
98. Matsuura, T.; Baxter, A.G.; Sourirajan, S. Ind. Eng. Chem. Process Des. Dev. 1977, 16, 82.
99. Kutowy, O.; Matsuura, T.; Sourirajan, S. J. Appl. Polym. Sci. 1977, 21, 2051.
100. Yeager, H.L.; Matsuura, T.; Sourirajan, S. Ind. Eng. Chem. Process Des. Dev. (in press).

101. Agrawal, J.P.; Sourirajan, S. Ind. Eng. Chem. Process Des. Dev. 1970, 9, 12.
102. Matsuura, T.; Sourirajan, S. Ind. Eng. Chem. Process Des. Dev. 1971, 10, 102.
103. Rangarajan, R.; Matsuura, T.; Goodhue, E.C.; Sourirajan, S. Ind. Eng. Chem. Process Des. Dev. 1978, 17, 46.
104. Rangarajan, R.; Matsuura, T.; Goodhue, E.C.; Sourirajan, S. Ind. Eng. Chem. Process Des. Dev. 1979, 18, 278.
105. Sourirajan, S.; Ohya, H. In "Reverse Osmosis and Synthetic Membranes"; Sourirajan, S., Ed.; National Research Council Canada: Ottawa, 1977; Chap. 4.
106. Kimura, S.; Sourirajan, S.; Ohya, H. Ind. Eng. Chem. Process Des. Dev. 1969, 8, 79.
107. Ohya, H.; Sourirajan, S. Ind. Eng. Chem. Process Des. Dev. 1969, 8, 131.
108. Ohya, H.; Sourirajan, S. Desalination, 1969, 6, 153.
109. Ohya, H.; Sourirajan, S. A.I.Ch.E.J. 1969, 15, 780.
110. Ohya, H.; Sourirajan, S. A.I.Ch.E.J. 1969, 15, 829.
111. Ohya, H.; Kasahara, S.; Sourirajan, S. Desalination,1975, 16, 375.
112. Ohya, H.; Sourirajan, S. "Reverse Osmosis System Specification and Performance Data for Water Treatment Applications"; The Thayer School of Engineering, Dartmouth College: Hanover, N.H., 1971.
113. Tweddle, T.A.; Thayer, W.L.; Matsuura, T.; Hsieh, F.; Sourirajan, S. Desalination, 1980, 32, 181.
114. Hsieh, F.; Matsuura, T.; Sourirajan, S. J. Appl. Polym. Sci. 1979, 23, 561.
115. Hsieh, F.; Matsuura, T.; Sourirajan, S. Ind. Eng. Chem. Process Des. Dev. 1979, 18, 414.
116. Hsieh, F.; Matsuura, T.; Sourirajan, S. J. Sep. Process Technol. 1979, 1, 50.

Issued as N.R.C. No. 18438.

RECEIVED December 4, 1980.

Application of Synthetic Membranes in Water Supply Systems in Israel

P. GLUECKSTERN, Y. KANTOR, and M. WILF

Mekorot Water Co. Ltd., Tel-Aviv, Israel

Israel is already exploiting all of its limited drinking water sources and reduction of the amount of potable water supplied to agriculture is being seriously considered.

During the next decade substantial additional water quantities will come from sewage reclamation. These will release some of the potable water used in agriculture for the increasing demand of municipal water supply. The next step in water development would have to be the desalination of remaining undeveloped brackish water resources as well as seawater. Presently, desalination is used to sovle regional water supply problems, especially at remote locations which are not yet connected to the national water supply grid.

The aim of this paper is to discuss and analyze the following topics:

(a) the role of desalination in solving regional water supply problems, emphasizing the chronological steps of introducing reverse osmosis technology for this purpose.

(b) the comparative economics of RO brackish water desalting as an alternative to the older thermal desalting plants.

(c) discussion of the most probable desalting options for long-term application and preparation of technology and operating experience for this purpose.

(d) overall economic analysis of desalting options and conclusions regarding the most promising technology for near and long-term application.

Present Status Of Desalting In Israel

With one exception all operating plants were built at locations not connected to the national water grid. The largest center is in Eilat a small town located on the Red Sea shore.

In Eilat and at other sites in Sinai located on the sea shore, seawater feed is used. At all other sites brackish feed water in the range of 2400 to 6000ppm TDS are desalted.

0097–6156/81/0153–0063$05.00/0

The first commercial desalting unit with a capacity of about 4000 cu. m/day has been operating in Eilat since 1965. By the end of 1979, 22 units with a combined capacity of 20,000 cu. m/day were operating or used as stand-by units at 11 sites.

All commercial types of processes, with the exception of freezing, namely, distillation, reverse osmosis and electrodialysis, are being applied in the above units; with various kinds of distillation processes being used for seawater desalting. Two of them, horizontal tube multieffect distillation and vapor compression units were developed and manufactured locally by the Israel Desalination Engineering Ltd. Recently, two small RO units with a combined capacity of approx. 100 cu. m/day were also used to desalt seawater. The main aim of these units is to test and demonstrate the feasibility of this new technology.

11 out of the 12 brackish water desalting units, with a combined capacity of 4500 cu. m/day, are using the RO process. Some of the smaller RO units, which supply drinking water to small and remote communities have a capacity of about 15 cu. m/day, while each of three larger RO units has a capacity of 1200 cu. m/day. These three units desalting brackish water of about 6000 ppm TDS comprise the current stage of an expanding RO desalting site near Eilat. At the final stage the RO systems will replace all currently operating seawater distillation plants at Eilat. The main reason for replacing these thermal units, which are still in good operating condition and can be considered as reliable water supply facilities is their prohibitive energy consumption.

It is generally accepted that the energy required for desalting brackish feeds by the RO process is much lower than for any thermal desalting process. The specific energy consumptions of the four different desalting units calculated from actual running conditions and compared in Fig. 1, illustrate this point. The specific energy requirement of the multistage flash units, coupled to an old power station, expressed in equivalent Kwhr/cu. m/day units, is shown for three different operating modes:

(a) without power generation, as operated presently, because the Israel Electric Company came to the conclusion that it is uneconomic to operate the power station.

(b) without power generation but after rebuilding the two units into a single more effecient unit, more or less to the limit of current technology.

(c) same as (b), but making use of the existing turbine to generate power for all pumping requirements.

The last two operating modes require several modifications which have not yet been made.

By comparing the most efficient dual-purpose operating mode with the total specific energy consumption of the RO units it is quite clear that the difference is more than an order of magnitude. It is therefore not surprising that at the prevailing energy prices, the replacement of thermal deslating is not only attractive, but an economic must.

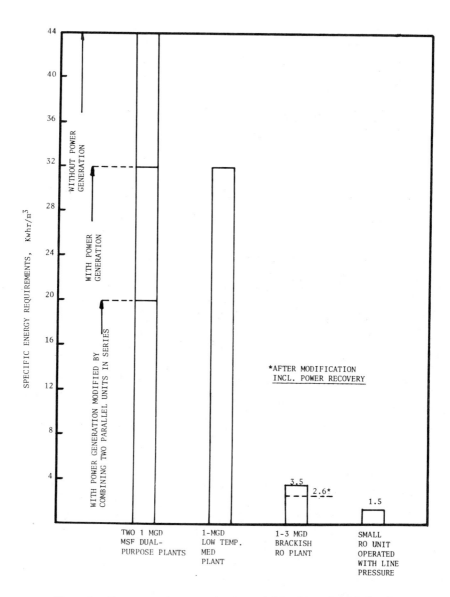

Figure 1.   Energy requirements of commercial desalting plants in Israel

The actual saving already obtained, and those predicted for the next year, due to the implementation of RO technology in Eilat are shown in Table I.

Table I: Energy saved by implementation of RO
               to replace thermal desalting in Eilat

Energy Cost For Thermal Desalting:

Annual Comsumption - 2.5×10^6 Cubic Meter
Annual Energy Cost - $\$ 5 \times 10^6$
                     $\$ 1000$ Per Family.

Saving by Replacement:

Fiscal Year	Total Annual	Annual per Family
1980	$\$ 2 \times 10^6$	$\$ 400$
1981	$\$ 4 \times 10^6$	$\$ 800$

Implementation Of RO Technology In Israel

Brackish Water Deslating. In the early 1970 Mekorot, the national water supplier, recognized the advantages of membrane de-salting processes, especially RO in regional water supplies, and started an applied research and evaluation program prior to commer-cial application. After theoretical economic evaluations (1), a test site was established and most commercial brackish water technologies were field tested (2). The results obtained during approximately two years of test operation, justified the application of RO technology for actual water supply. The small units used in the program were transferred to remote locations to supply drinking water.

Larger plants were considered for the growing water demand of Eilat. Due to the rising energy prices, Mekorot quickly came to the conclusion that RO desalting of the local brackish water should be used also to replace the distillation units. Consequently a large RO unit was designed and erected at Eilat. The first phase of de-velopment, consisting of a 700 cu. m/day unit, began commercial operation in March 1978 (3). As already mentioned, three units, with combined capacity of 3600 cu. m/day are operating presently. This capacity is now being expanded to 7000 cu. m/day and by the end of the next year the total distillation capacity will be rep-laced by an operating 10,000 cu. m/day RO plant.

The chronological steps of the implementation of RO techno-logy in Israel are shown in Fig. 2.

Seawater Desalting. In 1977 Mekorot also started a program for the evaluation of RO for seawater desalting (4). Presently

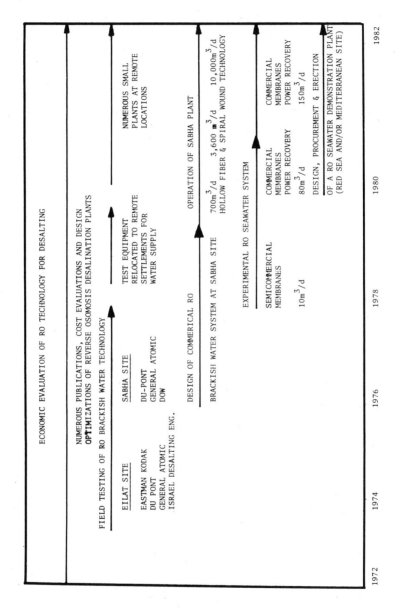

Figure 2. Research and implementation of RO technology by Mekorot Water Co. in Israel

two small units with a combined capacity of about 100 cu. m/day
are operated on the Red Sea shore. Along with other steps this
operation is essential in order to be ready to select RO for large
scale seawater desalting in the future if the water supply in
Israel will have to depend partially on desalting and RO will turn
out to be the more competitive means for this purpose. The objectives of the evaluation program are shown in Table II:

Table II: Objectives of RO evaluation program

---

1. Gain   Operating Experience With RO Equipment Under Actual
    Field Conditions.

2. Confirm The Adequacy Of All System Components And Evaluate
    Overall System Reliability.

3. Compare Under Parallel Operation The Performance Of Leading
    RO Seawater Technologies.

4. Establish Minimum Pretreatment Requirements For Local
    Conditions.

5. Establish Operating Experience And Demonstrate Applicability
    of Power Recovery Systems.

6. Evaluate The Economics Of Ro Seawater Desalting Based On
    Actual Field Experience.

These objectives are similar to those of the previous brackish
water RO evaluation program, with greater emphasis being placed on
power recovery, due to the higher energy consumption of seawater
desalting.
    The results obtained were partially reported elsewhere (4) and
they are quite similar to those obtained at other experimental
sites. Results of long term performance, some of them approaching
10,000 hours are shown in Fig. 3 and Fig. 4. As can be seen in
Fig. 3 the initial productivity values for all membranes were better
than the specified nominal values and continued to be better than
predicted. The results shown in Fig. 4 indicated that the normalized
rejection of the membranes tested,   except for one of the hollow
fiber membranes was better or within the limits specified by the
membrane producers. One of the membranes that showed an initially
low rejection   was successfully restored to the nominal value after
treatment as recommended by the manufacturer.
    The next step in the seawater RO development program will be
to construct and operate a large demonstration plant with a capacity
of several thousand cubic meters per day. This plant will be built
at a site on the Mediterranean Sea shore. This sea is much more
polluted than the Red Sea and one of the more important objectives

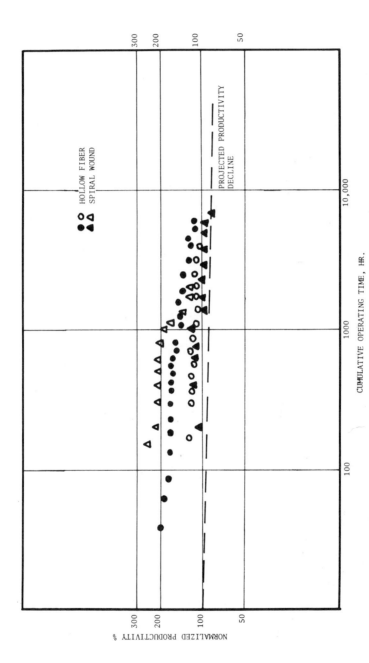

Figure 3. Productivity vs. operating time for seawater membranes tested at Eilat site

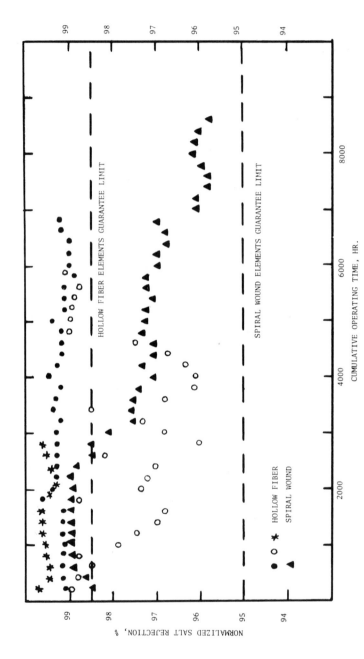

Figure 4. Normalized salt rejection vs. operating time for seawater membranes tested at Eilat site

of the demonstration plant is to investigate the pretreatment problems encountered with this type of feed water. At a later date the
demonstration plant will probably be transferred to Eilat, where
the value of desalted water is much higher.

The actual field results will enable to make a more realistic
comparison between RO and other desalting technologies and facili-
tate the selection of the best alternative at the date when large
scale desalting can not be further postponed.

At this stage no definite answer can be given about the date
and required capacity, but it is generally accepted that by the
end of the century, Israel will have to develop 500 to 700 million
cubic meters of additional water capacity. Of this 100-200 million
cubic meters would probably have to be supplied by desalting. At
least a part of the required capacity will be obtained by desalting
brackish waters which can not be used directly for agriculture.
The inventory of all brackish water resources is not completed as
yet, but the definite advantage of brackish water desalting over
seawater desalting, makes it essential to carry out a comprehensive
hydrological survey of brackish water potential in the country.

After full utilization of the brackish water feed the rest of
the required capacity would have to be obtained by seawater desalting. It was common belief in the past that the most feasible technology for large scale desalting would be seawater distillation
combined with power generation in large dual-purpose plants. In the
last few years this has changed, mainly because of the rapid progress in RO technology, and the gradually increasing recognition
that, due to various reasons, large dual-purpose plants would not
always be the best applicable solution.

Economic Comparison

The comparison between the two major seawater desalting alternatives, reverse osmosis and distillation, is more complex then
ever. The location, system size, time of implementation and economic parameters, especially the price of conventional energy and
also the possibility of use of non-conventional energy in the
future, such as solar or geothermal energy sources, may greatly
affect the final decision.

Non conventional energy options for desalting may eventually be
applied by utilizing solar or geothermal heat coupled to low temperature multieffect distillation plants and gravity pressure of
the feed water may eventually be applied as a partial power source
for RO plants located at the Dead Sea, in conjunction with the proposed Mediterranean-Dead Sea Hydroelectric Project. A conceptual
combination scheme of this alternative is shown in Fig. 5. In this
scheme the inlet of the process pump is connected to the regulating
reservoir of the hydroelectric plant through the reverse osmosis
filtration system. Pumping power is required only to build up the
differential pressure between the defined operating pressure of the
RO membranes and the available hydrostatic pressure at the pump

inlet. The power recovery turbine,shaft-connected directly to the
process pump, is designed to use the excess head of the reject
brine above that required to lift the brine back to the regulating
reservoir. The energy balance for the 40 MGD Plant shown on Fig. 5
indicates a very low energy requirement of approx. 2 Kwhr/cu. m.
This figure does not include however pumping power to lift the
product water to consumers located at levels higher than the Dead
Sea.

A summary of all feasible desalting options for Israel, sub-
divided according to the energy source, feed type and desalting
technology is given in Table III:

Table III: Desalting alternatives for Israel.

I   Conventional Energy:
      1.   RO
          1.1   Brackish Water Up To 8000 ppm TDS
          1.2   Reject Brine or High Saline Brackish Water
          1.3   Seawater
      2.   Low Temperature Multi-effect Distillation (LTMED)
                  Combined With Power Generation (Dual-Purpose)

II   Non-Conventional Energy:
      1.   Solar LTMED
      2.   Geothermal LTMED
      3.   RO Utilizing Hydrostatic Pressure of Feed Water
          3.1   RO Seawater Deslating In Conjunction With the
                  Mediterrnanean - Dead Sea Hydroeclectric Project.
          3.2   RO Brackish (Or Reject Brine) Located At The
                  Dead Sea

The energy requirements and a summary of the costing of the
listed alternatives, based on large capacity plants in the range
of 100,000 cu. m/day for seawater desalting and 20,000 cu. m/day
or larger for brackish feeds, are shown in Table IV.

The resulting unit water costs, were obtained by applying a 12
percent fixed charge rate and a unit power cost of 4.5 cents per
killowatt-hour which is predicted to be applicable in the early
nineties. It can be seen that for these economic ground rules, the
cost of desalted water from seawater, RO and dual-purpose plants
are in the same range of 60 ¢ to 70 ¢ per cubic meter. The specific
investments and energy consumption are considerable lower for RO
but its higher operation and maintenance cost, due mainly to membrane replacement, counterbalance the lower capital and energy cost
of the plants using current RO technology.

As for non-conventional energy, only utilization of the feed
gravity pressure in RO systems seems to have an economic advantage
when compared with the conventional energy option evaluated with

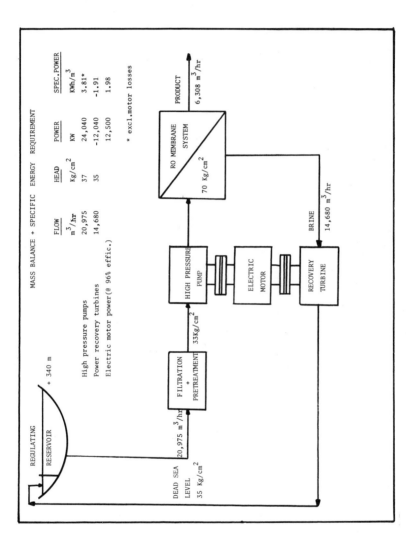

Figure 5. Connection diagram of a 40-mgd (151,000 cu m/d) RO plant to be operated in conjunction with the proposed Mediterranean–Dead Sea hydroelectric project

Table IV: Energy requirements and costing of desalting alterantives for Israel (current or near-term technology)

Energy Source	Conventional				Non-Conventional			
Feed Source ppm TDS	Brackish 2-6,000	Brackish 8-12,000	Seawater 42,000	Seawater 42,000	Seawater 42,000	Seawater 42,000	Brackish 10,000	Brackish 10,000
Process	RO	RO	RO	LTMED Dual-Purpose	LTMED Solar	LTMED Geo-thermal	RO	RO Hydrostatic Press. (Dead Sea)
Specifiec Energy Req., Kwhr/cu. m	1.5-2.0	2.5-3.5	4.0-5.0	6.5-7.5	-	-	2.0-2.5	0.5-1.5
Specific Investment $/cu. m - year	.6-1.0	1.0-1.4	1.7-2.1	2.3-2.8	1.9-2.1 excluding energy	1.9-2.1 excluding energy	1.6-2.0	.9-1.5
Operation & Maintenance Cost (Incl. chemicals and membrane replacement), cent.cu. m	10-12	12-18	22-25	4-5	4-5	4-5	22-25	12-18
Unit Water Cost,* cents/ cu. m	25-35	35-50	60-70	60-70	65-90	65-100	50-60	25-40

* @ 12% fixed charge rate and 4.5 ¢/Kwhr power cost.

Table V: Energy requirements and costing of desalting alternatives for Israel (advanced technology).

Energy Source	Conventional				Non-Conventional			
	Brackish		Seawater 42,000	Seawater 42,000	Seawater 42,000		Brackish 10,000	
Feed Source ppm TDS	2-6,000	8-12,000	42,000	42,000	42,000	42,000	10,000	
Process	RO		RO	LTMED Dual-Purpose	LTMED Solar	Geo-thermal	RO Hydrostatic Press (Dead Sea)	
Specific Energy Req., Kwhr/ cu. m	1.0-2.0	1.5-2.0	3.0-4.0	5.0-6.0	-	-	1.5-2.0	0.5-1.5
Specific Investment $/cu. m - year	.5-.8	.8-1.2	1.2-1.4	2.0-2.5	1.8-2.0	1.8-2.0	1.0-1.3	.8-1.1
					excluding energy source			
Operation & Maintenance Cost (incl. chemicals and membrane replacement), cents/cu. m	5-7	8-10	12-15	3-4	3-4	3-4	12-15	8-10
Unit Water Cost,* cents/ cu. m								
@ 4.5 cents/Kwhr	12-25	25-35	40-50	50-60	50-80	50-80	30-40	20-30
@ 9 cents/Kwhr	20-34	32-44	54-68	62-87	50-80	50-80	37-49	22-37

* @ 12% fixed charge rate

the rather optimistic energy prices. The effect of different energy prices: low (4.5 ¢/Kwhr)and high (9¢/Kwhr), on product water cost obtained by projected technologies is shown in Table V. This comparison is based on more advanced technologies, such as less expensive and more efficient membranes, and parallel improvements in the distillation technology.

It is believed that RO has more potential for further improvments. This is reflected by the comparative figures shown. Due to its lower energy requirement RO is less affected by increasing energy prices and is significantly more competitive in this undesirable situation. RO has in addition several more advantages which are outlined in Table VI.

Table VI: Main advantages of RO technology
                   in comparison to other alternatives

---

1. Lower Energy Requirement Than Any Other Process, Including Dual-Purpose Plants.

2. Sizing, Timing and Location Of Desalting Plants Are Not Dependent On The Development Of the National Power Grid.

3. Capacity Can Be Staged According To Demand Within a Short Time After Decision.

4. Large Potential For Flexibility.

5. Large Potential For Improvement.

6. Technological Improvement Can Also Be Applied In Operating Plants.

Some of the listed factors are very important for Israel's conditions and therefore the RO technology will probably be the most suitable for near term and long term needs.

Summary

Desalting in Israel, initiated in the mid-sixties to solve the regional potable water shortage, would have to be enhanced in the future to supply an additional amout of 100-200 million cubic meters per year of desalted water required for the country's development.

According to the present status of deslating technologies and forseen developments, the prospective optional methods can be classified in the following feasibility order.
   1. Reverse osomosis desalting of all available brackish water feeds.

2. Seawater reverse osmosis, especially when feed gravity pressure can be utilized.

3. Low temperature multieffect distillation, especially if solar or geothermal energy can be applied economically.

Literature Cited:

1. Glueckstern, P., Arad, N., Kantor, Y., Greenberger, M., "Proceedings of the 4th International Symposium on Fresh Water from the Sea", Athens, 1973, 2 335.

2. Glueckstern,P., Greenberger, M., "Proceedings of the 5th International Symposium on Fresh Water from the Sea", Athens, 1976, 4, 301.

3. Glueckstern,P., Kantor, Y., Mansdorf, Y., "Proceedings of the 6th International Symposium on Fresh Water from the Sea", Athens, 1978, 3, 278.

4. Glueckstern, P., Wilf, M., Kantor, Y., "Desalination",1979, 30, 235.

RECEIVED December 4, 1980.

Durability Study of Cellulose Acetate Reverse-Osmosis Membrane Under Adverse Circumstances for Desalting

Laboratory Investigation and Its Field Application Results

HIROTOSHI MOTOMURA and YOSHIO TANIGUCHI

Kurita Water Industries Ltd., 1723 Bukko-cho Hodogaya-ku, Yokohama 240, Japan

In 1968 we started investigations of RO applications for desalting brackish water. In the course of the investigations, we have found the spirally wound module of asymmetric cellulose acetate RO membrane shows excellent durabilities against fouling materials and free chlorine.

In 1971, we first installed a then-world-largest RO plant in KASHIMA industrial complex Ibaragi, Japan. The plant produced 3,000 m³/day (0.8 MGPD) of fresh water from brackish water of the KITAURA Lake. This RO system has been expanded and now produces 13,400 m³/day (3.54 MGPD). The success of the operation of the plant was reported in detail at the Mexico Conference in 1976 (1), and also at Niece in 1979 (2). Until now the RO system has been keeping the salt rejection well above 90 % with the module replacement rate of less than 5 % per year.

The total capacity of RO production in Japan came up to 80,000 m³/day (21.14 MGPD) in 1979, and KURITA's installations produce more than 70 % of the total production. Figure 1 shows the development of our installations. The rapid increases in the fields of ultrapure water polishing and the waste water reclamation are remarkable. This success of RO applications for the variety of fields are supported by
1) the proper pretreatment system and the appropriate standard for feed water quality which were established by KURITA WATER INDUSTRIES LTD.,
2) the durability studies of cellulose acetate membranes under adverse conditions.
In 1976, the importance of pretreatment for stable RO operation was presented at the Mexico Conference (1).

This presentation will discuss the membrane performance and its physical and chemical changes under unfavourable conditions. This kind of studies will give us information on trouble-shooting counter-measures for unexpected membrane deteriorations, and on the durability of a cellulose acetate membrane under adverse conditions.

Process of Membrane Deterioration

Table I shows processes of membrane deteriorations. They can
be classified into the three categories; physical, chemical and
biological process.

Physical deterioration includes compaction by creeping and
surface deteriorations by scratching and vibration. Creeping is
accelerated at higher temperatures and pressures, resulting in
the membrane compaction. This phenomenon is well analyzed and
the membrane characteristics of compaction can be estimated in
terms of m-value. Scratching and vibration can develop the microscopic defects in the surface structure of membranes, and give
poor performances. We discussed this type of deterioration in
Mexico in 1976 (1).

The major chemical processes of membrane deteriorations are
hydrolysis and oxidation. Cellulose acetate is most stable at the
level of around pH 4.7, and at the pHs lower or higher than that
value, membrane hydrolysis is accelerated. In practical applications of cellulose acetate membranes, feed water pH is usually
controlled between 5 to 6. But it is impossible to control the pH
of demineralized pure water for electronic and pharmaceutical uses,
i.e. for ultrapure water polishing. In such cases feed water pH 7
should be supplied to cellulose acetate material. Studies of
membrane behaviour under such conditions will give good information for estimating the membrane life.

Adverse oxidation of membrane occurs at higher concentrations
of oxidizers such as chlorine, ozone and hydrogen peroxide. The
chemicals are important for slime control, and rather high concentrations of the chemicals are dosed for sterilization of RO feed
system, especially in cases of ultrapure water system, and of
waste water treatment system. The evaluation of membrane durability against oxidizing chemicals informs us the proper procedures
for RO maintenance.

Any biological deterioration of cellulose acetate membranes
is always by "accidental". To prevent this kind of deteriorations, chlorine injection to feed water is common practice.
Inadequate control of chlorine injection may result in the enzymic
deterioration of cellulose acetate membrane.

Influences of Deterioration on Membrane Characteristics

As membrane deteriorations can be seen in case of performance
degradations or changes in membrane structure, we have investigated into these two aspects. Information about the relation
between membrane characteristics and deterioration processes is
useful for trouble-shooting. Even if operation records showed no
implication of deteriorating process of a membrane, the analysis
of the deteriorated membrane will reveal its own history.

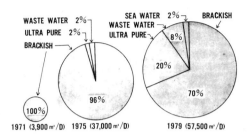

Figure 1.   Development of RO installations by Kurita Water Industries Ltd

Table I.   Processes of Membrane Deteriorations

MEMBRANE DETERIORATIONS

- **PHYSICAL**
  CREEPING
  SCRATCHING & VIBRATION
- **CHEMICAL**
  HYDROLYSIS
  OXIDATION
- **BIOLOGICAL**

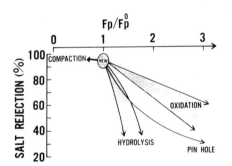

Figure 2.   Rejection–flux pattern of deteriorated cellulose acetate membrane: F_p, permeate flux of new membrane; F_p, permeate flux of deteriorated membrane.

Performance. Figure 2 shows a rejection-flux pattern (R-F pattern). Compaction, as it is well known, results in the flux decline with salt rejection increase. Contrary to this, other types of membrane deterioration give the flux increase with salt rejection decline. In case of scratching, vibration, or microbiological deterioration, small cracks or pinholes develop over membrane surfaces. If the flux increase is solely attributed to the crack or pin-holes, and these sites do not reject salt at all, the relation between salt rejection and flux can be calculated. The pattern in Figure 2 shows the result of this calculation, and agreed well with the actual performance of the deteriorated membrane.

Hydrolysis gives almost the same pattern as in the case of pin-holes at higher salt rejection but less permeate flux at lower salt rejection.

Oxidation gives much higher water flux increase comparing with the cases of pin-hole and hydrolysis. In both cases of hydrolysis and oxidation, the R-F pattern varies somewhat with membrane types.

Physical and Chemical Structure. The analyses of physical and chemical structures include electronmicroscopic analysis, IR spectrophotometric analysis, X-ray diffractometry, and burst tests.

Figure 3 shows the surface structure of a physically deteriorated membrane by scanning electronmicroscopes. Hard crystals of an inorganic salt might have scratched the membrane surface and the rough surface was developed. The salt rejection decreased to 60 % and the water flux doubled comparing that of normal membranes.

Figure 4 shows surface heavily hydrolyzed by a concentrated alkaline solution. This membrane could reject only 17 % of salt. It looks like the stormy sea surface. This surface seems to have dissolved, and then reprecipitated.

Figure 5 shows the optical microscopic view of a stained membrane surface which were biologically deteriorated. Microbiological colonies of 1 to 10 $\mu^{\star}$ size can be seen spreading over the surface. The density of microorganism over the surface determined by ultrasonic dispersion technique was 2×10^6 cells/ cm^2. Figure 6 shows the electronmicroscopic view of the same surface. When the colonies of microorganism were removed, the surface defects were found. The pattern of the defects is similar to that of the optical microscopic view. The enzymic hydrolysis occurred just below the colonies of microorganism. Figure 7 shows the defect penetrating the active surface. This structual change gives the R-F pattern similar to that of the membrane with pin-holes. This membrane shows the salt rejection of 25 %, and permeate flux of 2.50 m/D.

The X-ray diffraction spectrum in Figure 8 shows the crystalline structure of a normal cellulosic membrane. Diffraction peaks appeared around 10, 11, 16, and 21 degrees of 2θ. This spectrum

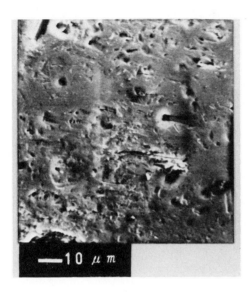

Figure 3.   Surface structure of physically deteriorated membrane

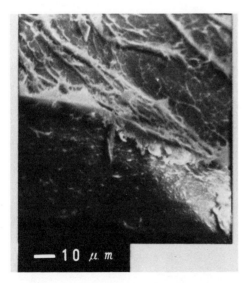

Figure 4.   Surface structure of heavily hydrolyzed membrane

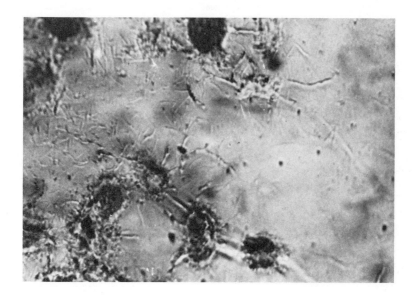

Figure 5.   Optical microscopic view of membrane surfaces that were biologically deteriorated

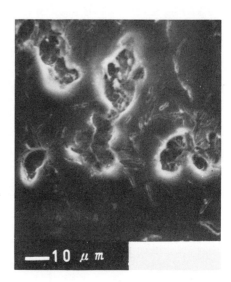

Figure 6.   Scanning electron microscopic view of membrane surfaces that were biologically deteriorated. Colonies of the microorganism on the surface were removed.

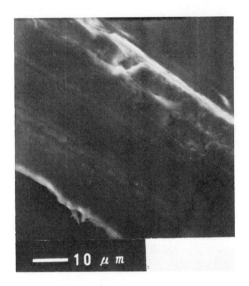

Figure 7. Cross section of biologically deteriorated membrane

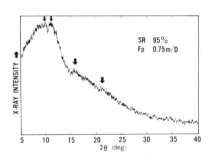

Figure 8. X-ray diffraction pattern of normal cellulose acetate membrane

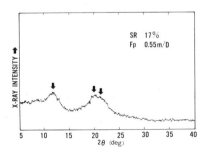

Figure 9. X-ray diffraction pattern of hydrolyzed cellulose acetate membrane

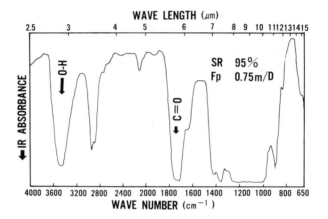

Figure 10.   IR spectrum of normal cellulose acetate membrane

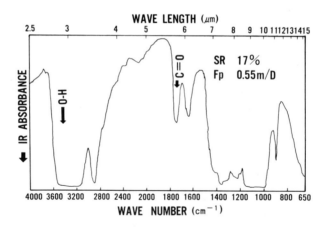

Figure 11.   IR spectrum of hydrolyzed cellulose acetate membrane

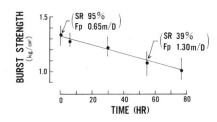

Figure 12. Burst strength of oxidized membrane that was soaked in NaClO of 0.1% AsCl₂

Table II.   Process of Membrane Deterioration and Its Influences on the Characteristics of Membrane

DETERIORATION   MEMBRANE CHARACTERISTICS

● PHYSICAL

Creeping	Fp ↓, SR
Scratching & Vibration	R-F pattern of "pin-hole" Rough Surface

● CHEMICAL

Hydrolysis	Typical R-F pattern IR : C=O↓, O-H↑ Rough Surface
Oxidation	Typical R-F pattern Decrease of Burst Strength

● BIOLOGICAL

	R-F pattern of "pin-hole" Pin-holes under colonies

can be assigned to that of cellulose triacetate II crystal.
Figure 9 shows a spectrum of the hydrolyzed membrane, and peaks
appeared at 11, 20, and 22 degrees. The crystal structure changed
to that of cellulose II type.

Figure 10 shows the IR spectrum of a normal cellulose acetate
membrane. Figure 11 shows the spectrum of the hydrolyzed membrane. The decrease of absorption around 1,720 cm^{-1}, and the
increase of absorption around 3,200 to 3,500 cm^{-1} are shown. The
first peak correspond to the C = O double bond, and the second to
the O - H single bond. These spectra show the decrease of the
acetyl content in the membrane.

X-ray and IR spectra of an oxidized membrane gave no information, but physical strength of the membrane was highly decreased.
Figure 12 shows the burst strength of the oxidized membrane. The
membrane was immersed in sodium hypochlorite solution of 0.1 %,
and the burst strength was determined from time to time. The
strength decreased gradually.

Table II shows the processes of membrane deteriorations and
its influences on the characteristics of membrane.

Concluding Remarks

Our investigation on durability and membrane characteristics
changes under adverse conditions have much contributed to
development of RO applications. Among these applications are
those for ultra-pure water in electronic and pharmaceutical
industries. Even under the circumstance of pH 7 and with 2 to 4
times per year of sterilization by H_2O_2 of as high as 1 %, the
cellulose acetate membrane proved to show membrane life of more
than 3 years.

Our investigation will also contribute to improvement in the
system design, and techniques of operation and maintenance.

We have tried to relate the performance of a deteriorated
membrane to its structure by classical methods. Recent advancement in the techniques of morphological and physicochemical
analyses is remarkable, and is much contributing to better understanding of the membrane behaviour. We have now various types of
RO membranes made of synthetic polymers available, and most these
analytical procedures are applicable for the analysis of these
membranes. Investigations on the membrane structures are much
more required, and they will reveal the relations between
materials and structure, and structure and performance. We
believe these investigations will contribute to development not
only in the membrane itself, but in the application of the membrane. We hope the progress of membrane science will expand RO
market.

Literature Cited

1. Taniguchi, Y. DESALINATION, 1977, 20, 353-364.
2. Horio, K. DESALINATION, 1979, 32, 211-220.

RECEIVED December 4, 1980.

Membranes for Salinity Gradient Energy Production

K. L. LEE, R. W. BAKER, and H. K. LONSDALE

Bend Research, Inc., 64550 Research Rd., Bend, OR 97701

The free energy of mixing 1 m^3 of fresh water with seawater is about 0.65 kilowatt-hours. This free energy is now wasted in considerable quantity where the fresh waters of the earth mix with the oceans. Previous studies by Loeb suggested that some of this energy may be recovered by a process known as pressure-retarded osmosis (PRO). In PRO, fresh water permeates across a semipermeable membrane into a brine pressurized to a point below its osmotic pressure. The volume increase can then be released through a turbine to generate power. In the present work the potential of PRO has been evaluated using eight reverse osmosis desalination membranes, including cellulose acetate, polyamide, polybenzimidazolone, and various composite membranes. A transport model has been developed whereby the PRO performance of a membrane can be predicted based on reverse osmosis (RO) and direct osmosis characterization data. It has been shown that a wide range of osmotic phenomena can be explained in terms of three intrinsic membrane properties: the permeability coefficients for salt and water, and the resistance to salt diffusion in the porous support layer of the membrane.

Based on this analysis and accompanying experimental work, we conclude:

(1) PRO power generation is technically feasible, but not economically viable with currently available RO membranes and a seawater/fresh water salinity gradient resource.

(2) Concentration polarization is a major problem in PRO. External concentration polarization occurs in the liquid boundary layers on either side of the membrane. External concentration polarization can be minimized by stirring the solutions to reduce the thickness of these boundary layers.

(3) Internal concentration polarization occurs as a result of salt accumulation in the porous substrate of asymmetric membranes, and is unaffected by stirring. Internal concentration polarization can only be reduced to an acceptable level by using membranes with an open substrate. Without due regard for internal concentration polarization, it is unsafe to project PRO performance from RO performance.

0097–6156/81/0153–0089$05.00/0

(4) Of the existing flat-sheet RO membranes, cellulose acetate membranes of the Loeb-Sourirajan type give the best results because their open microporous substrate minimizes internal concentration polarization. Conventional interfacial composite membranes, despite their high water permeabilities and good salt rejections, are not suitable for PRO because of severe internal concentration polarization.

(5) Useful PRO membranes do not require the very high permselectivity necessary in reverse osmosis, and a trade-off between flux and salt rejection in conventional RO membranes is possible. If the salt rejection is too low, however, internal concentration polarization due to excessive salt leakage can limit the water flux.

(6) As a result of internal concentration polarization, the effective osmotic pressure difference across the membrane can be significantly below the osmotic pressure difference between the bulk solutions. The effective osmotic pressure can be calculated from the salt permeation coefficient and the salt diffusion resistance in the porous membrane substrate. The highest power output for a membrane is obtained at an operating pressure equal to about one half of the effective osmotic pressure.

(7) Based on a simple economic analysis, it appears that, when seawater is used as the salt solution, a membrane with a water flux in PRO of about 1×10^{-2} cm^3/cm^2-sec ($\sim$200 gal/ft^2-day) is required to make the process economically viable in today's economy, even if the installed membrane cost is as low as \$100/m^2. The highest flux we projected under these PRO conditions among the RO membranes tested was only somewhat greater than 1×10^{-4} cm^3/cm^2-sec ($\sim$2 gal/ft^2-day), for a power output of 1.6 watt/m^2.

(8) The economics of PRO systems using brines and fresh water sources and current membranes are more favorable, with estimated power outputs as high as 200 watt/m^2. However, surface brines exist in deserts where there is limited fresh water, and brines that might be produced from salt domes pose a difficult effluent disposal problem. If PRO systems can be produced at an installed cost of \$100/m^2 of membrane, the projected economics are competitive with other power-generating techniques. This appears to be the only salinity gradient resource worthy of further study.

Acknowledgment

This work was supported in part by the U.S. Department of Energy under Contract EG-77-C-05-5525.

Reference

K.L. Lee, R.W. Baker, and H.K. Lonsdale, "Membranes for Power Generation by Pressure-Retarded Osmosis," Journal of Membrane Science, in press.

RECEIVED December 4, 1980.

Seawater Reverse Osmosis: The Real Experience

R. BAKISH

Director of Desalination Programs, Fairleigh Dickinson University, Teaneck, NJ 07070

Seawater RO today is a proven water conversion process with a respectable, though still most limited past and truly exciting future. While the total worldwide distillation based capacity has exceeded the 1 billion gallons-per-day mark, that of seawater RO has just about reached 10 million gallons per day. When one is to speak of experience, I believe that one should only talk about a process after it has become commercial. The most accurate statement as to the time for commercialization of seawater reverse osmosis plants is to say that it appears to be sometime between late 1974 and early 1975. As a criterion for commercialization, I consider the actual sale of a plant by a manufacturer to a user. One, of course, speaks here of relatively small plants, in fact, plants with capacity in the 2,500 to 20,000 gallons-per-day range. The difficulty in establishing the accurate date is the apparent fact that in the early installed plants, it is virtually impossible to establish with certainty whether the plant was being field tested or purchased on the open market as a plant for the purpose of water production. To me, at least, the commercialization is an important fact of a successful water conversion technique, because before it takes place, one cannot truly speak of it as part of the technology contributing to water conversion, or of experience with it. In fact, it is even more complex than this as to some, real commercialization means the above stated definition, but applied to plants with minimum capacity of 1MGD.

Pretreatment

As you well know seawater around the world varies extensively. This variability is further extended by the nature and location of the plant intakes and introduces factors beyond composition differences, which are relevant to the quality of the raw seawater to be converted. Is one withdrawing water from a sea well?

What kind of a well is it? Does the water originate from a
shallow bay or does it come out of deep coastal waters? What
is the nature of the bottom? Is it withdrawn from deep open
ocean, etc? Each of these facts affect factors such as suspended
solids, bio-content, and last but not least, depend on local
atmospheric conditions induced variability.

Table I shows the composition of some natural seawaters
around the world. This wide seawater composition variation
affects the quality of the product, i. e. the product salinity.
This, of course, in the unlikely case that all we had to contend
with in the RO conversion were the composition variations. In
fact, the other variables such as: the number and the nature of
microorganisms, the amount, size, and nature of suspended
solids and their variability, presence or absence of pollutants,
each and all of which can be affected by the prevailing atmospheric conditionspresent, are much more consequential to
trouble-free operations than the seawater composition variations.

TABLE I - SALINITY VARIATION AROUND THE WORLD

Approximate Salinities ppm

Baltic Sea	7,000
Black Sea	13,000
Adriatic Sea	25,000
Pacific Ocean	33,600
Indian Ocean	33,800
Caribbean (W.I.L.)	38,500
Atlantic Ocean	39,400
Arabian Gulf	43,000
Red Sea	43,000

The SDI[1] of a water is the accepted criterion of its
quality for RO conversion and some SDI's of water around the
world are given on Table II. The manufacturers usually require
values of waters reaching permeators to have an SDI below 3 if
they are to warranty their membrane design life. This requirement of seawater for RO conversion is accomplished through pretreatment. The quality of the raw seawater determines the need
for, and the specific type of pretreatment required to produce
the water quality requisite to satisfy a specific permeator
manufacturer's requirements.

TABLE II

SEAWATER SILT DENSITY INDEX AS OBSERVED AT DIFFERENT LOCATIONS

LOCATION	TYPE OF INTAKE	S.D.I.
Paradise Island, Bahamas	Open Ocean	35-75*
Paradise Island, Bahamas	Beach Well	2.0-3.5**
New Providence, Bahamas	Well	3.4**
New Providence, Bahamas	Well – 5U Filtration	1.9
Cat Cay, Bahamas	Open Ocean	6.0
Cat Cay, Bahamas	Natural Beach Sand Filter	2.5
Wrightville Beach, U.S.A.	Pipe	45*
CADAFE, Venezuela	Channel	16* up to 45
Jeddah, Red Sea, Saudi Arabia	Pipe	6.2
Ral Al Mishab, Arabian Gulf, S.A.	Channel – Infiltration Gallery	4.0**
WIL St. Croix USVI	Tague Bay – 6'depth 150' from shore	18

* Total Time $<$ 15 Minutes

**Iron in System

A variety of situations ranging from virtually no pretreatment to elaborate multistep pretreatment processes are encountered in the field today. In the case of systems,[3,4] withdrawing water from open ocean and from sites far removed from shallow coastal zones with coastal influences, limited filtering referred to as mechanical filtering is satisfactory. We might have a sand filter followed by a 5 micron filter providing all the pretreatment needed to assure the necessary quality. When water is withdrawn from properly designed sea wells, only minimal pretreatment consisting of a sand filter and the 5 micron cartridge filter is needed. This is not unlike pretreatment used for the processing of deep ocean water for the production of water with acceptable SDI's.

On the other end of the spectrum, we have water withdrawn directly from shallow bays near the shore containing high bacteria, algae, and suspended solid counts. Such sources are also subject to notable weather induced fluctuations. In these cases experience dictates need for elaborate pretreatment. One pretreatment approach[5,6,7] which appears to have met with excellent success, though also notably increasing water costs, begins with chlorination, followed by in-line coagulation and filtration with mixed bed and zeolite filters. In some cases polyelectrolytes are added to improve in-line coagulation. The water is then reacted with bisulphite for dechlorination in the case where chlorine sensitive membranes are used, and there are cases on record where as much as double anticipated chlorine stoichiometry is added to insure complete dechlorination. The water then passes through a 5 micron cartridge filter to round up the pretreatment cycle prior to pH adjustment for scale control. Figure 1 gives a schematic of this type of pretreatment which, in principle, appears widely used. Depending on the specific content of the seawaters being processed, one can either carry out the complete set of steps as shown in Figure I or only part of them. One can use an activated carbon filter instead of the bisulphite for dechlorination though it is felt by some that activated charcoal filters tend to promote bacterial growth.

The proper operation of pretreatment systems, including duly scheduled backwashing of filters, and correct and continuous dosing of the requisite chemicals is necessary to assure a steady supply of pretreated water with the requisite by the permeator manufacturer quality. While I have been unable to obtain concrete data, there are indications that an alternate prefiltration system combining a 5 micron cartridge filter, ultrafiltration unit, and a UV sterilizer produces an SDI lower than 3. Experience with ultrafiltration at our West Indies laboratory, a couple of years ago, indicated excessive costs mainly caused by rapid plugging of associated cartridge filters. The literature has at least a reference of successful coupling of ultrafiltration and RO.[8]

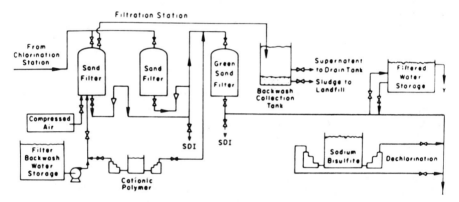

Figure 1.   Pretreatment schematic

Before entering the permeator for salt removal, the feed is
either acidified or modified with proprietary chemicals for scale
control. While both approaches have their followers, despite its
handicaps, acid dosing today appears predominant in the industry;
in fact some RO permeator manufacturers will only warranty their
product for acid. Studies[9] to be initiated shortly at our laboratory should hopefully quantitatively evaluate the relative
merits of these approaches. It is hoped that at least equivalence
if not superiority for proprietary scale control chemicals will
be unequivocally established so that one can drop acid use and
satisfy many who are justifiably reluctant to use acid, for
reasons familiar to all.

RO systems today accomplish the conversion either with a
single or a double pass. From the information provided to me by
permeator and system manufacturers, and from discussions with
individuals active in the industry, it appears that about 60% of
seawater systems use single pass conversion. One must add here
that there are also differences in the configuration of RO
membranes within the permeators. While there are others, the
spiral wound and the hollow fiber designs truly command the
market place today. Again, estimating, it appears that the
hollow fiber design also has about 60% of the market.

A third relevant factor is the chemical composition of the
membranes, with cellulose acetate, polyamide and a number of
composite membranes sharing the seawater installed capacity. It
is my estimate that polyamide membranes have at least 90% of
the market.

A few comments on the size of commercial seawater RO plants
are appropriate at this point. While in principle any size plant
can be built, it appears that commercial plants today start at
1000GPD. The largest operational plant in the world today is the
Jeddah 3.2MGD plant[10] on stream since February 1979, followed
by 800,000 GPD plant[11] at CADAFE, which has been on stream since
the beginning of this year, and was recently expanded to
1,000,000 GPD. Next in size is the 400,000 GPD plant at the
Caspian Sea[12]. Two additional plants exceeding the 800,000 GPD
capacity appear to be in various stages of completion; one of
them is second, 1,000,000 GPD capacity plant in CADAFE, and the
other is in Yanbu[13]. Saudi Arabia, where I understand a
500,000 GPD expansion is planned for the 800,000 GPD plant, which
will bring capacity to 1,300,000 GPD. Last May, ground-breaking
ceremonies on a 3MGD plant, for the Florida Aqueduct Authority
took place. When completed, this will be the second largest seawater RO plant, and the largest single pass seawater plant in the
world. In total, I suspect there are about 300 plants with
capacities above 5,000 GPD, and perhaps more than twice as many if
one counts all seawater plants, including those on yachts and
drilling platforms.

The Experience

Let us now attempt to review the field experience of sea-water RO plants, perhaps the most important aspect of any commercial process, information most critical to the potential plant buyer. My comments here are biased by our experience at the Desalination Technology Transfer Center in St. Croix, where we have been operating seawater RO plants for more than four years. While it is certain that no two facilities have equivalent operational practice, experience, and problems, and I wish to emphasize this, nevertheless, I believe that by discussing the most limited operations information available, in light of our experience, it will make my comments more meaningful.

Let me begin by saying that regretfully only very limited data on the 600 or more seawater RO systems, which are operational around the world today, have reached the printed stage. In fact, so little operational data have been published, that reference to these few reports might provide even biased impression. In fact, most of the published reports habitually contain comments such as: "excellent experience," "performance was quite satisfactory." Some of the operators[14] state that while experience appears satisfactory, longer operation will be needed and preferably from larger plants, before they will be prepared to make a full commitment to this technology. In another report[8] comments were to the effect that the ultrafiltration was superior pretreatment to the in-line coagulation approach, and that the systems as a whole performed well. Other reports with minor exception provide similar comments.

In principle this speaks of an endorsement of the process, but based on my personal involvement in RO operations, these "operations" reports are not quite satisfactory. My remarks here should not be construed as critical of the performance of the systems, or the technology. They only express my sentiment to the effect that if there were more detailed information available it would materially enhance the potential user's ability to decide for himself on the virtues of the process, and provide a strong growth impetus. Also, I feel that today there are no accepted standards either for judgement or for comparison of seawater RO system performance.

The following is the kind of data which should be most useful:

Data to judge the efficiency of the pretreatment operation including SDI's along the pretreatment cycle. Assuming that customarily only requisite quality water reaches the permeators effort should be made to establish direct cause and effect relationship associated with deviations from pretreatment objectives and possible damage to permeators.

Regarding the permeators themselves, information on the percent salt rejection, and the productivity over the period of time the unit or units operated should be generated and supplied. Specific information on cleaning of the permeators including

frequency and effects of cleaning on performance should be made
available. Biological presence, fouling and their possible effect
on performance, if any, should be provided. Last, but not least,
reference to permeator failures, if any, with detailed reports
on "postmortem" examination of the permeator and the suspected
causes of the failure, should be presented. More and better
cost information is also needed.

Now let us look at the systems and the components of the
systems. Reports in the field are virtually mute on many small
but annoying problems, which almost invariably accompany the
operation of seawater RO systems. Here are some which have
plagued us, starting with the pumps. I will not identify
manufacturers, as I have avoided reference to any in this write-
up. It is not my objective to accuse anyone. I just offer these
comments in the hope to encourage those who I hope are aware of
their product problems in the field and failures to rectify
those for the benefit of all. I feel that considerably greater
attention must be placed on pumps and pump materials selection
for seawater RO use in order to improve reliability, simplify
maintenance, and reduce failure frequency in the pump operations,
and in turn improve on the RO system water supply capability.
There is need for greater care in motor alignment, and attention
to this problem will reduce even further the frequency of bearing
failures. Additional attention could be given to flow meters,
and while most appear satisfactory, both in terms of durability
and accuracy, some are most difficult to service. Knowing the
alien-to-many materials ambient in the vicinity of seawater RO
plants, I wonder why manufacturers do not pay more attention to
materials selection here.

Flow switches, pressure relief valves, and high pressure
switches, all tend to be less than compeltely reliable, and while
we have in no way checked all available models and manufacturers,
our experience indicates need for additional attention. Components
related to switches, and pressure relief valves, could be of
particular concern in semi-attended and fully automated installations.

For chlorination we graduated from hypochlorite tanks to in
situ chlorine generation by electrochemical means, a major improvement indeed, which we highly recommend. However, we have had
more than our share of problems with the chlorine generator we
used.

In conclusion, while it can be stated that the apparent facts
on seawater RO will certainly support the continuous growth of
this technique for seawater conversion, the reality is that there
are only very limited real operations generated and reported firm
facts on which one can concretely and unequivocally base decision
to justify a more rapid growth here. Unless some of these concrete
operational facts on the large and largest RO installations
operating around the world today are made available, the desired
by all rapid growth of large seawater RO systems will come at

rates that could be disappointing to many in the camps of both users and manufacturers. There is no substitute to good operations data on what I believe is a truly outstanding process for fueling its further rapid growth.

Acknowledgements

This work was prepared as part of the activities under contract No. 14-34-0001-0447 of OWRT, and I wish to thank OWRT for its support. I also wish to thank Ajax International Corporation, Basic Technologies, Inc., Degremont, Dow Chemical, DSS Engineers, Inc., Fluid System, Div. of UOP, Inc. Kobe Steel, Ltd., Permutit Co., Inc., and Polymetrics, Inc. for reference material and information,which they were kind enough to supply. I also wish to thank Mr. William Root, the first graduate of the Fairleigh Dickinson University Desalination Program for information which he supplied.

References

1. Du Pont, Technical Bulletin, p. 491
2. S. R. Latour, DSS Engineers, Inc., Private Communication and other sources.
3. S. M. Rovel, Desalination 22, (1977), pp. 485–493.
4. H. Lerat, Proceedings 6th International Symposium, "Fresh Water From the Sea" (1971), pp. 317–325.
5. A. C. Epstein, Proceedings 39th Annual International Water Conference, Pittsburgh, Pennsylvania, Seawater Pretreatment, available NITS (1979), p. 590.
6. A. C. Epstein, Proceedings International Water Conference, Pittsburgh, Pennsylvania, Pretreatment of Seawater for Membrane Processes, (1978), pp. 149–160
7. A. B. Mindler and S. T. Bateman, Pilot Plant Study on Marine Microorganisms and Organic Matter, Permutit, May 1980, OWRT Contract No. 14-34-0001-8538.
8. R. Tidball, D. Kuiper, P. H. Lange, and R. Kadai, Desalination, 3 (1978 pp. 319–330.
9. OWRT, Contract in Negotiation
10. A. Al Golaikah, N. El Ramly, Isam Jamjoom, and R. Seaton, Technical Proceedings 7th Annual Conference of NWSIA,(1979).
11. R. Quinn, Proceedings IDEA Conference, Nice (1979)
12. G. Leitner, Technical Proceedings 7th Annual Conference of NWSIA (1979)
13. W. Andrews, Private Communication
14. P. Glueckstern, Y. Kantor, and M. Wilf, Proceedings 6th International Symposium "Fresh Water From the Sea," 3 (1978), pp. 319–330.

RECEIVED December 4, 1980.

An Electrical Study of Ion Transport in C Acetate

M. A. CHAUDRY[1] and P. MEARES

Chemistry Department, University of Aberdeen, Scotland

Although cellulose acetate is not inherently a polyelectrolyte there are reports which indicate that it contains a low concentration of weak acid, presumably carboxylic, groups (1). Water absorbed by cellulose acetate membranes might be preferentially located, to some extent, in the region of these ionogenic groups and so assist in their dissociation.

When ions permeate through cellulose acetate their transport pathways will tend to follow the regions where water is most concentrated. Thus they will meet and interact with the dissociated, fixed carboxylate ions. The concentrations of ions absorbed from salt solutions by swollen cellulose acetate are small for reasons connected with the low dielectric constant of the latter (2). The electro-chemical potentials of ions undergoing transport may therefore be influenced significantly by the presence of the fixed charges. Such influences are familiar with normal ion-exchange membranes.

Because such behaviour would affect the performance of cellulose acetate membranes in desalination, it was studied twelve years ago by one of the authors using methods similar to those described here. The results were not widely publicized at that time (3). The work has now been repeated in greater detail and the earlier findings confirmed. This new work is reported here. In the intervening period other workers have referred to the effect of ion-exchange capacity of cellulose acetate on its membrane properties but their studies have been carried out differently from ours (4).

Outline of Experimental Procedures

We seek to determine an effective fixed-charge density which influences ion uptake and transport. This may be different from an analytical determination of total carboxyl content because some groups may not be in swollen regions of the polymer and so may not

[1] Current address: Chasma Nuclear Power Project, Pakistan Atomic Energy Commission, P.O. Box No. 1133, Islamabad, Pakistan.

be exposed to the ion fluxes.   Three types of electrochemical
measurements are required in our procedure.   They are: the time
course of the decrease in resistance of a membrane, previously
cooked in water at a very dilute salt solution at a controlled pH,
after immersion in a more concentrated salt solution (5);   the
membrane conductance at equilibrium in that solution, membrane
concentration potentials measured with the membrane interposed
between a series of solutions of the same salt over a range of
concentrations.

All measurements have been made on homogeneous membranes of
Eastman Kodak 398-3 cellulose acetate (6).   The membranes were
cast on glass plates and evaporated slowly to dryness from 2% w/v
solution in pure acetone in a controlled atmosphere.   The
membranes were carefully outgassed under vacuum at 40°C before
annealing in water for 30 minutes at 80°C during which they became
detached from their casting plates.

The membranes, of thickness usually about 40 μm, were mounted
in a Perspex cell in which all measurements were carried out.   The
membrane faces were not obstructed by supports as zero pressure
difference was maintained in the cell.   A.C. conductances at
1400 Hz were measured with platinum disc electrodes parallel to the
membrane and of area 7 cm^2, equal to that of the membrane.
Potentials were measured with reversible Ag/AgCl electrodes.
Large volumes of solutions, circulating through external
thermostatted reservoirs were used.   The entire set up was housed
in an air thermostat and the half-cells were each stirred by small
motor-driven Perspex helices.

Analysis of Experimental Data

Provided one may neglect the small osmotic shrinkage that
occurs when a membrane previously swollen in a very dilute
solution is transferred to a somewhat more concentrated solution,
and provided no exchange of counterion-type occurs (by pre-
conditioning in a 10^{-4} M salt solution rather than in water, a
hydrogen ion/metal cation exchange was prevented from interfering
with the results) the absorption of salt by the membrane will
follow Fickian diffusion kinetics.   The molar concentration $\bar{c}_t$ of
salt at a plane distant x from one face and time t is given by

$$\frac{\bar{c}_t}{\bar{c}_\infty} = 1 - \frac{4}{\pi} \sum_{n=0}^{\infty} \frac{1}{(2n+1)} \sin[(2n+1) \pi x/\ell] \exp\{-[(2n+1)\pi/\ell]^2 Dt\} \quad (1)$$

where c_∞ is the concentration everywhere in the membrane when $t = \infty$.
ℓ is the membrane thickness and D the diffusion coefficient of the
salt in the membrane.
When t exceeds a few minutes only the first term in the
summation is important and equation 1 may be reduced to

$$\bar{c}_t = \bar{c}_\infty [1 - Q \sin(\pi x/\ell)] \quad (2)$$

where Q is defined by

$$Q = \frac{4}{\pi} \exp(-\pi^2 D t/\ell^2) \tag{3}$$

While salt is entering the membrane its electrical resistance falls progressively.   If the equivalent conductance Λ of the salt in the membrane may be regarded as constant, which is consistent with the equilibrium conductance data to be discussed later, integration of the local resistance across the thickness of the membrane leads to

$$\frac{K_\infty - K_o}{K_t - K_o} = \frac{1}{(1-Q^2)^{\frac{1}{2}}} \left[1 + \frac{2}{\pi} \tan^{-1} \left\{ \frac{Q}{(1-Q^2)^{\frac{1}{2}}} \right\} \right] \tag{4}$$

where K_o, K_t and K_∞ are the membrane conductances at times 0, t and ∞ respectively.

To evaluate D from experimental data a table was prepared of the right side of equation 4 at selected values of Q over the range $0.7 > Q > 0.0005$.   From the experimental plot of the left side of equation 4 versus t a set of values of t can be read off at the selected values of Q by using the table.   Equation 3 shows that a plot of log Q versus t should be a straight line of slope S and intercept 0.105 on the log Q axis.   D then follows from

$$D = -2.303 \, S \, (\ell/\pi)^2 \tag{5}$$

Figure 1 shows a typical plot.   The curvature at early times exists because higher terms in the summation of equation 1 cannot then be neglected.

Assuming that the salt is dissociated within the membrane, D is related to the individual ionic conductances Λ_+ and Λ_- by

$$D = \frac{RT\nu}{F^2 \nu_+ \nu_-} \frac{\Lambda_+ \Lambda_-}{(\Lambda_+ + \Lambda_-)} \tag{6}$$

where ν_+ and ν_- are the stochiometric numbers of moles of cations and anions per mole of salt and ν is their sum.

If the membrane has cation exchange properties the transport numbers t_+ and t_- will be functions of concentration.   In fact t_+ will rise sharply at low concentrations.   At high concentrations the ion exchange properties become swamped and limiting values of transport numbers $t_+(\ell)$ and $t_-(\ell)$ are approached such that

$$D = \frac{RT\nu}{F^2 \nu_+ \nu_-} \Lambda \, t_+(\ell) \, t_-(\ell) \tag{7}$$

The molar distribution coefficient λ_s of salt between the membrane and a solution of molar concentration c_s is defined as the value of the ratio $\bar{c}_\infty/c_s$ at high concentration when ion exchange effects are swamped.   A straightforward consideration of the equilibrium conductance of the membrane leads to the relation

$$\lambda_s = \frac{RT\nu}{F^2 \nu_+\nu_-} \frac{K_\infty \ell}{c_s DA} t_+(\ell) t_-(\ell) \tag{8}$$

where K_∞ divided by c_s is to be evaluated at high concentration.

To make further progress $t_+(\ell)$ and $t_-(\ell)$ must be determined. Membrane potentials can be used for this purpose. The potential difference ΔE between a pair of anion-reversible electrodes immersed in solutions of molalities m_1 and m_2 bathing opposite sides of the membrane is given by

$$\Delta E = -\frac{\nu RT}{\nu_- F} \int_{m_1}^{m_2} t_+ d \ln (\gamma_\pm m) \tag{9}$$

provided, as we have confirmed experimentally, the electro-osmotic transport of water is negligible. $\gamma_\pm$ is the mean molal activity coefficient of the salt.

Membrane potentials were measured across a number of contiguous small concentration intervals in order to build up a curve of ΔE versus $\ln(\gamma_\pm m)$ relative to a single reference concentration by using the now well-established additivity rule (7,8). Some measurements were made over wider concentration intervals to check that additivity held for each system studied.

The ΔE versus $\ln (\gamma_\pm m)$ plots were gentle smooth curves as shown in Figure 2. They were differentiated at any concentration of interest by fitting a second order polynomial to the curve in the region of that concentration and differentiating the polynomial. The derivative $dE/d \ln (\gamma_\pm m)$ gives $(- \nu RT/\nu_- F)t_+$. Hence plots of t_+ versus m were constructed.

To estimate the limiting value $t_+(\ell)$ and to introduce the molal fixed charge concentration $\bar{X}$, expressed in equivalents of univalent fixed anions per kg of water sorbed by the membrane, we have treated the ion concentrations in the membrane as being governed by a Donnan distribution.

If $\bar{m}_+$ and $\bar{m}_-$ are the molalities of cations and anions respectively in the membrane, electroneutrality requires that

$$z_+ \bar{m}_+ = \bar{X} + z_- \bar{m}_- \tag{10}$$

where z_+ and z_- are the charge numbers (i.e. both are positive numbers). The Donnan distribution leads to

$$\bar{m}_-^{\nu_-} \left(\frac{\bar{X} + z_-\bar{m}_-}{z_+} \right)^{\nu_+} = \lambda_m^\nu m^\nu (\nu_+^{\nu_+} + \nu_-^{\nu_-}) \tag{11}$$

where λ_m is $\gamma_\pm/\bar{\gamma}_\pm$ and $\bar{\gamma}_\pm$ is the mean molal activity coefficient of the salt in the membrane.

It is convenient to note here that all the salts studied had univalent anions; hence we may set $z_- = \nu_+ = 1$ and $\nu_- = z_+$. Equation 11 then reduces to

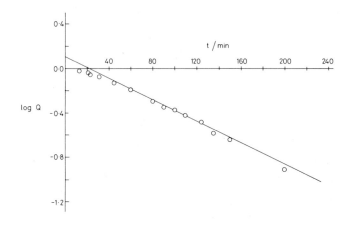

Figure 1.   Kinetic conductance experimental plot of log Q vs. t for 0.20M KCl at 25°C

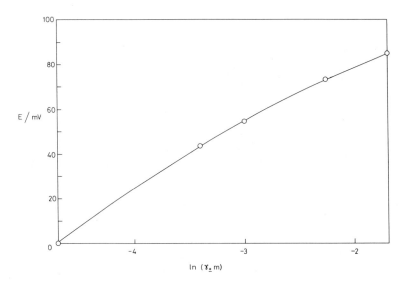

Figure 2.   Membrane potential E vs. ln ($\gamma_\pm$m) relative to 0.01M KCl at 25°C

$$\bar{m}_-^{\bar{\nu}_-} (\bar{X} + \bar{m}_-) = (\nu_- \lambda_m m)^\nu \tag{12}$$

The high concentration limit of interest is reached when $\bar{X} \ll \bar{m}_-$. Under this condition equation 12 becomes

$$\lambda_m = \bar{m}/m \tag{13}$$

where $\bar{m}$ is the molal concentration of sorbed salt, $\bar{m}_-/\nu_-$. Thus λ_m is seen to be the molal distribution coefficient. It is related to the molar coefficient λ_s by

$$\lambda_m = \lambda_s/W \tag{14}$$

where W is the weight of water in kg absorbed by 1 dm^{-3} of swollen membrane. This quantity is not difficult to determine in cellulose acetate by conventional means.

It seems reasonable to expect that $\gamma_+/\bar{\gamma}_+$ will not be greatly concentration dependent i.e. that λ_m is a constant of the system at a given temperature and can be treated as such in equation 12 which applies at all values of m, large and small.

The details of the treatment from this point onwards depends on the value of ν_-; detailed consideration here will be limited to uni-univalent salts, $\nu_- = 1$. Equation 12 then becomes, after rearrangement,

$$\bar{m}_-^2 + \bar{X}\bar{m}_- - \lambda_m^2 m^2 = 0 \tag{15}$$

The solution of the quadratic equation 15 is

$$\bar{m}_- = \tfrac{1}{2}[(\bar{X}^2 + 4\lambda_m^2 m^2)^{\frac{1}{2}} - \bar{X}]$$
$$\bar{m}_+ = \tfrac{1}{2}[(\bar{X}^2 + 4\lambda_m^2 m^2)^{\frac{1}{2}} + \bar{X}] \tag{16}$$

The ratio of the transport numbers r is defined by

$$r = t_+/t_- = t_+/(1 - t_+) \tag{17}$$

When m is large such that $\bar{X} \ll \bar{m}_-$ and $\bar{m}_+ = \bar{m}_-$ the transport numbers reach their limiting values and r becomes r(ℓ) given by

$$r(\ell) = t_+(\ell)/t_-(\ell) = \Lambda_+/\Lambda_- \tag{18}$$

At lower concentrations when $\bar{m}_+$ and $\bar{m}_-$ are given by equations 16 one has

$$r = \bar{m}_+\Lambda_+/\bar{m}_-\Lambda_- = r(\ell)\bar{m}_+/\bar{m}_- \tag{19}$$

r at various values of m can be calculated from the transport numbers evaluated from the membrane potential data.

Introducing equation 16 into equation 19 and rearranging gives

$$\frac{1}{m\,r^{\frac{1}{2}}} = \frac{\lambda_m}{\bar{X}\,r(\ell)^{\frac{1}{2}}} - \frac{\lambda_m\,r(\ell)^{\frac{1}{2}}}{\bar{X}\,r} \tag{20}$$

A plot of $1/m\,r^{\frac{1}{2}}$ versus $1/r$, as illustrated in Figure 3, gives a straight line of measurable slope and intercept on the $1/m\,r^2$ axis. Thus one finds

$$r(\ell) = -\text{slope/intercept} \tag{21}$$

$$\lambda_m/\bar{X} = (-\text{slope} \times \text{intercept})^{\frac{1}{2}} \tag{22}$$

From the definition of $r(\ell)$ it is easily seen that

$$t_+(\ell) = r(\ell)/[1 + r(\ell)]$$
$$t_-(\ell) = 1/[1 + r(\ell)] \tag{23}$$

Putting these relations and equation 14 into equation 8 gives, when $\nu_+ = \nu_- = 1$,

$$\lambda_m = \frac{2\,RT}{W\,F^2}\,\frac{K_\infty\,\ell}{c_s\,DA}\,\frac{r(\ell)}{[1 + r(\ell)]^2} \tag{24}$$

since every quantity on the right side of equation 24 has now been determined, λ_m can be evaluated.   Equation 22 is then used to find $\bar{X}$.

Some doubt might be expressed about the concentration dependence of the membrane conductance and the evaluation of the limiting ratio K_∞/c_s in equation 24.   We have found the ratio $(K_\infty - K_o)/c_s$ to be almost constant.   If it is plotted against $1/c_s$ (see Figure 4) and extrapolated to $1/c_s = 0$ one obtains the limiting value of K_∞/c_s at high concentration since K_o becomes negligible then.

It may be noted that data on the diffusion coefficient of the salt and on the limiting transport numbers permit the individual ionic mobilities and diffusion coefficients in the membrane to be evaluated by conventional means.

When $\nu_- > 1$ the equation equivalent to equation 15 is of order higher than quadratic, a cubic when $\nu_- = 2$ and a quartic when $\nu_- = 3$.   The solution of these equations, though possible, does not lead to a value of $\bar{X}$ of acceptable precision. Alternative schemes for analyzing the data on 2:1 and 3:1 salts have been devised and will be discussed in a later publication.

Results

The results obtained with NaCl at $25^{\circ}C$ and with KCl at 25°, 35° and $45^{\circ}C$ in Eastman Kodak 398-3 cellulose acetate are listed in Table I.   When examining the data it should be remembered that the fixed charge capacity measured here is that effective in electro-kinetic properties of the membrane;   it is not a quantity of analytical chemistry.   Nevertheless, because NaCl and KCl are very similar in their electrochemical properties, one would expect the apparent number of moles of fixed charges per unit mass of dry

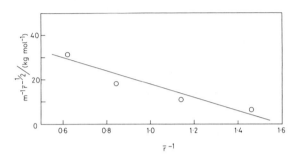

Figure 3.   Plot of $1/m\,r^{\frac{1}{2}}$ vs. $1/r$ for KCl at $25\,°C$

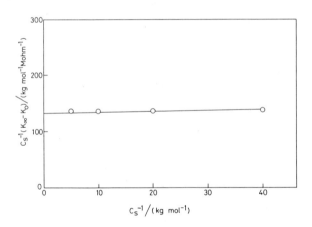

Figure 4.   Equilibrium membrane conductance plot for KCl at $25\,°C$

polymer, $\bar{M}$, to be a constant.   The value found here is 0.74 ± 0.1 mequiv kg^{-1}.

Table I. Electrochemically measured data on cellulose acetate

Property	Salt and Temperature			
	NaCl, 25°	KCl, 25°	KCl, 35°	KCl, 45°
$\bar{X}$/m equiv (kg H$_2$O)$^{-1}$	5.51	5.38	6.71	5.61
$\bar{M}$/m equiv (kg CA)$^{-1}$	0.737	0.720	0.836	0.654
λ_m (molal)	0.264	0.207	0.236	0.207
λ_s (molar)	0.0404	0.0318	0.0335	0.0276
$D/10^{-14}$ m^2 s^{-1}	2.24	2.90	3.44	5.36
$D_+/10^{-14}$ m^2 s^{-1}	1.81	2.37	2.73	4.25
$D_-/10^{-14}$ m^2 s^{-1}	3.21	3.64	4.64	7.34

On account of the relatively low water regain of cellulose acetate, the molal concentration of ionic groups in the swollen material exceeds 5 mmolal.   This is comparable to the concentration of 300 ppm sodium chloride, a typical reverse osmosis product solution.   Our homogeneous membranes are believed to be very similar to the active layer of an asymmetric membrane as developed by Loeb and Sourirajan.   It is evident therefore that the concentration of fixed charges in the membrane is sufficient to exercise a significant Donnan exclusion of co-ions on the downstream side of the membranes in a reverse osmosis plant.

Lonsdale (1) quoted 0.009% by weight of carboxyl groups from chemical analysis.   This is equivalent to a value of $\bar{M}$ of 2 m equiv kg^{-1}, almost three times our value.   This suggests that only about one third of the carboxyl groups detectable by analysis are effective in influencing the ion transport phenomena.

The value of $\bar{X}$ found here appears to agree well with the values 5.0 and 2.3 m equiv dm^{-3} absorbed water found by Demisch and Pusch (4) by analytical and electro-chemical measurements respectively in cellulose acetate from a different manufacturer. The agreement is deceptive however because their value is based on the total water held in an asymmetric membrane.   A value of $\bar{M}$ estimated from their data is almost ten times our $\bar{M}$.   It may be noted that their electrochemical method and their assumptions are quite different from ours.

The most dubious assumption in our work lies in the use of

the Donnan equilibrium and the implicit choice of an ideal 1 molal
solution as the standard state for salt in the solution and in the
swollen membrane.   The more highly clustered in the neighbourhood
of the ions is the water sorbed by the polymer the better founded
is this assumption.   There is good evidence from water sorption
isotherms and water transport data in favour of such clustering in
cellulose acetate (9).

The fact that λ_m for both salts lies in the range $0.20 - 0.25$
shows that water in the membrane is a less effective solvent for
ions than is bulk water i.e. the low-dielectric-constant matrix
polymer lies well within the range of the electrostatic fields
around the ions.   Our value of λ_s, the molar distribution
coefficient of sodium chloride between polymer and solution, is in
good agreement with values obtained by direct measurement (1,5,10,
11,12).   This is further evidence in favour of our theories and
assumptions.

The diffusion coefficients of potassium and sodium chlorides
in the membrane we have found to be independent of solution
concentration within experimental error.   The value of sodium
chloride agrees well with those found by others bearing in mind
the differences in the polymer and in the membrane casting
procedures (5,13).

Just as in free aqueous solution, K^+ is more mobile than Na^+
but in the membrane K^+ is less mobile than Cl^- whereas in water
their mobilities are equal.   Perhaps this indicates that the
degrees of hydration of K^+ and Cl^- are modified in the membrane to
different extents.

Our data at three temperatures on KCl do not permit
activation energies to be evaluated with precision.   Clearly the
activation energy for transport in the polymer is considerably
larger than it is in free solution and seems larger for Cl^- than
for K^+.

In conclusion, it can be claimed that a combination of
kinetic and equilibrium conductance and membrane potential
measurements provides a powerful method for investigating the
permselective properties of membranes of low fixed charge density.
Such methods should be applicable also to other polymers useful in
hyperfiltration if they can be prepared in the form of homogeneous
membranes.

Literature Cited

1.   Lonsdale, H.K. in Merten, U. Ed. "Desalination by Reverse
      Osmosis"; M.I.T. Press: Cambridge, Mass., 1966; p.93-160.
2.   Glueckauf, E. Desalination, 1976, 18, 155.
3.   Craig, J.B.; Meares, P.; Webster, J. "Physico-chemical
      studies on semi-permeable membranes"; Final report on EMR
      1799, United Kingdom Atomic Energy Authority: Harwell, 1968.
4.   Demisch, H.-U.; Pusch, W. J. Electrochem. Soc., 1976, 123, 370.

5. Saltonstall, C.W.; King, W.M.; Hoernshemeyer, D.L.
    Desalination, 1968, 4, 309.
6. Meares, P.; Craig, J.B.; Webster, J. in Sherwood, J.N.;
    Chadwick, A.V.; Muir, W.M.; Swinton, F.L., Ed. "Diffusion
    Processes"; Gordon & Breach: London, 1971; Vol. 1, p.609.
7. Krämer, H.; Meares, P. Biophys. J., 1969, 9, 1006.
8. Foley, T.; Meares, P. J. Chem. Soc. Faraday Trans. I, 1976,
    72, 1105.
9. Williams, J.L.; Hopfenberg, H.B.; Stannett, V. J. Macromol.
    Sci.-Phys. (B), 1969, 3, 711.
10. Lonsdale, H.K.; Merten, U.; Riley, R.L. J. Appl. Polymer Sci.,
    1965, 9, 1341.
11. Thomas, C.R.; Barker, R.E. J. Appl. Polymer Sci., 1963, 7, 1933.
12. Heyde, M.E.; Peters, C.R.; Anderson, J.E. J. Colloid Interf.
    Sci., 1975, 50, 467.
13. Kimura, S. Proc. Int. Symp. Fresh Water from Sea, 4th, 1973,
    4, 204.

RECEIVED December 4, 1980.

Prediction Method for the Life of Reverse-Osmosis Membranes

H. OHYA, Y. NEGISHI, K. KAMOTO[1], K. MATSUI[2], and H. INOUE[3]

Yokahama National University, Yokahama, Japan

Economics of reverse osmosis depends mainly on membrane life. If membrane can be in service over a long period, the depreciation cost of membrane per unit permeate becomes smaller. When we are planning to treat any aqueous solution by reverse osmosis, the treatment cost may be estimated assuming membrane life and others. At present, long term operation of pilot plant is nescessary to make accurate estimation. Because we don't have any good and accurate method to estimate membrane life at higher pressure range, sea water desalination in particular and in the case of treating water containing materials which may deteriorate membranes, except to treat well pretreated feed at medium pressure range.

These facts shift cost estimation to much safer side, resulting into over-investment, which may reduce the advantage of reverse osmosis process over other processes. For the further prosper of reverse osmosis, we definetely need more accurate and easier method to predict membrane life which may be determined by decrease in either flux through it or separation of solute.

Compaction Effects

The decrease in flux with time under pressure has been attributed to membrane compaction.

Log-Log Plot. Riley and others(1) showed the flux date are plotted as logarithm water flux versus logarithm time, a rather straight line results. This correlation is widely used now to estimate flux decline. But as shown in Fig. 1, water flux data obtained from the plant operating at higher pressure and/or with least pretreatment system show a steeper decline after a longer period than that predicted from the straight line obtained at the initial period. For the convenience of reading the scale of vertical axis is expanded in Fig.1.

[1] Current address: Sasakura Engineering.
[2] Current address: Nitto Electric Industries.
[3] Current address: Nippon Denso.

0097–6156/81/0153–0113$05.00/0

Membrane Structure and Compaction. Membrane compaction has been considered as results of an increase in the effective thickness of the active surface layer and/or an added viscous flow resistance in the porous region underneath.[1,2] It will be more reasonable to consider that water flux is inversely proportional to the effective thickness of the membrane which can be assumed to increase with time.

New Plotting. After a careful scruniny into various sets of data, plotting the reciprocals of membrane constants or water flux against time elasped, a rather straight line can be obtained than the previous one as shown in Fig.2, using the same data. A straight line can be obtained from the data at 2000 psi. But the data at 1500 and 1000 psi scatter slightly around the lines. The reason why the data scatter may be that water flux is a function of operating temperature, pressure and concentration and so on.

Plotting the reciprocals of membrane constant(pure water permeability) against time elasped as shown in Fig. 3, a much more straight line can be obtained for each operating pressure 2000, 1500,1000 and 600 psi. But during the initial period of the operation of less than seven to three hours, the reciprocal values increase steeply untill they reach the straight lines.

This phenomenon might be mainly due to the compaction of porous region of the membrane since the significant reduction of the total thickness of membrane after pressurization is well observed (1,etc),even if the duration is a short period. And also it is a common phenomenon to encounter a great deal of flux recovery during a short period of restart of the operation after reverse osmosis equipment is stopped for some period, and to reduce soon to its original flux observed just before stopping the equipment. The recovery phenomenon might be due to the elasticity of the porous region. Plotting logarithmic values of the differences between the the solid straight line and the data in the Fig.3 against time, a linear relation can be obtained for each operating pressure. Hence these differeces can be well expressed as an exponential function of time which diminishes quickly as can be seen in Fig.3.

The resultant form of the function will be expressed as the following equation.

$$1/A = 1/A_0 + at + be^{-t/\tau} \qquad (1)$$

For operational pressure, the constants in the equation (1) are listed on the Table 1.

Table 1   Constants of Equation (1)

pressure(psi)	$1/A_0$(MPa.s.m^{-1})	a(MPa.s.m^{-1}.h^{-1})	b(MPa.s.m^{-1})	τ(h)
2000	1.37×10^6	4.89×10^3	$- 4.3 \times 10^6$	3.15
1500	1.09	3.26	$- 2.9$	1.17
1000	0.76	0.33	$- 1.2$	1.46
600	0.65	0.00	$- 1.2$	0.89

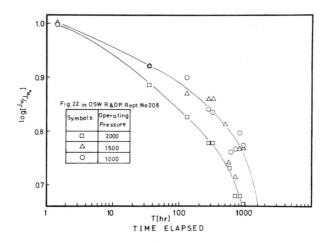

Figure 1.   log[J$_w$/J$_{wo}$] vs. log time (data from Ref 1, Figure 22). Scale of log-[J$_w$/J$_{wo}$] is increased for easy reading.

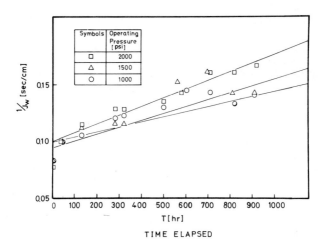

Figure 2.   1/J$_w$ vs. t (data are the same as in Figure 1)

The third term of the right side of the equation vanishs in a short period and may correspond to the compaction term of the porous region. The time constant in the exponent increases as the operational pressure increases. This means that the transitional effect of compaction is not so important at lower operational pressures, but long and serious at higher pressures. The second term may correspond to the compaction term of the active layer and be a linear function of time. At the operational pressure of 600 psi, there is essentially no compaction effect in the long term. Increasing the operational pressure, this term becomes serious and its gradient increases steeply.

Data of WRPC. The Water Reuse Promotion Center(WRPC) in JAPAN has been engaged in development of sea water desalination by reverse osmosis since 1974. At IDEA meeting at Mexico city 1976,the first redults were reported with two types of modules, du Dont hollow fine fiber module B-10 and UOP's cellulose triacetate ultrathin spiral wound module,tested at their laboratory at Chigasaki beach. Then the WRPC has adopted two types of modules made in Japan, Toray new type of spiral wound module made from cellulose acetate and Toyobo's cellulose triacetate hollow fine fiber module.

Toray's data are plotted as the reciprocal of membrane constants against time elasped like Fig. 4. The first generation of Toray module tested at the laboratory might have some defect in the membrane backing material. After 6000 hours in operation, they exchanged half of the modules for the second generation chlorine resistant. The second had been improved about twice in its resistance against flux decline.

The same type of plot for Toyobo's hollow fine fiber is shown in Fig.5. As far as the half time concerns when the flux reduces to half of its initial value,Toyobo's hollow fine fiber mosule is the best among the modules tested at the laboratory as shown on the Table 2.

Table 2   a,b and half time $t_1/2$

	$1/A_0 (MPa.s.m^2.mol^{-1})$	$a(MPa.s.m^2.mol^{-1}.h^{-1})$	$t_1/2$ (h)
Toray SC-5000	9.4	0.7×10^{-3}	1.34×10^4
Toyobo Hollosep	54.6	1.33	4.10
du Pont B-10	72.6	4.14	1.75
Toray SC-5000(new)	10.0	0.32	2.62

Still we have to obtain relationship between half time or the slope of the lines and the operating conditions such as operational pressure, temperature and so on. But taking pilot plant data only for 1000 to 2000 hours at some designated conditions, this type of plot proved to be able to predict the flux decline over 10 000 hours quite accurately.

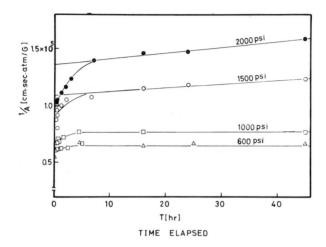

Figure 3. 1/A vs. t *(data from Ref 1, Figure 23)*

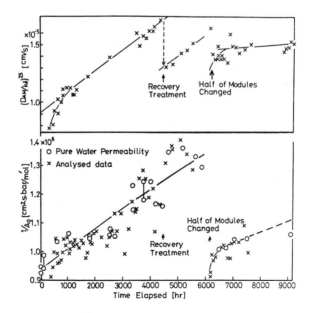

Figure 4. *Characteristics of Toray's spiral wound modules over a long period: SC-5000A; 12 modules used for the first stage (6).*

Deterioration of Asymmetric Cellulose Acetate Membranes with NaOCl
           Structural and Chemical Change

For the purpose to shorten the time needed to decrease separation to a certain level, membranes were subjected to contact
with aqueous solution of high concentration at elevated temperature.
Here is reported the results obtained only with sodium hypochlorite
as a solute which is widely added to R.O. feed as bactericide and
of which effect on the membranes is not well understood. Only al-
lowable concentration is said about 2 mg/l as sodium hypochlorite
or 1 mg/l as chlorine.

Experimental. Films were cast from Manjikian's standard casting solution(acetane 45wt%, formamide 30wt%, cellulose acetate
type E-398-3 25wt%) by his preparation method.(3) Before use, membranes were cured in water at 85°C for 10 minutes.
     Fig.6 shows the experimental apparatus in which seven batch-
wise R.O. cells were installed. Effective area of membranes was 19
cm^2. Compressed nitrogen gas was used to pressurize the R.O. cells
at 1.0 MPa. About 750 cm^3 of the feed solution was kept well stirred by means of a magnetic stirrer fitted in the cell about 0.5 cm
above the membrane surface to avoid the effect of concentration
polarization. Temperature inside the constant temperature chamber
was controlled within $\pm$ 1°C at a fixed point using a fun and two
heaters of 500W.
     Characterization of membranes was carried out at 1.0 MPa and
25°C, using pure water and aqueous solution of sodium chloride,(
3 500 mg/l) to obtain pure water permeability and rejection of NaCl
at the beginning of the each run, every 15-20 hours, and the end.
The procedure of deterioration experiments at each concentration
of NaOCl was like follows: About 750 cm^3 of aqueous sodium hypochlorite solution concentration of which is listed on Table 3, were
used each time. About 100-150 cm^3 of solution permeated through
the membrane during overnight and the permeate was recharged to
the cell every day. The entire solution were renewed every week.
     The concentration of NaOCl was determined by iodometry and of
NaCl by electroconductivity.

Table 3   Experimental Conditions

operating temp.(°C)			initial conc. of NaOCl (mg/l)		
10			40	50	100
20			40	50	100
35	10	20	30	40	50
45	10		30	50	

Effect of Temperature on Separation and Pure Water Production
Rate(P.W.P.). Fig. 7 shows some results obtained at various temperature with the concentration of NaOCl as 50 mg/l. At lower temperature, separation and pure water production rate kept almost
constant value. But with increasing temperature, separation decreases and pure water production rate increases steeply.

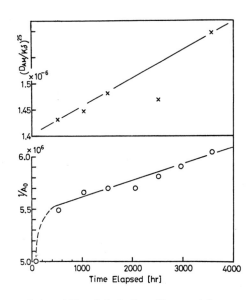

*Figure 5.   Characteristics of Toyobo's hollow fiber modules over a long period:
Hollowsep; 5 modules used for the first stage (6).*

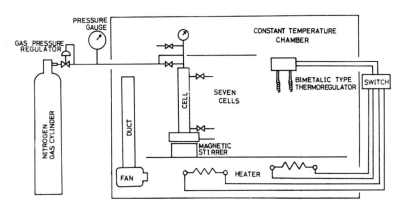

*Figure 6.   Batchwise reverse osmosis equipment in constant temperature chamber
with forced draft*

Effect of Concentration on Separation and P.W.P. Fig. 8 shows
the effect of concentration on decrease of separation of membranes
at 35°C. At lower concentration, separation kept almost constant
and pure water production rate decreased. But increasing the concentration 30,40, and 50 mg/l, separation decreases steeply and
pure water production rate contrary increases. At 20 mg/l, deterioration phenomenon is observed after 100 hours as an increase of
pure water production rate. In the case of 40 and 50 mg/l, steep
decrease of separation and increase of pure water production rate
are observed.

Analysis of Chemical and Structural Change. Membranes of
separation between 90% to 30 % were examined in their chemical and
structural change. All samples of membranes were dissolved into
acetone completely and any trace of undissolved matter could not
seen. This means acetyl content of any deteriorated membranes is
still over 32.6%.
    Typical infrared absorption spectra of the thin membranes cast
on mercury surface from the acetone solution above are shown in
Fig. 9. But there were not found any change on the spectra between
control membrane and the most deteriorated. This means there were
not occurred any chemical change in the deteriorated membranes as
a whole. Infrared absorption spectra of the active surface layer
were measured by the attenuated total reflexion method, using Fourier transformation infrared spectrometer. The ratio of absorbance
of esteric bonding and hydroxyl bonding are listed on Table 4. The
absorbance ratio of all the deteriorated membranes show that absorption of hydroxyl bonding increases and this means that hydrolysis or oxidation occurred on the active surface layer. But at the
present stage, quantitative measurement can not be expected, because
ATR IR spectra are strongly affected also by the surface conditions.
    A typical example of ESCA spectra of the active surface layer
is shown in Fig.10. Pattern of carbon ls orbit changes as shown in
this figure. From the measurement of these two spectra, we might
say that we have an evidence that chemical change is occurred in
the active surface layer of the deteriorated membranes.

Table 4 Ratio of Absorption of IR-Spectrum Using ATR Method

Separation of Membrane	26.2%	48.3%	80.6%	91.4%(control)
Wave Number (cm^{-1})				
1030/1215 (ν_{C-OH} /ν_{C-O})	1.12	1.09	1.12	1.03
1030/1735 $(\nu_{C-OH} /\nu_{C=O})$	1.76	1.61	1.78	1.45
1030/1365 (ν_{C-OH} /ν_{C-H})	3.28	2.89	3.37	2.46

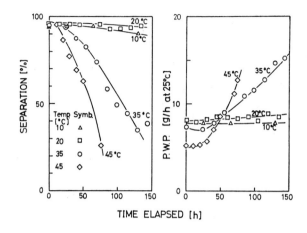

Figure 7. Effect of temperature on the change of separation and pure water production rate due to membrane deterioration by sodium hypochlorite: [NaOCl] = 50 mg L⁻¹.

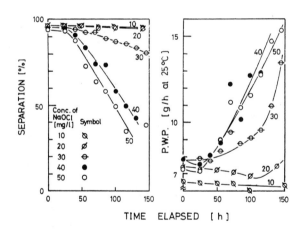

Figure 8. Effect of [NaOCl] on the change of separation and pure water production rate due to membrane deterioration; T = 35°C.

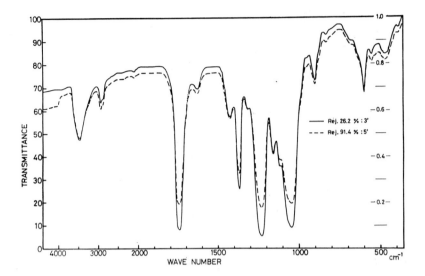

Figure 9.   IR spectra of the control sample (No. 5') and the deteriorated sample
(No. 3')

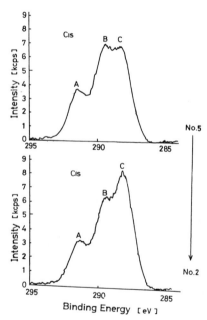

Figure 10.   ESCA spectra of the active
surface layer of the control sample (No.
5) and the deteriorated sample (No. 2)

Scanning electrin micrographs of the control membrane and deteriorated membrane are shown in Fig.11. Two micrographs of membranes are essentially same. particularly in the surface active layer. From these two micrographs, structural change does not occurred as far as the SEM scale concerns.

Analysis of the Mechanisum of Deteriorationof Asymmetric Cellulose Acetate Membrane by Sodium Hypochlorite

Membrane deterioration may be merely caused by decrease of acetyl content(C_A) in the active surface layer as a result of hydrolysis or oxidation, not by structure change. Analysis was carried out based on solution-diffusion model proposed by Lonsdale etal([4]), using their measured values of solute diffusivity and partition coefficient in homogeneous membrnaes of various degree of acetyl content and also using those values of asymmetric membranes heat treated at various temperatures measured by Glueckauf([7]).

Model of Deterioration Mechanisum. As acetyl content decreases due to hydrolysis or oxidation of ester bonding, solute permeability increases. Then concentration of solute(in this case sodium hypochlorite) in the membrane increases and the hydrolysis or oxidation rate increases and so on. It will be more reasonable to assume that hydrolysis or oxidation rate of cellulose acetate in the active surface layer may be accelerated by the action of the nascent oxygen generated from sodium hypochlorite.

$$2NaOCl \longrightarrow 2NaCl + O_2 \qquad (2)$$

Then the decrease rate of acetyl content may be expressed as the second order reaction of the solute concentration in the membrane.

$$-\frac{dC_A}{dt} = k_d\, C_{dm}^2 \qquad (3)$$

Concentration of solution in the membrane may be proportional to that in the permeate(C_{d3}). Then, the rate equation may be written as follow:

$$-\frac{dC_A}{dt} = k_d'\, C_{d3}'^2 \qquad (4)$$

Concentration in the permeate is expressed by that in the feed as Equation (5), using solution-diffusion model assuming no concentration polarization.

$$C_{d3} = R_d/(\Delta p - \Delta\pi + R_d) \qquad (5)$$

where

$$R_d = D_{sm}K_{sm}RT/D_{wm}C_{wm}\bar{v}_w^{0\,2} \qquad (6)$$

Substituting equation (5) into equation (4) and integrating the equation (4), we can obtain equation (7), where $f_1(C_A)$ and $f_2(C_A)$ are function of acetyl content and f_T is a function of temperature of heat treatment.

$$k_d' C_{d_1}^2 t = -\left(\frac{\Delta p - \Delta \pi}{f_T}\right)^2 f_2(C_A) - 2(\Delta p - \Delta \pi)f_1(C_A)/f_T + (0.398 - C_A) \tag{7}$$

$$f_1(C_A) = \int_{0.398}^{C_A} dC_A/R_d^* \quad (8), \quad f_2(C_A) = \int_{0.398}^{C_A} dC_A/R_d^{*2} \tag{9}$$

$$R_d = f_T R_d^*(C_A) \tag{10}$$

Symbol * in equation (10) means for homogeneous membrane of acetyl content C_A, and $R_d(C_A)$ without * for asymmetric membrane. $R_d^*(C_A)$ for NaOCl in membrane of any degree of acetyl content are obtained and shown on Table 5, assuming that relation of solute permeabilities in homogeneous membrane for NaCl and NaOCl may be expressed as follows

$$(D_{sm}K_{sm})_{NaOCl} = 0.0846(D_{sm}K_{sm})_{NaCl}^{0.885} \tag{11}$$

Equation (11) is obtained using several asymmetric membranes heat treated at various temperatures. $f_1(C_A)$ and $f_2(C_A)$ calculated from $R_d(C_A)_{NaOCl}$ on Table 5 are shown in Figure 12 where pure water and sodium chloride permeabilities in homogeneous membranes obtained by Lonsdale etal(4) are also shown.

Procedure of Analysis. Rate constant k_d' can be calculated as a slope of the line plotted right hand side of equation (7) against time elasped. At first acetyl content is estimated from the ratio of sodium chloride permeability of the deteriorated membrane and the initial by Fig.12. Using the estimated acetyl content, $f_1(C_A)$ and $f_2(C_A)$ can be obtained from Fig. 12. Using these values and f_T the right hand side of equation (7) can be calculated and plotted against time elasped as shown in Figure 13 and can be obtained the rate constant as 6.8×10^{-7} $(mg/l)^{-1}h^{-1}$ for this case.

Arrhenius plot is done using concentration averaged rate constant against reciprocals of absolute temperatures. The activation energy is found 71.4 $kJ.mol^{-1}$ and rate equation is expressed like the next equation.

$$-\frac{dC_A}{dt} = 1.02 \times 10^6 \exp(-71.4 \times 10^3/RT) C_{d3}^2 \tag{12}$$

Verification of the Deterioration Rate Model. For the purpose to examine the agreement of the rate equation with the measured data, separation change along with time is calculated for three cases, at the severest condition, at medium and at least and shown in Figure 15. The agreement seems rather good.

Table 5 Diffusion, concentration, and distribution of homogeneous membranes from cellulose acetate of various degree of acetylation. [All data except data for NaOCl are from ref. ($\underline{4}$).]

Acetyl content [wt%]	K^*_{mNaCl} [-]	D^*_{mNaCl} [cm²·s⁻¹] (adopted)	D^*_{wm} [cm²·s⁻¹]	C^*_{wm} [mol·m⁻¹]	R^*_{dNaCl} [MPa]	$(KD)^*_{mNaOCl}$ [cm²·s⁻¹]	R^*_{dNaOCl} [MPa]
43.2	0.015	$0.39 {+.13 \atop -} \times 10^{-10}$ (0.39)	1.2×10^{-6}	5.83×10^3	6.3×10^{-4}	0.0149×10^{-9}	0.0161
39.8	0.035	$9.4 {+1.1 \atop -}$ (9.4)	1.6	8.55	0.0181	0.528	0.291
37.6	0.060	$43.0 {+20 \atop -}$ (43.0)	2.9	11.1	0.0604	3.27	0.765
33.6	0.170	$290 {+60 \atop -}$ (290)	5.7	14.0	0.562	52.5	4.97

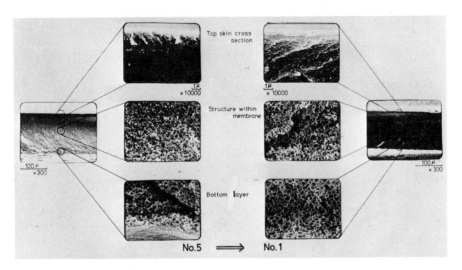

Figure 11.   SEMs of the control sample (No. 5) and the deteriorated sample (No. 1)

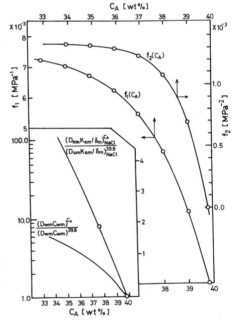

Figure 12.   An increase of the solute and pure water permeabilities for homogeneous membranes due to a decrease of acetyl content and $f_1(C_A)$ and $f_2(C_A)$ vs. acetyl content

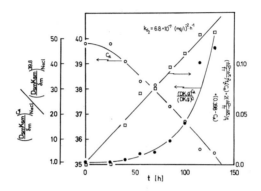

Figure 13. A typical analytical procedure for the data shown in Figure 8; [NaOCl] = 40 mg L⁻¹ at 35°C.

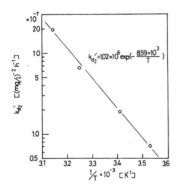

Figure 14. Arrehenius plot of the rate constants of the hydrolysis of oxidation

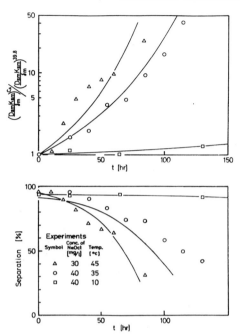

Figure 15. Typical example of the decrease of the separation and the increase of the solute permeabilities by the prediction method (———) assuming $k = 1.8 \times 10^{-4}$ cm s^{-1}, $\Delta p = 1.0$ MPa, $T = 25°C$, and the experimental data for three cases are 30 mg L^{-1}, 45°C, 40 mg L^{-1}, 35°C, and 40 mg L^{-1}, 10°C.

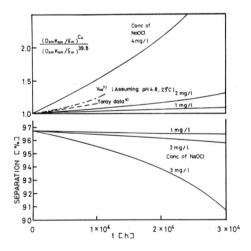

Figure 16. Decrease of separation (or increase of solute permeabilities) of seawater reverse osmosis desalination at several concentration levels of NaOCl. Initial membrane constants: pure water permeability constant = 97.0 nmol m^{-2} Pa^{-1} s^{-1} and the solute permeability constant for NaCl = 0.9×10^{-5} cm s^{-1}. Operational conditions: $k = 1.01 \times 10^{-3}$ cm s^{-1}, $\Delta p = 6.0$ MPa, and $T = 25°C$.

Long Term Deterioration. As an example, suppose two stage
sea water desalination and cellulose acetate membranes are used
for the first stage. The membrane constants are assumed as $D_{wm}C_{wm}$
$\overline{v}_w^0/(RT\delta_m) = 97$ nmol.m^{-2}.Pa.$^{-1}$s^{-1} and $D_{sm}K_{sm}/\delta_m = 0.9 \times 10^{-5}$cm.s^{-1}, and
the operating conditions are assumed as k = 1.03×10^{-3}cm.s^{-1}, $\Delta P=6$
MPa, and T = 25 °C. For the purpose to kill microorganism, chlorine
is supposed to be added to the feed sea water about 1 mg/l which
corresponds to about 2 mg/g of sodium hypochlorite.

Decrease of separation and increase of solute permeability
predicted by the oxidation or hydrolysis rate data are shown in
Figure 16. If we increase the concentration of NaOCl from 2 mg/l
to 4 mg/l, decrease of separation is accelerated because the deterioration rate is proportional to the square of the concentration
of the solute. The dotted line shows the tendency of solute decline
of the first stage membranes of Toray's spiral wound module which
was tested at the Chigasaki Laboratory of Water Reuse Promotion
Center over 9 000hours(5)

The initial membrane constants and the operating conditions
were almost same as those assumed for the calculation of this graph.
The concentration of chlorine in the feed had been controlled minimum 1.2 mg/l or about 2.3 mg/l as NaOCl.

The increase of solute permeability due to the oxidation or
hydrolysis by NaOCl is estimated about half of the measured data.
There will be several another causes to deteriorate membranes, PH
as an example. Using Vos'es data(6) at PH 4.8 and 22°C, the broken
line in Fiure 15 is calculated and seems overestimate the deterioration of membranes.

Conclusions

As for the flux decline over long term operation 10 000 hours
at high pressure, the reciprocals of flux through the membranes
may be expressed as a linear function of time elasped.

The prediction method of separation decrease using short term
experiments at high temperature and at high concentration of solute
has proved to be quite effective.

Symbols

a	– coefficient of compaction defined by Eq.(1),MPa.s.m^{-1}. h^{-1} or MPa.s.m^2.mol^{-1}.h^{-1}
A	– pure water permeability constant,m.MPa^{-1}.s^{-1} or mol. MPa^{-1}.s^{-1}.m^{-2}
A	– extrapolated value of A to time zero using Eq.(1)
b	– coefficient of short term compaction in Eq.(1),MPa.s. m^{-1}
C	– concentration, mg.l^{-1} or mol.m^{-3}
C_A	– acetyl content,wt fraction
D	– diffusion coefficient in the membrane,cm^{2}s^{-1}

$f_1(C_A)$ - a function of C_A, defined by Eq.(8), MPa^{-1}
$f_2(C_A)$ - a function of C_A, defined by Eq.(9),MPa^{-1}
f_T - heat treatment coefficient, defined by Eq.(10),-
k_d,k_d' - rate constant,defined by Eq.(3) and (4), $(mg/l)^{-2}.h^{-1}$
K_{sm} - distribution coefficient for the solute between the
                 membrane and the brine,-
R   - gas constant,$J.mol^{-1}.K^{-1}$
R_d - defined by Eq.(6), MPa
t - time elasped,s or h
T   - temperature,K or °C
t   - half time,h
$\overline{v}^0$ - partial molar volume for water,$m^3.mol^{-1}$
δ^w - thickness of membrane,μm
Δp - pressure difference,MPa
$\Delta\pi$ - osmotic pressure difference,MPa
τ - time constant in the exponential Eq.(1),h

Subscript
d   - sodium hypochlorite
m   - in the membrane
NaCl   - sodium chloride
NaOCl   - sodium hypochlorite
s   - solute
w   - water
1   - in the bulk solution at high pressure side
2   - on the membrane surface at the high pressure side
3   - in the permeate

Superscript
*   - homogeneous membrane

Literature Cited

1 Merten,U.Lonsdale,H.K.;Riley,R.L.;Vos.K.D. Office of Saline
   Water,Res. Develop. Progr. Rept., 1966,No. 208.
2 Baayens,L.;Rosen,S.L. J.Appl.Polymer Sci.,1972, 16, 663.

3 Manjikian,S. I&EC PRD. 1967, 6, 23.
4 Lonsdale,H.K.;Merten,U.;Riley,R.L. J.Appl. Polymer Sci.,1965,
   9, 1341.
5 Ohya,h,;Kunisada,Y.;Hirai,M.;Murayama,Y. Proc. of Sixth Int.
   Symp. on Fresh Water from the Sea,1978, 3, 341.
6 Vos,K.D.;Hatcher,A.P.;Merten,U. I&EC PRD,1966, 5, 211.
7 Glueckauf,E.;Sammon,D. Proc. of 3rd Int. Symp. on Fresh Water
   from the Sea,1970, 2, 397.

RECEIVED January 5, 1981.

Model and Preliminary Experiments on Membrane Fouling in Reverse Osmosis

R. F. PROBSTEIN, K. K. CHAN[1], R. COHEN, and I. RUBENSTEIN[2]

Department of Mechanical Engineering, Massachusetts Institute of Technology, Cambridge, MA 02139

One of the principal limitations to the optimum performance of reverse osmosis systems is membrane fouling, which leads to a decrease in membrane flux with time. Materials that form fouling films on the flow side of membrane surfaces include colloidal impurities, macromolecules, biological contaminants, and inorganic precipitates. Moreover, the foulant film may be electrically neutral or carry a fixed charge. The rate of formation, the extent, and the nature of the fouling film will depend on the properties and characteristics of the foulant, the membrane surface, the working fluid, and the operating conditions. An understanding of how fouling films grow as a function of these parameters might make it possible to minimize or delay the fouling by suitable variations of the process design or operating conditions.

The general problem of fouling is a complex one and the aim of this paper is limited to presenting a summary of some preliminary results on the kinetics of the colloidal fouling of asymmetric reverse osmosis membranes. A simple model is suggested for the rate of growth of a colloidal fouling film in steady, obstruction free, laminar and turbulent reverse osmosis systems. Preliminary experimental results are presented on the fouling of cellulose acetate membranes by colloidal iron hydroxide suspended in a flowing saline solution.

Fouling Model

The fouling process may be characterized as a rate dependent kinetic process describable by the material balance relation

$$c_f \frac{d\delta_f}{dt} = \dot{m}_d - \dot{m}_r \qquad (1)$$

[1] Current address: General Electric Co., Wilmington, MA 01887.
[2] Current address: Weizmann Institute of Science, Rehovot, Israel.

Here, c_f is the mean concentration of foulant in the film whose thickness at any time t is δ_f, and $\dot{m}_d$ and $\dot{m}_r$ are, respectively, the mass of foulant deposited and removed per unit area per unit time. Assuming the deposition rate to be independent of the foulant film thickness and the removal rate to be linearly dependent on the film thickness, we may write a first-order rate equation for the film growth. From Eq. (1) this equation is given by

$$\frac{d\delta_f}{dt} = \frac{\delta_f - \delta_f^*}{\tau} \qquad (2)$$

where δ_f^* is the asymptotic equilibrium film thickness at large time and τ is a characteristic film buildup time. The film thickness as a function of time is given from the integration of Eq. (2) by

$$\delta_f = \delta_f^* (1 - e^{-t/\tau}) \qquad (3)$$

Based on considerations to be discussed in a more detailed version of this work we assume that the deposition rate is diffusion controlled, and the characteristic buildup time is controlled by the chemical and physical properties of the foulant and associated foulant-membrane surface forces. The consequence of the first assumption is that

$$v_d = \frac{\delta_f^*}{\tau} \sim \frac{\Delta c}{\bar{c}} \sim \frac{V_o \delta_c}{D} \qquad (4)$$

Equation (4) states that the linear deposition rate v_d is a diffusion controlled boundary layer effect. The quantity Δc is the difference in foulant concentration between the film and that in the bulk flow and $\bar{c}$ is an appropriate average concentration across the diffusion layer. The last term approximately characterizes the "concentration polarization" effect for a developing concentration boundary layer in either a laminar or turbulent pipe or channel flow. Here, V_o is the permeate flux through the unfouled membrane, δ_c the foulant concentration boundary layer thickness and D the diffusion coefficient.

In reverse osmosis systems the permeate flux is expressible by the semi-empirical relation

$$V = \frac{\Delta p - \Delta \pi}{R} = \frac{\Delta p_e}{R} \qquad (5)$$

where Δp is the applied pressure difference across the membrane, $\Delta \pi$ the osmotic pressure difference, R the total hydraulic resistance and Δp_e the effective driving pressure. The total resistance may be taken to be the linear sum of the membrane and foulant film resistance:

$$R = R_m + R_f \tag{6}$$

The apparent resistance due to the reduction in driving force from concentration polarization is generally small in most reverse osmosis systems and is neglected. The resistance can also be written in terms of a characteristic thickness and permeability

$$R_i = \delta_i / \kappa_i \tag{7}$$

where $i = m$ or f. The permeability is proportional to the liquid diffusion coefficient and its temperature dependence is given by

$$\kappa_i \sim D(T)/T \sim 1/\eta \tag{8}$$

where η is the liquid viscosity. We can therefore write for the flux through the unfouled membrane

$$V_o = \Delta p_e / R_m \sim \Delta p_e / \eta \tag{9}$$

with the membrane thickness δ_m assumed to be constant and independent of temperature and the applied pressure.

For developing concentration diffusion layers in channel or pipe flow the concentration boundary layer thickness is expressible by the proportionality

$$\delta_c \sim D^{1/3} U^{-1/3} \tag{10}$$

and in turbulent flow by

$$\delta_c \sim D^{1/3} \eta^{5/12} U^{-3/4} \tag{11}$$

Both D and η have an exponential dependence on temperature but over the narrow range of temperatures of interest we approximate the temperature behavior by the power-law relations

$$D \sim T^{8.1} \tag{12a}$$

$$\eta \sim T^{-7.1} \tag{12b}$$

Inserting Eqs. (9)-(12) into Eq. (4) we find that the deposition rate may be written in laminar flow as

$$v_d \sim \Delta p_e U^{-0.33} T^{+1.7} \tag{13}$$

and in turbulent flow as

$$v_d \sim \Delta p_e U^{-0.75} T^{-1.3} \tag{14}$$

The second assumption of the model that the characteristic buildup time is chemical-physical controlled, implies that this time is dependent on the chemical, physical and electrical properties of the foulant and the membrane but not on the flow. We may lump all of the temperature effects into a van't Hoff-type relation by writing the characteristic time in the form

$$\tau = \tau_o \, e^{-\Delta G/\mathcal{R}T} \tag{15}$$

where ΔG is an "effective" association energy, which correlates the probability of foulant association in the film or with the membrane. For purposes of comparison with the preceding relations we may approximate Eq. (15) over the temperature range of interest by the power-law proportionality

$$\tau \sim T^m \qquad (m > 0) \tag{16}$$

Experiments and Data Reduction

Experiments were carried out in a continuous flow tubular reverse osmosis module with intentional fouling of the membrane by mixing in with the saline feed solution a high concentration of colloidal iron hydroxide, a known fouling material. The use of iron hydroxide in membrane fouling experiments has been previously employed by Jackson and Landolt ($\underline{1}$), however, their tests were not of long enough duration to enable a determination of the fouling kinetics.

The basis for the experiments as carried out was that the flux decline with time, which is an easily measured quantity, could be correlated with the foulant film growth by the model of Eq. (2), or some other appropriate semi-empirical model. In this way the fouling film thickness could be deduced indirectly. To show this we write from Eqs. (5)-(7)

$$\frac{V_o - V_f}{V_f} = \frac{R_f}{R_m} = \frac{\delta_f/\kappa_f}{\delta_m/\kappa_m} \tag{17}$$

where V_f is the permeate flux when the membrane is fouled. So long as the reduction in flux due to fouling is not large then $\delta_f/\kappa_f \ll \delta_m/\kappa_m$ and from Eqs. (17) and (5)

$$\delta_f = \frac{\kappa_f}{\kappa_m} \left(\frac{V_o - V_f}{V_o}\right) \delta_m \tag{18a}$$

$$= \kappa_f \left(\frac{\Delta p_e}{V_o}\right) \left(\frac{V_o - V_f}{V_o}\right) \tag{18b}$$

This shows the film thickness is linear in the relative flux decline. Although this result has been developed using the semi-empirical Eq. (5), it can be derived on more rigorous grounds.

From Eq. (3) it follows that

$$V_o - V_f = (V_o - V_f^*)(1 - e^{-t/\tau}) \tag{19}$$

But $V_o - V_f$ is known from experiment so that we can solve for $V_o - V_f^*$ and τ, assuming of course that the exponential growth law is followed in the experiments. With $V_o - V_f^*$ known we can determine the asymptotic resistance δ_f^*/κ_f from Eq. (18). To determine the behavior of δ_f^* alone for purposes of comparing with the results of the theory, it is sufficient to assume the temperature dependence of κ_f as given by Eq. (8). This is not necessary, however, if only a comparison of the pressure and velocity dependence are of interest.

For estimation purposes the film permeability can be calculated from (2)

$$\kappa_f = \frac{Dv}{\mathcal{R}T} \tag{20}$$

where v is the molar volume of the colloidal solution. From the relation that $D\eta/T$ is a constant for liquids (see Eq. 8), and from data on the viscosity of water we have

$$\kappa_f = 1.91 \times 10^{-6} e^{-17.3/\mathcal{R}T} \quad m^2/s \cdot MPa \tag{21a}$$

with $\mathcal{R} = 8.314$ kJ/mol·K. In approximate power-law form for the temperature range of interest

$$\kappa_f \simeq 4.84 \times 10^{-27} T^{7.10} \quad m^2/s \cdot MPa \tag{21b}$$

The permeability so calculated ranges from 1.24×10^{-9} $m^2/s \cdot MPa$ at $10°C$ to 1.79×10^{-9} $m^2/s \cdot MPa$ at $25°C$.

A diagram of the experimental setup is given in Figure 1. The membranes were of the Loeb-Sourirajan asymmetric cellulose acetate type and were manufactured by the Abcor Corp. The membranes are inserted inside a 3/8 inch (0.95 cm) diameter porous tubular housing 5 feet (1.52 m) in length. The solution used in the tests contained 5,000 mg/L of sodium chloride. At these concentrations polarization effects were negligible. Iron hydroxide in an amount equal to 7.3 mass percent was mixed into the saline solution. The resulting iron hydroxide concentration of 50 mg/L was sufficiently large that despite deposition on the membrane surface during the course of the experiment the composition in solution remained roughly constant. This colloid concentration is from one to two orders of magnitude larger than that found in common brackish ground water where such fouling has been shown to be significant. The large concentrations used enabled the experimental time scales to be correspondingly lower to achieve the same level of fouling as in long term operation with much lower concentrations.

Four parameters were varied in the experiments - pressure, temperature, volume flow rate, and pH. However, in this paper we shall not discuss the effect of pH variation. Before running the tests each new membrane was compacted at about 600 psig (4.14 MPa) for about 10 hours. The permeability of the unfouled membrane was measured using pure water and the saline solution. A typical fouling experiment was run for about 10 hours with the permeate flux measured at 30 minute intervals during the first 3 to 4 hours and at somewhat longer intervals after that. The ranges covered in the tests were: pressures 500-800 psig (3.45-5.52 MPa); temperatures 10-25°C; and flow rates that gave a range of Reynolds numbers based on tube diameter from 1,330 to 15,500. The flow inside the tube thus spanned the completely laminar to completely turbulent flow regimes.

Results and Comparison with Theory

Figures 2 and 3 show typical test results for flux decline in laminar flow where the pressure and temperature are varied and the Reynolds number is held fixed. Similar behaviors are found with variations in Reynolds number and for turbulent flow. The important feature of the data is that the flux decline is exponential with time and an asymptotic equilibrium value is reached. Each solid curve drawn through the experimental points is a least-square fit exponential curve defined by Eq. (19). It is interesting to note that Merten et al (3) in 1966 had observed an exponential flux decay in their reverse osmosis experiments. However, Thomas and his co-workers in their later experiments reported an algebraic flux decay with time (4,5).

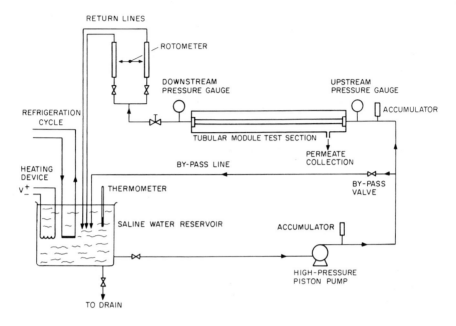

Figure 1. Reverse osmosis experimental set-up

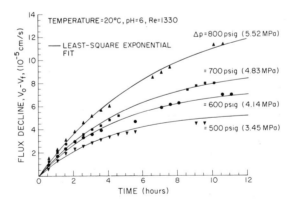

Figure 2. Flux decline vs. time at different pressures in laminar flow

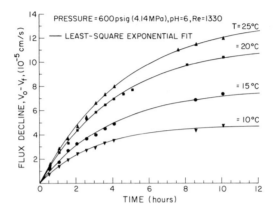

Figure 3. Flux decline vs. time at different temperatures in laminar flow

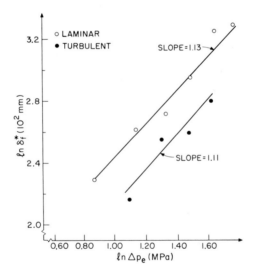

Figure 4. Dependence of equilibrium foulant film thickness on effective trans-membrane pressure

Using fitted curves such as those shown in Figures 2 and 3, the dependence of δ_f^* and τ on Δp_e, U and T could be determined. The results for the equilibrium foulant film thickness are shown plotted on a log-log scale in Figures 4 to 6. The experimental points were reduced using Eqs. (18b) and (21). Absolute thicknesses are shown for δ_f^* only to give some idea of the magnitudes involved. The use of absolute units does not, of course, affect the slope of the data, which within the experimental accuracy is seen to follow a straight line in these plots, indicating a power-law dependence on the independent variables. In order to reduce the data by means of Eq. (18b) it is necessary to know the behavior of the unfouled membrane flux V_o. The experiments showed that V_o is linear in Δp_e and independent of U as Eq. (9) would predict. However, the data plotted in Figure 7 indicate that $V_o \sim T^{8.9}$, whereas Eqs. (9) and (12b) give $V_o \sim T^{7.1}$. The difference is not explained but is probably associated with the experimental procedure. In any case, the experimentally determined values were employed.

In Figures 8 and 9 are shown the data for the dependence of the characteristic film buildup time τ on Δp_e and U. In accord with the model, τ is found to be independent of U, with only a very weak dependence on Δp_e indicated. This latter result could in part be a function of experimental inaccuracy. The data reduction for τ introduces no assumptions beyond that needed to draw the exponential flux decline curves such as those shown in Figures 2 and 3. However, an error analysis shows that the maximum errors relative to the exponential curve fits occur at the earlier times of the experiment. This is seen in the typical error curve plotted in Figure 10. The error analysis indicates that during the early fouling stage the relatively crude experimental procedure used is not sufficiently accurate or possibly that the assumed flux decline behavior is not exponential at the early times. In any case, it follows that the accuracy of the determination of δ_f^* is greater than that for τ.

In Figure 11 a van't Hoff-type plot is given of the characteristic buildup time as a function of $1/T$. The data clearly indicate a linear behavior in this plot with one value of the slope ($\Delta G/\mathcal{R}$ ratio) for laminar flow and another for turbulent flow. Two lines are shown for the turbulent case, one in which only three of the data points were correlated, with what appears to be an inconsistent point left out, and one in which all four points were correlated. The effective association energies of Eq. (15), as defined by these correlations, are relatively low, ranging between 6.5 and 19 kJ/mol, which is in the range of values corresponding to physical adsorption. These results indicate that the foulant film buildup is controlled by physical rather than chemical phenomena.

The reason for a higher association energy for laminar flow than for turbulent flow may be explained by the fact that the turbulence alters the colloid size by increasing the particle

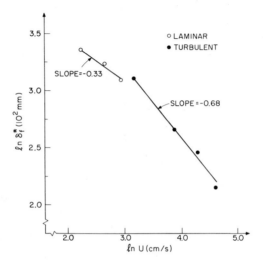

Figure 5.   Dependence of equilibrium foulant film thickness on flow velocity

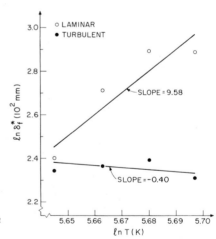

*Figure 6.   Dependence of equilibrium
foulant film thickness on temperature*

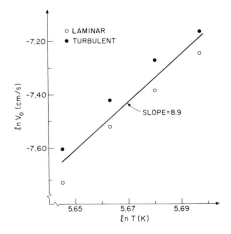

Figure 7. Dependence of unfouled membrane flux on temperature

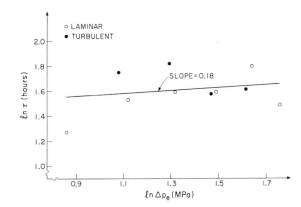

Figure 8. Dependence of characteristic film build-up time on effective transmembrane pressure

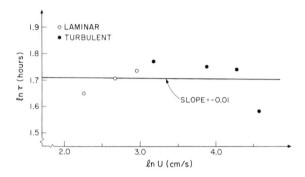

Figure 9.   Dependence of characteristic film build-up time on flow velocity

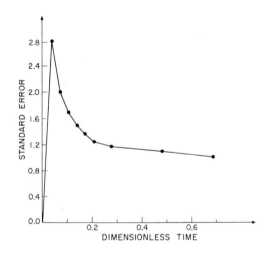

Figure 10.   Typical error curve for exponential fit of data

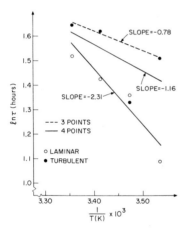

Figure 11. Dependence of characteristic film build-up time on temperature in van't Hoff-type plot

agglomeration rate. We may approximate the exponential dependence shown in Figure 11 by a power law fit and find $\tau \sim T^{7.9}$ for laminar flow and $\tau \sim T^{2.7 \to 4.0}$ for turbulent flow.

The results for δ_f^* and τ in laminar and turbulent flow are summarized in Table I. In Table II the experimentally derived deposition rate dependences given from $v_d = \delta_f^*/\tau$ are compared with the theoretical values of Eqs. (13) and (14). The comparison is seen to be quite good and in some instances the excellent agreement should be considered fortuitous.

Table I

Experimental dependence of equilibrium film thickness and characteristic buildup time in laminar and turbulent flow.

	Laminar	Turbulent
$\delta_f^* \sim$	$\Delta p_e^{1.13} U^{-0.33} T^{9.6}$	$\Delta p_e^{1.11} U^{-0.68} T^{-0.40}$
$\tau \sim$	$\Delta p_e^{0.18} U^{-0.01} T^{7.9}$	$\Delta p_e^{0.18} U^{-0.01} T^{+2.7 \to 4.0}$

Table II

Comparison of experimental and theoretical deposition rate dependences in laminar and turbulent flow.

	Laminar	Turbulent
Exp't. $v_d \sim$	$\Delta p_e^{0.95} U^{-0.32} T^{1.7}$	$\Delta p_e^{0.93} U^{-0.67} T^{-3.1 \to -4.4}$
Theory $v_d \sim$	$\Delta p_e^{1.00} U^{-0.33} T^{1.7}$	$\Delta p_e^{1.00} U^{-0.75} T^{-1.3}$

In concluding it must be emphasized that fluid shear can and does control the foulant film thickness. For example, higher velocities reduce the film thickness as shown in Table I. However, insofar as the characteristic kinetic buildup time is concerned the flow appears not to play a direct role, according to the experimental data reported here. Rather, it is only the properties of the foulant and the membrane that are controlling, although the flow may have an indirect effect by altering foulant size.

Acknowledgment

This research is presently supported by the Office of Water Research and Technology under Grant No. 14-34-0001-8536. Initial support was provided by the National Science Foundation under Grant No. ENG 76-18565.

Literature Cited

1. Jackson, J.M., and Landolt, D., "About the Mechanism of Formation of Iron Hydroxide Fouling Layers on Reverse Osmosis Membranes," Desalination 12, 361-378 (1973).

2. Belfort, G., and Marx, B., "Wastewater Treatment by Membranes: What Can be Done About Fouling?" in Proc. 33rd Industrial Waste Conference, May 9-11, 1978, Purdue University. Ann Arbor Science, Ann Arbor, Mich., 1979.

3. Merten, U., Lonsdale, H.K., Riley, R.L., and Vos, K.D., "Reverse Osmosis for Water Purification," Res. & Dev. Progress Report 208, U.S. Office of Saline Water, Washington, D.C., September, 1966.

4. Thomas, D.G., and Mixon, W.R., "Effect of Axial Velocity and Initial Flux on Flux Decline of Cellulose Acetate Membrane in Hyperfiltration of Primary Sewage Effluents," I&EC Process Design and Development 11, 339-343 (1972).

5. Sheppard, J.D., Thomas, D.G., and Channabasappa, K.C., "Membrane Fouling Part IV: Parallel Operation of Four Tubular Hyperfiltration Modules at Different Velocities with Feeds of High Fouling Potential," Desalination 11, 385-398 (1972).

RECEIVED December 4, 1980.

Intrinsic Membrane Compaction and Aqueous Solute Studies of Hyperfiltration (Reverse-Osmosis) Membranes Using Interferometry[1]

DAVID MAHLAB[2], NISSIM BEN YOSEF, and GEORGES BELFORT[3]

School of Applied Science and Technology, Hebrew University of Jerusalem, Israel

This paper is the third in a series and a direct continuation of our first publication.[1,2] In the first paper, we described the theory and a nominal experiment to show the goodness of fit of the concentration polarization for dissolved species for an unstirred batch system with a plane infinite membrane. An explicit general solution was derived and presented for the time-dependent convective diffusion equation for the case $\pi_0 << \Delta P$. Interferometry was used to measure the steady state feed-side concentration build-up at $28\pm1°C$ for a constant applied differential pressure of 30 atm for a dilute solution of 62 mg/ℓ NaCl. Theoretical analysis of the electromagnetic wave propagation in an inhomogeneous medium (i.e. ray tracing of the bended beam) was analytically solved for the *stationary* form of the diffusion equation.

The second paper is concerned with the numerical solution to the general *transient* form of the diffusion equation and its parametric fit to the changing interferometric fringe pattern.[2]

Here we are concerned with applying the same model and optical methods to analyze (1) the influence of applied pressure on intrinsic compaction, and (2) aqueous solution effects on intrinsic transport parameters and concentration polarization. The reader is referred to our first paper for details including the relevance of the work and previous significant developments.[1]

The major significance of this work is that *intrinsic compaction* for one solute and *aqueous solution effects* for different solutes are measured for a commercial hyperfiltration membrane as a function of applied differential pressure. The results are obtained via simulation of the steady state concentration profile adjacent to the planar surface of the membrane for $\pi_0 << \Delta P$.

[1] This is the third in a series of papers dealing with this particular topic.

[2] Current address: Ormat Turbines, P.O. Box 68, Yavne, Israel.

[3] Current address: Department of Chemical Environmental Engineering, Rensselaer Polytechnic Institute, Troy, NY 12181. To whom correspondence should be addressed.

0097–6156/81/0153–0147$05.00/0

II.   Theory

Boundary Value Problem.   The relevant transformed boundary value problem and solutions will be presented without derivation since the details have been published previously (Mahlab et al., 1977).   Thus, the problem can be stated as follows:

$$\frac{\partial \psi}{\partial \tau} = \frac{\partial^2 \psi}{\partial \xi^2} + \frac{\partial \psi}{\partial \xi} \tag{1}$$

with the boundary conditions,

$$\psi(\xi,0) = 0 \text{ and } \psi(\infty,t) = 0 \tag{2a}$$

and

$$\left. \frac{\partial \psi}{\partial \xi} \right|_{\substack{\xi=0 \\ \tau=\tau}} + R\psi(0,\tau) = -R \tag{2b}$$

with the following transformations

$$\tau = V_{w_o}^2 \, t/D, \qquad \xi = V_{w_o} \, x/D \tag{3a}$$

and

$$\psi(\xi,t) = c(x,t)/c_o - 1 \tag{3b}$$

After taking the Laplace Transform of Eqs(1) and (2) and rearranging the solution into partial fractions, the inverse Laplace transformation results in a solution divided into 3 cases: where $R \leq 1/2$, $1/2 < R < 1$,   and R=1 (for continuity).   The solutions are:

$$\psi_{R \leq 1/2}(\xi,\tau) = \frac{R}{1-R} \, e^{-\xi/2} \int_0^\tau \xi/2 \, \frac{e^{-[\xi^2/(4u)+u/4]}}{\sqrt{\pi u^3}} du$$

$$- \frac{1}{2(1-R)} \, \text{erfc} \, [\sqrt{\tau}/2 + \xi/(2\sqrt{\tau})]$$

$$+ \frac{1-2R}{2(1-R)} \, e^{-R\xi} e^{R(R-1)\tau} \text{erfc}[(1-2R)\sqrt{\tau}/2$$

$$+ \xi/(2\sqrt{\tau})] \tag{4}$$

and

$$\psi_{1/2 \leq R < 1}(\xi,\tau) = \frac{R}{1-R} \, e^{-\xi/2} \int_0^\tau \xi/2 \, \frac{e^{-[\xi^2/(4u)+u/4]}}{\sqrt{\pi u^3}} du$$

$$- \frac{1}{2(1-R)} \, \text{erfc}[\sqrt{\tau}/2 + \xi/(2\sqrt{\tau})]$$

$$+ \frac{2R-1}{2(1-R)} e^{(R-1)\xi} e^{R(R-1)\tau} \text{erfc}[2R-1)\sqrt{\tau}/2$$

$$+ \xi/(2\sqrt{\tau})]$$

$$- \frac{2R-1}{1-R} e^{R(R-1)\tau} e^{-\xi/2}$$

$$\int_0^\tau \xi/2 \frac{e^{-[\xi^2/(4u) + (R-1/2)^2 u]}}{\sqrt{\pi u^3}} du \qquad (5)$$

and

$$\Psi_{R=1}(\xi,\tau) = (1+\tau) e^{-\xi/2} \int_0^\tau \xi/2 \frac{e^{-[\xi^2/(4u) + u/4]}}{\sqrt{\pi u^3}} du$$

$$- \xi/2 e^{-\xi/2} \int_0^\tau \frac{e^{-[\xi^2/(4u) + u/4]}}{\sqrt{\pi u}}$$

$$- (1 + \tau/2 + \xi/2) \text{erfc}[\sqrt{\tau}/2 + \xi/(2\sqrt{\tau})]$$

$$+ \sqrt{\tau/\pi} e^{-[\sqrt{\tau}/2 + \xi/(2\sqrt{\tau})]^2} \qquad (6)$$

where $\text{erfc}(z) = (2/\sqrt{\pi}) \int_z^\infty e^{-u^2} du$ is the complementory error function.

Ray Tracing. An electromagnetic wave propagating perpendicular to the gradient of the refractive index of the medium will bend in the direction of this gradient. The bending phenomenon is completely described by the ray equation:

$$\frac{d(n\underline{\tau})}{ds} = \nabla n \qquad (7)$$

where n = refractive index; s = actual optical path; and $\underline{\tau}$ = is the unit vector tangent to s. The objective here is to solve Eq(7) in one-dimension for s thereby obtaining the total optical path $\ell = \int n ds$ from the general or transient functional dependence of the refractive index,

$$n(\xi,\tau) = n_o + c_o \frac{dn}{dc_o} \psi_{R \triangleleft 1}(\xi,\tau) \qquad (8)$$

where n_o = refractive index at c_o as $x \to \infty$. For the steady state case as $\tau \to \infty$ for R<1, we get from Eqs (4) and (5)

$$\psi_{R<1}(\xi,\infty) = \frac{R}{1-R} e^{-vx} \tag{9}$$

where $v = V_{w_0}/\mathcal{D}$, the reduced flux. Thus the refractive index $n(\xi,\infty)=n(x)$ can be represented by a simple decreasing exponential function of x.

For a complete description of the ray path, integration of the x-component of Eq (7) results in (see Eq(C4) in Appendix C of Ref 1):

$$0 = \int_{x_0}^{x} (\frac{1}{\sqrt{k_1 n(u)^2 - 1}} - \frac{y}{x-x_0}) \, du. \tag{10}$$

Using the relation $\ell = \int n ds$ to find the optical path length ℓ, the following equation is derived in terms of the difference between the object and reference path for high relative accuracy:

$$\Delta\ell = \int_{x_0}^{x} [\frac{n(u) k_1^{1/2}}{\sqrt{k_1 n(u) - 1}} - \frac{n_0 y}{x-x_0}] \, du \tag{11}$$

This equation with n(u) from Eqs(8) and (9) was solved using the Newton-Ralston method.

Membrane Transport. Yasuda and Lamaze[3] have shown that salt rejection R of a water-swollen membrane can be expressed as follows:

$$R = \{ g + P_2 RT/[P_1 v_1 (\Delta P - \sigma\Delta\pi)]\}^{-1} \tag{12}$$

where P_1 and P_2 are the diffusive permeabilities of water and salt respectively and v_1 is the molar volume of water. g is defined as the ratio of the hydraulic to diffusive flow by

$$g = K_1 RT/(P_1 v_1) \tag{13}$$

The total water flux is given by

$$J_1 = (K_1/\Delta x) (\Delta P - \sigma\Delta\pi) \tag{14}$$

where σ is the Staverman reflection coefficient and equals 1 in the solution-diffusion model, K_1 is the hydraulic permeability and Δx is the thickness of the membrane or active skin in this case.

If g=1 the solution-diffusion model is said to hold.[4] By plotting R^{-1} versus $(\Delta P - \sigma\Delta\pi)^{-1}$ from Eq(12), the intercept is g and the slope is $(P_2 RT/P_1 v_1)$.

III. Experimental

Details of the stainless steel hyperfiltration cell and the optical system were presented previously.[1] A flat cellulose acetate membrane (type 990 obtained from the Danish Sugar Corp. Ltd., RO-Division DK-4900 Nakskov, Denmark) was used at 28+°C at pressures ranging from 5 to 30 atm with an initial feed concentration ranging from c_o =50 to 182 mg/ℓ NaCl for the intrinsic compaction studies and at several different concentrations for the aqueous solute studies. In each case, intrinsic parameters - rejection R and reduced flux v - were obtained by fitting the steady-state solutions of Eqs(4),(5) and (6) and incorporating the ray tracing to the experimental interferogram. Additional details are presented in Ref.1.

IV. Results and Discussion

Two applications of the above model and experimental set-up are described below.

Intrinsic Compaction. Reciprocal intrinsic rejection is plotted against reciprocal applied pressure according to Eq(12) in Fig.1a, while reduced flux is plotted against applied pressure according to Eq(14) in Fig.1b. Osmotic effects are neglected due to the low initial feed concentration. ($\Delta\pi/P$ ranges from approximately 0.01 to 0.0019 for ΔP from 5 to 30 atm, respectively.

Two phase behaviour is apparent in both plots of Fig.1 i.e. at low applied pressure and high applied pressure above 10 atm. In Fig.1a a lower slope (ϕ=2.25) and higher intercept (g=1.32) is obtained for the low pressure region as compared to the slope (ϕ=2.60) and intercept (g=1.09) for high pressure region. Since from Eq(13), a value of g close to 1 implies adherence to the solution-diffusion model, it appears that at low pressures where g = 1.32>1.0, a combined model of viscous and diffusive flow is operative. This correlates with previous SEM studies in our laboratory (unpublished), where micro-pin holes were postulated to exist in the skin. The presence of such *micro-pin holes* in the surface can be used to explain the high g-value. Above 10 atm, the DDS-990 membrane is compressed or compacted and the micro-pin holes filled. Thus g = 1.09≈1.0 implies adherence to the solution-diffusion model.

From Eq(12), the slopes in Fig.1a are equal to P_2RT/P_1v_1. The results above together with the slopes (=$K_1\Delta x$) of the low and high pressure regions of Fig.1b and Eq(14), enable P_1 and P_2 to be calculated for an estimate of the skin thickness of $\Delta x \approx 0.2 \times 10^{-4}$ cm (Ref 5). The results are summarized in Table 1. The results for P_1 and P_2 reported in Table 1 compare favorably with those found in the literature. For NaCl (0.9 moles/ℓ) Blunk (see Ref 5 p.134) obtained $P_1 = 2.60 \times 10^{-7}$ gm/cm-sec and $P_2 = 2.0 \times 10^{-6}$ cm^2 sec^{-1} at 102 atm.[1] Compaction at such high applied pressures could

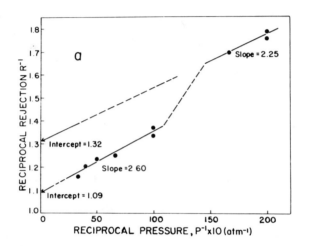

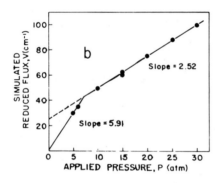

Figure 1.   Intrinsic parameters vs. applied pressure

Table I

Intrinsic Water and Salt Permeabilities as Function of Pressure

Pressure range	g-factor	Permeability ratio[a] $\phi = P_2RT/P_1v_1$	Hydraulic permeability[b,c] $K_1 = P_1v_1g/RT$	Diffusive Permeabilities		
				water, P_1	salt, P_2	Ratio, P_1/P_2
atm	--	dynes cm^{-2}	cm^3 s g^{-1}	cm^{2}sec^{-1}	cm^2 sec^{-1}	--
low 0-9	1.32	2.28×10^6	1.866×10^{-15}	1.958×10^{-6}	3.224×10^{-9}	607
high 10-30	1.09	2.63×10^6	7.958×10^{-16}	1.011×10^{-6}	1.920×10^{-9}	527

[a] multiply atm×1.0133×10^6 to get dynes cm^{-2}.

[b] $K_1 = \Delta x$(slope from Fig 11b)x $D/(1.0133 \times 10^{-6})$, where $D=1.6 \times 10^{-5}$ cm^2 sec^{-1} for NaCl @ 25°C and $\Delta x = 0.2 \times 10^{-4}$ cm.

[c] Choose $v_1 = 18.06$ cm^3 mole^{-1}, $R = 82$ cm^3 atm/(°K mole) and $T = 273 + 28°C = 301°K$, Thus

$\frac{v_1}{RT} = 7.221 \times 10^{-10}$ cm sec^2 g^{-1}.

explain these low values. Also, Blunk's values are observed and
not intrinsic permeabilities such as ours.

By increasing the pressure above 10 atm, P_1 and P_2 decrease
by 48 and 40%, respectively, suggesting a compaction phenomenon.
By filling up the micro-pin-holes and reducing the viscous flow
component through compaction, P_1 and P_2 are reduced by about the
same order of magnitude while the ratio P_1/P_2 remains essentially
constant during the process.

Aqueous Solution Effects. Using the simulation developed
previously[1], the intrinsic parameters R and v were calculated
and measured as a function of applied pressure for several
different solutes. The solutes chosen were based on their
ability to "make structure" (ie. $MgCl_2 \cdot 6H_2O$, $AlCl_3$) or to "break
structure" (ie. KCl, $NaNO_3$) of bulk water. In addition to the
inorganic solutes, a strong hydrogen bonding organic solute urea,
was chosen. The results are summarized in Table II where the
permeability ratio $\phi [= P_2RT/(P_1v_1)]$ has been calculated from
Eq(12) for R^{-1} versus ΔP^{-1} and the hydraulic permeability
$K_1 \times 10^{10}$ has been calculated from Eq(14) for $J(= v\bar{v})$ versus ΔP.
Again osmotic effects have been neglected because very dilute
feed concentrations, c_o were used.

Two effects are immediately apparent from Table II. The
solute species appears to have a prenounced effect on the permeability ratio ϕ, while the hydraulic permeability K_1 and the g-
ratio appears to hardly be effected by the type of solute used
(within experimental error). There also appears to be excellent
agreement between experiment and theory for prediction of v and
K_1. Thus, for constant K_1 and hence P_1 with solute type, from
Eq(12) ϕ should vary with P_2 or diffusive permeability of the
solute within the membrane. For the inorganic ions the best
"structure breaker" $NaNO_3$ exhibits the highest ϕ, while the best
"structure maker" $AlCl_3$ exhibits the lowest ϕ. Confirming the
well-known fact that urea is poorly retained by cellulose acetate
membranes, low theoretical intrinsic rejections are predicted
with an extremely high permeability ratio ϕ. Excluding urea, the
g-ratio is essentially equal to one for all the inorganic solutes,
strongly suggesting solution-diffusion type behavior for water
transport. This also explains why K_1 should be independent of
solute type since in the solution-diffusion model, the water and
solute move independently (ie. friction between salt and water,
$f_{sw}=0$) at their respective diffusive permeability rate.

A qualitative comparison of the ϕ values (normalized to NaCl)
from Table II with reverse osmosis and spectroscopic results of
aqueous solutions is presented in Table III.

The normalized ϕ ratios are in good qualitative agreement with
those calculated from Sourirajan[6] and with his free energy
parameter $\Sigma\{-\frac{\Delta\Delta G}{RT}\}$[7]. For the spectroscopic parameters of aqueous
solutions from infrared overtone studies of Luck[8] and spin echo
and continuous wave nuclear magnetic resonance studies of Hertz[9],

Table II

Intrinsic Parameters Versus Pressure for Different Solutes

Solute	Conc. c_0 mg/ℓ	Diff.coef. $D \times 10^5$ cm² sec⁻¹	Appl.press. ΔP atm	Reduc.flux Exp v cm⁻¹	Reduc.flux Theor cm⁻¹	Salt reject R Theor	Perm.ratio ratio, ϕ atm	g^a --	Hydr.perm.^{b} Exp cm³ sec g⁻¹	Hydr.perm.^{b} Theor. cm³ sec g⁻¹	$K_1 \times 10^{10}$
NaCl	85	1.36	11 / 15 / 20	60 / 70 / 88	55 / 70 / 90	0.84 / 0.87 / 0.91	2.105	0.994	8.516	10.589	
KCl	198	1.69	10 / 15 / 20	50 / 59 / 73	50 / 63 / 72	0.80 / 0.84 / 0.87	2.770	1.051	7.774	7.436	
MgCl$_2$ 6H$_2$O	50	1.05	10 / 15 / 20	87 / 101 / 118	85 / 95 / 110	0.93 / 0.95 / 0.97	0.758	0.999	6.510	5.250	
NaNO$_3$	197	1.33	10 / 15 / 20	74 / 87 / 102	75 / 85 / 100	0.67 / 0.75 / 0.82	4.770	0.961	7.448	6.650	
AlCl$_3$	35.5	1.05	10 / 15 / 20	84 / 107 / 124	85 / 110 / 125	0.96 / 0.98 / 0.98	0.403	0.998	8.400	8.400	
Urea	1200	1.15	10 / 15 / 20	71 / 80 / 104	70 / 80 / 100	0.14 / 0.18 / 0.21	68.30	2.38	7.590	6.900	

a From the solution-diffusion model $R^{-1} = \{g + \phi(\Delta P - \sigma \Delta \pi)^{-1}\}$

b From the equation $J = vD = K_1(\Delta P - \sigma \Delta \pi)/\Delta X$.

Table III

Parameters From the Solution-Diffusion Model[a]

And Spectroscopic Results of Aqueous Solutions

Parameter		Ref.	Solute					
			NaCl	KCl	NaNO$_3$	MgCl$_2$6H$_2$O	AlCl$_3$	Urea
$\frac{\phi}{\phi_{NaCl}}$	This work[b]	--	1	1.32	2.27	0.36	0.19	32.5
	Sourirajan	6	1	1.27	3.00	0.56	--	42.0
$\Sigma\{-\frac{\Delta\Delta G}{RT}\}$		7	1.37	1.48	2.24	0.30	--	--
$(T_{str}-T)_{20°C}$		8	2.0	2.5	--	-8.0	--	--
T_1, sec		9	3.448	3.637	--	2.500	--	--
$\delta \times 10^7$		9	0.9	0.9	0.6	-0.7	--	--

a Calculated from $R^{-1} = \{g + \phi(\Delta P - \sigma\Delta\pi)^{-1}\}$, where $\phi = P_2RT/(P_1 v_1)$.

b Results obtained from Table II.

ϕ/ϕ_{NaCl} varies in the same direction as structure temperature $(T_{str}-T)_{20°C}$, longitudinal relaxation T_1, and chemical shift δ, respectively. Thus, it appears that the same properties of aqueous inorganic solutes that effect water structure and mobility (as measured by the spectroscopic parameters above) also effect the ability of a solute to move or diffuse through a membrane. Diffusion of electrolytes is usually dependent on their concentration, hydrated size and ionic atmosphere, their effect on water structure, and their dissociation. Also, the internal surface properties or structural properties of the membrane will directly influence the electrolyte mobility. These details have yet to be clarified with respect to the mechanism of desalting.

ABSTRACT

A previously reported interferometric method is used to study the effects of both *intrinsic compaction* and *aqueous solution effects* on transport through a commercial cellulose acetate hyperfiltration membrane. By fitting the theoretical model to the experimental interferogram, the intrinsic solute rejection R and the reduced flux $v(=v_{w_o}/D, cm^{-1})$ thus obtained, are studied as a function of applied pressures from 5 to 30 atm. and for six different solutes (NaCl, KCl, $MgCl$, $NaNO_3$, $AlCl_3$, and urea). For the pressure studies, two phase compaction behavior is observed with an inflection point between 7 and 11 atms. For the aqueous solution studies, the hydraulic permeability K and the g-ratio are hardly effected by solute type (within experimental error). The solute diffusive permeability P_1, however, varies with solute type in good qualitative agreement with free energy parameters, infrared overtone shifts, and spin echo and continuous wave nuclear magnetic resonance spectroscopy results from the literature.

ACKNOWLEDGEMENTS

The authors thank Amotz Weitz for technical assistance and advice. This work was sponsored by the US-Israel Binational Foundation under Grant No. 186.

LITERATURE CITED

1. Mahlab, D., Ben-Yosef N. and Belfort G., "Interferometric Measurement of Concentration Polarization Profile for Dissolved Species in Unstirred Batch Hyperfiltration (Reverse Osmosis)", Chem. Eng. Commun. 6, 0-000. (1980)

2. Mahlab, D., Ben-Yosef N. and Belfort G., "Concentration Polarization Profile for Dissolved Species in Unstirred Batch Hyperfiltration (Reverse Osmosis) - II Transient Case." Desalination, 24, 297-303 (1978)

3. Yasuda, H., and Lamaze, C.E., J. Polym. Sci., A-2, 9, 1537
    (1971).

4. Thau-Alexandrowicz G., Bloch R. and Kedem O., Desalination 1,
    66 (1966).

5. Lonsdale H.K., Chap 4, p.93–160, in Desalination by Reverse
    Osmosis (ed. U. Merten) The MIT Press, Mass. (1966).

6. Sourirajan S., Reverse Osmosis, Logos Press, London (1970).

7. Sourirajan S. and Matsuura T., Chap 3 of Reverse Osmosis and
    Synthetic Membranes (ed. S. Sourirajan), National Research
    Council Canada, NRCC No. 15627 (1977).

8. Luck W.A.P., Chap iii.3 of Structure of Water and Aqueous
    Solutions (ed. W.A.P. Luck) Verlag Chemie Physik Verlag
    (1974).

9. Hertz, H.G., Chap VII.2 of Structure of Water and Aqueous
    Solutions (ed. W.A.P. Luck) Verlag Chemie Physik Verlag
    (1974).

RECEIVED December 4, 1980.

Pressure Drop Across Polarization Layers in Ultrafiltration

MICHAEL WALES

Abcor, Inc., 850 Main Street, Wilmington, MA 01887

In his plenary lecture at this symposium, (1) honoring Drs. Loeb and Sourirajan, Dr. Sourirajan expressed the view that ultrafiltration is really a special case of reverse osmosis. The theoretical work of this paper, combined with literature data, is fully in accord with this viewpoint. The dynamic resistance to flux of water through an ultrafiltration membrane can be expressed in terms of an osmotic pressure or osmotic pressure-like function, even in many cases of ultrafiltration of lyophobic colloids. We shall distinguish between lyophilic systems, which are stable in the absence of a phase change at the membrane (precipitation, gel formation) and lyophobic systems which are unstable and can be coagulated by passage over a finite energy barrier. The position is taken that in lyophilic systems which are not capable of forming true gels, resistance is always osmotic pressure controlled. The difference between a true gel and a semi-dilute (2) macromolecular solution is explained.

Lyophilic Systems-Laminar Boundary Layers

It is assumed that the layer of solution next to the membrane is in laminar flow, and that molecular diffusion is operative. It was also surmised, both by the present author, and by Dejmek (3) that the relative motion of solvent (water) with respect to solute, since it gives rise to an energy dissipation, should manifest itself as an observable frictional pressure drop. While there is indeed an energy dissipation (entropy production) from this cause, under steady state conditions only an increased osmotic pressure at the membrane results and no frictional pressure drop as such is observed. Consider the motion of a particle or molecule through a fluid under laminar conditions. A force F* is produced by this relative motion such that

$$F^* = f^* (U_1 - U_2) \tag{1}$$

0097–6156/81/0153–0159$05.00/0

where U_1 = fluid velocity with respect to some external reference, U_2 = particle velocity with respect to the same reference. Signer and Egli (4) by comparing flow of water through crosslinked methyl cellulose gels and ultracentrifugal sedimentation of linear methyl cellulose in water, showed that it was irrelevant whether fluid moved with respect to solute, or vice versa. It was also shown that in the semi-dilute concentration region, f*, the molecular friction factor, depended only on concentration and not on molecular weight, and was the same for the linear polymer and crosslinked gel. For a solution of C_2 mols/cm^3, the energy dissipated per unit volume per unit time is then, from Equation (1),

$$\Phi = C_2 \ f \ (U_1 - U_2)^2 \tag{2}$$

where f is now a molar frictional factor. From the thermodynamics of irreversible processes, in one dimension

$$\Phi = - \sum_i J_i \frac{d\mu_i}{dx} \tag{3}$$

for a system of i components (5) where the J_i are fluxes, moles/area x time and the μ_i are chemical potentials, x = distance. We also have

$$\mu_i = \mu_i{}^c + \overline{V}_i P \tag{4}$$

where $\mu_i{}^c$ is the concentration dependent part of μ_i, $\overline{V}$ the partial molar volume, P = pressure. Furthermore,

$$\sum_i c_i \ d\mu_i{}^c = 0 \tag{5}$$

This is the Gibbs-Duhem relation.

In a binary system, where component 1 is solvent (water)

$$\overline{V}_1 \ d\pi = - \ d\mu_1{}^c \tag{6}$$

where π = osmotic pressure. Combining Equations (2) through (6) we obtain, for a binary system

$$C_1 \overline{V}_1 \frac{d\pi}{dx} (U_1 - U_2) - J_v \frac{dp}{dx} = C_2 \ f(U_1 - U_2)^2 \tag{7}$$

where the volume flux is

$$J_v = C_1 \overline{V}_1 U_1 + C_2 \overline{V}_2 U_2 \tag{8}$$

For the case of permeation through a gel column (4), $\frac{d\pi}{dx} = 0$ since

the gel column is everywhere in equilibrium with pure water.   In
this case,

$$\frac{dp}{dx} = \frac{-f\ C_2\ J_v}{(C_1 \overline{V}_1)^2}$$

(9)

expressing a linear dependence of head loss on J_v.   In obtaining
this result, the expressions

$$J_1 = C_1 U_1$$

(10a)

$$J_2 = C_2 U_2$$

(10b)

were used so that

$$U_1 - U_2 = \frac{C_2\ J_v - J_2}{\overline{V}_1 C_1 C_2}$$

(11)

(in this case $J_2 = 0$).

Also,

$$C_1 \overline{V}_1 + C_2 \overline{V}_2 = 1$$

(12)

However, in the case of a concentration polarization layer, $\frac{d\pi}{dx}$
is not zero.

If we evaluate f from the diffusion coefficient at concentration C_2,

$$D = \frac{C_2}{f} \frac{d\mu_2^c}{dC_2} = \frac{-C_1 d\mu_1^c}{f\ dC_2} = \frac{C_1 \overline{V}_1 d\pi}{f\ dC_2}$$

(13)

This is the Onsager-Fuoss relation.
or

$$f = \frac{C_1 \overline{V}_1}{D} \frac{d\pi}{dC_2}$$

(14)

Then, combining Equations (7), (11) and (14)

$$\frac{dp}{dx} = \frac{1}{D} \frac{d\pi}{dC_2} \left(1 - \frac{J_2}{C_2 J_v}\right) \left(D \frac{\partial C_2}{\partial x} - C_2 (U_1 - U_2)\right)$$

(15)

But under steady state conditions, since the material balance at
the membrane must be satisfied, the term in the second brackets
is zero.   Thus, there is no observable frictional head loss and

across the polarization layer

$$\frac{dp}{dx} = 0 \tag{16}$$

However, an osmotic pressure at the membrane must be over-come in order to obtain flux.
For unit reflection coefficient

$$\Delta P = R_m J_v + \pi(C_2^{\ m}) \tag{17}$$

where ΔP = applied transmembrane pressure, R_m = hydraulic re-sistance of (fouled) membrane, $C_2^{\ m}$ = solute concentration at the membrane.

$C_2^{\ m}$ is given in theory by Brian's relation (6), which for unit rejection is

$$C_2^{\ m} = C_2^{\ b} e^{J_v/k} \tag{18}$$

where k is a mass transfer coefficient and $C_2^{\ b}$ is the concentra-tion in the bulk solute at some point (tube, spiral, Amicon cell, etc.), under steady state conditions. If we substitute Equation (11) in the term in the second brackets of Equation (7), letting this term equal zero,

$$D \frac{dC_2}{dx} = \frac{C_2 J_v - J_2}{\overline{V}_1 C_1} = \frac{(C_2 - C_p) J_v}{\overline{V}_1 C_1} \tag{19}$$

where C_p = permeate concentration. This is the basis of Brian's (6) treatment of concentration polarization. For dilute solu-tions, $C_1 \overline{V}_1 = 1$. Lyophilic colloids may be fairly concentrated at the membrane and $C_1 \overline{V}_1 < 1$. However, we shall ignore this term because of variation of k across the polarization layer.

Some facts about solutions of lyophilic colloids (chain polymers, proteins) which seem not to have been fully appreciated heretofore should be reiterated at this point.

1) Osmotic pressures of chain polymers in the semi-dilute region (2-20% v) are appreciable and no longer molecular-weight dependent. At 50% v, osmotic pressures of chain polymers are of the order of 100 atm, far greater than any transmembrane pressure used in ultrafiltration (7).

2) Osmotic pressures of globular proteins are less than those of chain polymers, but at so-called "gel" concentrations are still very high, and are increasing rapidly with concentra-tion.

As an illustration of these facts, we show calculated flux

vs. transmembrane pressure curves for polyvinyl alcohol in water. These curves were calculated from the flux vs. flow data of Shen and Hoffman (8) at three concentrations shown. The membrane resistance was approximately known, so that Equation (17) was used to calculate the osmotic pressure at the membrane at a series of flows at constant ΔP. From Equation (18) and C_2^m from the Flory-Huggins osmotic pressure function (7), values of k were estimated at each flow and concentration. Using these values of k and the Flory-Huggin osmotic pressure function with chi for dilute polyvinyl alcohol solutions from the Polymer Handbook, the curves of Figure 1 were calculated by going back to Equations (17) and (18). They are, in fact, typical for polyvinyl alcohol ultrafiltration. Number average molecular weight was assumed to be 250,000. It should be mentioned that concentrated polyvinyl alcohol solutions will gel on standing at room temperature. However, the preceding data were obtained at an elevated temperature (82°C).

This brings up the question of "gel control" of boundary layer resistance vs. "osmotic pressure control." If in a given system, gel formation cannot be seen at any realistic concentration in vitro in the laboratory, it certainly is contrary to physical chemistry and polymer science to assume "gel control" in ultrafiltration. While all true gels are semi-dilute or concentrated polymer solutions, all (or most) semi-dilute or concentrated polymer solutions are not gels. Gels (2) have sharp phase boundaries, zero diffusion coefficients and well-defined melting points. Concentrated polymer solutions may actually have larger diffusion coefficients than at infinite dilution and always have diffuse phase boundaries. It would be expected that only such materials as agar, pectin, gelatin, etc. would give gel-controlled polarization layers. Also, some proteins might be denatured at the membrane to give true gels.

Returning to Equation (15), it is noted that $\frac{dp}{dx} = 0$ for the steady state because although energy is being dissipated, this is supplied exactly by transfer of water at high chemical potential in bulk to low chemical potential at the membrane. For the unsteady state, the second term in brackets is not zero and this is no longer true. Equation (15) must then be evaluated from the solution of a partial differential equation which describes the particular unsteady state in question.

Turbulent Boundary Layers

Here we no longer have molecular diffusion operating exclusively (9) and the diffusion coefficient, frictional factor and chemical potential are no longer interrelated. Also, the energy dissipation function is probably no longer quadratic. For simplicity, at unit rejection, for the steady state

$$\frac{dp}{dx} = \frac{J_v C_2}{C_1 \bar{V}_1 D^*} \frac{d\pi}{dC_2} - \frac{\Phi}{J_v} \tag{20}$$

This was obtained from Equation (7), where D^* is an eddy diffusion coefficient. Thus, we have no assurance that $\frac{dp}{dx} = 0$ in this case.

Lyophobic Systems: Rigid Particles

The essential difference between lyophobic and lyophilic systems is that in the latter the potential function between molecules increases without limit as intermolecular distance decreases, to yield ever greater repulsive forces. Thus, in the absence of phase change, the osmotic pressure in lyophilic systems increases without limit with increasing solute concentration. In lyophobic systems, on the other hand, the stability of charged colloidal systems is described by the DLVO theory (10). A similar situation is also present in uncharged sterically stabilized systems. That is, there is a potential barrier which prevents coagulation, but this barrier may be large or small depending on the type and condition of the sol. When the barrier is of the order of 2kT, a slow coagulation occurs (10).

It may not be generally realized that the potential energy barrier which opposes particle approach can lead to what are quite appreciable "osmotic" or "disjoining" pressures when it is attempted to concentrate a lyophobic sol by expressing the fluid component through a membrane. These pressures have been measured experimentally using the apparatus shown in Figure 2 (11). Other types of apparatus have also been used (12, 13). A schematic of curves obtained on one electrostatically stabilized latex is shown in Figure 3 (11). In this case, the dispersion (latex) could be cycled back and forth to very high pressures reversibly, without coagulation. For a number of reasons (shape and position of energy maximum), the vertical asymptote corresponds to a volume fraction less than that of spherical close packing. Note that pressures of more than 60 psi can be developed, which are fairly typical of transmembrane pressures in ultrafiltration. Needless to say, there are also cases where the expected asymptotic pressure is not reached because the energy barrier is overcome on the way there and coagulation occurs (14, 15). However, for the case of a stable latex, we can approximate the curves of Figure 3 by

$$\pi = - \alpha \ln \left(1 - \frac{v}{v^*}\right) \tag{21}$$

Here v = volume fraction latex, v^* = asymptotic volume fraction, α = constant, π = "osmotic" pressure. Then, also

$$\Delta P = R_m J_v - \alpha \ln \left(\frac{v^* - v_b e^{J_v/k}}{v^*}\right) \tag{22}$$

by the use of Equations (17) and (18). ΔP is the applied transmembrane pressure as before. v_b = volume fraction of bulk latex.

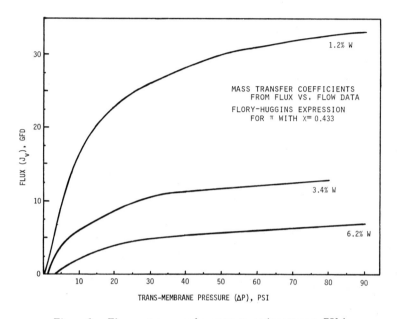

Figure 1.   Flux vs. transmembrane pressure for aqueous PVA

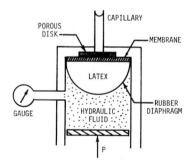

*Figure 2.   Barclay–Harrington–Ottewill
apparatus*

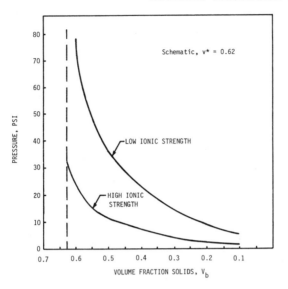

Figure 3. *Experimental pressure vs. volume, Latex*

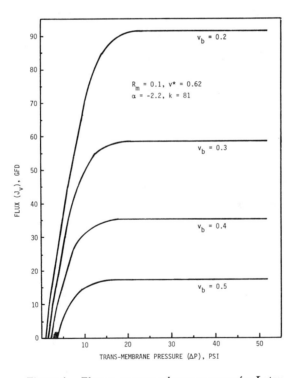

Figure 4. *Flux vs. transmembrane pressure for Latex*

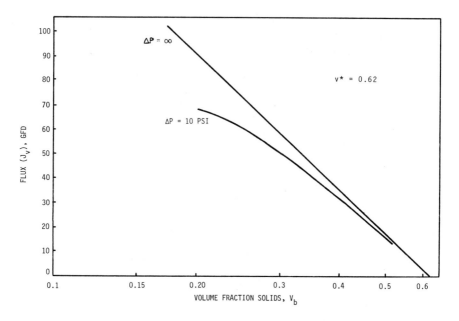

Figure 5.   Influence of solids content on flux for Latex

As $v_b e^{J_v/k}$ becomes close to v^*

$$J_v = k \ln \frac{v^*}{v_b} \tag{23}$$

This is empirically found to be the case in the ultrafiltration of latex where v^* is found by extrpolation to $J_v = 0$. v^* from this experiment and from the measurement of Figure 2 should be identical. This experiment has not yet been done. Equations (22) and (23) are plotted in Figures 4 and 5. Note that in Figure 5, the simple form of Equation (23) is a good approximation from $\Delta P = 10$ psi to infinity. These figures look quite typical for latex ultrafiltration.

It is proposed that the apparatus of Figure 2 would be a useful tool in monitoring ultrafiltration of latex and electrophoretic paints and in systems design (11).

To consider briefly the case where the dispersion coagulates at the membrane, this could lead to an apparent "gel controlled" ultrafiltration depending on the nature of the coagulum. Or, it might progress to total plugging of the tube if all particles had the same degree of instability. If only some particles were unstable, a slower but possibly eventual fatal fouling would ensue. Presumably, backing off on transmembrane pressure would be beneficial since the system tends to be a pressure-independent mode. There is also the question of interaction of particle and membrane double layers which will not be addressed here.

Symbols

b	Refers to bulk (location)
C_i	Concentration of i'th component, moles/cm^3
d	Differential operator
D	Diffusion coefficient, cm^2/sec
f*	Molecular frictional factor
f	Molar frictional factor
i	Subscript referring to component
J, J_i	Flux, moles/cm^{2}sec
J_v	Volume flux, cm/sec
k	Mass transfer coefficient
m	Refers to membrane (location)
P	Pressure
R_m	Hydraulic resistance of membrane
U_i	Velocity of i'th component, cm/sec
v*	Critical volume fraction

v   Volume fraction

$\overline{V}_i$ Partial molar volume of i'th component

x   Distance

$\propto$ Constant in relation for latex osmotic pressure

Δ Change in

μ_i Chemical potential of i'th component

$\mu_i c$ Concentration dependent part of chemical potential

Σ Summation sign

Φ Energy dissipation function

χ_1 Constant in Flory-Huggins equation

Acknowledgement

The writer is indebted to Dr. J.J.S. Shen for discussions on mass transport theory and to Dr. Leon Mir for encouragement and for instruction in the practical aspects of ultrafiltration.

Literature Cited

1. Sourirajan, S., Plenary Lecture, Symposium on Synthetic Membranes and Their Application, Las Vegas, Nevada, August 25, 1980.

2. de Gennes, P.-G., "Scaling Concepts in Polymer Physics"; Cornell University Press: Ithaca and London, 1979; pp. 133-160.

3. Dejmek, P. Ph.D. Thesis, Dept. of Food Science, Lund Institute of Technology, Lund, Sweden, 1975.

4. Signor, R.; Egli, H. Rec. Trav. Chim., 1950, 69, 45.

5. Katchalsky, A.; Curran, P. F., "Non-Equilibrium Thermodynamics in Biophysics"; Harvard University Press: Cambridge, MA, 1965; Chapter 9.

6. Brian, P.L.T. in "Desalination by Reverse Osmosis"; U. Merten, Ed., MIT Press: Cambridge, MA, 1966; Chapter 5.

7. Flory, P. J., "Principles of Polymer Chemistry; Cornell University Pressure: Ithaca, N.Y., 1953; pp. 514-515.

8. Shen, J.J.S.; Hoffman, C. R., 5th Membrane Seminar: Clemson University, Clemson, S.C., May 12-14, 1980.

9. Colton, C. K.; Friedman, S.; Wilson, D. E.; Lees, R. S., J. Clin. Investigation, 1972, 51, 2472

10. Kruyt, H. R., "Colloid Science"; Elsevier: Amsterdam, 1969; Vol. I., Chapters 2, 6, 8.

11. Barclay, L.; Harrington, A.; Ottewill, R. H., Kolloid Z.-Z. Polymers, 1972, 250, 655

12. Homola, A.; Robertson, A. A., J. Colloid Interface Sci., 1976, 54, 286.

13. Ottewill, R. H., J. Colloid Interface Sci., 1977, 58, 357.

14. Dickinson, E.; Patel, A., Colloid and Polymer Sci., 1979, 257, 431.

15. Ottewill, R. H., Progr. Coll. and Polymer Sci., 1976, 59, 14.

RECEIVED December 4, 1980.

The Effect of Halogens on the Performance and Durability of Reverse-Osmosis Membranes

JULIUS GLATER, JOSEPH W. McCUTCHAN, SCOTT B. McCRAY,
and MICHAEL R. ZACHARIAH

Chemical, Nuclear, and Thermal Engineering Department, School of Engineering
and Applied Science, University of California, Los Angeles,
405 Hilgard Avenue, Los Angeles, CA 90024

The rapid expansion of reverse osmosis technology during the
past two decades has resulted in the development of a variety of
new membranes. Unique polymer systems and fabrication methods
have led to the production of membranes with significantly improved performance and reliability. In spite of these developments little is known about chemical sensitivity or life expec-
tancy of reverse osmosis membranes used in desalting applications.
Manufacturers are consequently reluctant to guarantee their products for long runs especially in unique chemical environments.

Commercial reverse osmosis units employ two basic membrane
designs, homogeneous films and thin film composite membranes. The
chemical systems involve cellulose acetate and a variety of linear
or cross linked aromatic polymers. The functional groups princi-
pally consist of amides, ureas, and ethers. Each membrane type is
characterized by specific chemical and physical properties. Little
is presently known about chemical interactions between the membrane
polymer and pretreatment chemicals dissolved in make-up water.
Chemical agents are used in water treatment for disinfection,
oxygen scavenging, scale control, etc. When added alone or in
combination with other chemicals, these agents may influence the
performance of reverse osmosis membranes. The response of membranes to changing chemical environments has been discussed to some
extent in the literature but few definitive studies have appeared.

Chlorine is the oldest and most widespread method of water
disinfection. In reverse osmosis systems, chlorine may be added
to feedwater for control of micro-organisms and, in addition, to
prevent membrane fouling by microbiological growth. According to
Vos et al. [1,2], chlorine will attack cellulose diacetate membranes at concentrations above 50 ppm. Membranes were found to
show a sharp increase in salt permeability and a decrease in
strength after one week of continuous exposure. Under milder conditions (10 ppm chlorine for 15 days) no detectable change in performance was observed. Spatz and Friedlander [3] have also found
cellulose acetate membranes to be resistant to chlorine when exposed to 1.5 ppm for three weeks.

0097–6156/81/0153–0171$05.00/0

Limited testing on chlorine sensitivity of poly(ether/amide)
and poly(ether/urea) thin film composite membranes have been reported by Fluid Systems Division of UOP [4]. Poly(ether/amide)
membrane (PA-300) exposed to 1 ppm chlorine in feedwater for 24
hours showed a significant decline in salt rejection. Additional
experiments at Fluid Systems were directed toward improvement of
membrane resistance to chlorine. Different amide polymers and
fabrication techniques were attempted but these variations had
little effect on chlorine resistance [5]. Chlorine sensitivity
of polyamide membranes was also demonstrated by Spatz and Friedlander [3]. It is generally concluded that polyamide type membranes deteriorate rapidly when exposed to low chlorine concentrations in water solution.

Chlorine dioxide has been used as a water disinfectant, showing fewer undesirable side effects than chlorine [6]. This agent
was shown by Vos et al. [1] to be unreactive toward cellulose
acetate membranes. The compatibility of chlorine dioxide with
other membrane types has not been studied.

Iodine has had limited application for disinfection of swim-
ming pools [7] and small public water supplies [8]. One application in a reverse osmosis system has also been reported by Turby
and Watkins [9]. Advantages of iodine are greater stability than
chlorine, lower residual requirement, and diminished chemical
reactivity toward dissolved organic compounds.

Bromine is another candidate for water disinfection. This
element is very corrosive and requires special techniques for
handling, however, a bromine derivative, BrCl* is much less corrosive and is known to be a more effective bactericide [10].

Motivation for this research arose from the present interest
in membrane response to changing chemical environments. This interest is shared by membrane manufacturers as well as operators
of reverse osmosis plants. Although some results of chlorine-
membrane interaction have been published, few of these studies
are definitive in terms of experimental conditions. Bromine,
iodine, and chlorine dioxide were selected for investigation since
these agents are being considered in certain feedwater disinfection applications. A search of the literature revealed an absence of controlled experimental studies involving exposure of
membranes to halogen agents other than chlorine.

Experimental Procedures

All membrane exposures were carried out by soak testing under
equilibrium conditions at fixed concentrations and constant pH.
Pretreatment chemicals were added to buffer solutions at pH 3.0,
5.8 and 8.6. These buffers, representing an arbitrary pH range
were prepared according to directions given by Perrin and Dempsey

---
* BrCl is presently being tested but results are not included in
this paper.

[11]. The two lower pH levels were phosphate buffers whereas the 8.6 buffer consisted of a boric acid, sodium borate system. The buffers showed no reaction with pretreatment chemicals used, and had sufficient buffer capacity to maintain constant pH during experiments of long duration.

Soak tests with chlorine were carried out in heavy walled pyrex test chambers of approximately 28 liter capacity. The contents were stirred magnetically by six synchronized stirring bars. Membrane samples were hung from the lucite lid by pyrex hooks. All membranes studied in this work were flat sheets. Samples of approximately eight square inches were rolled into cylinders of 1 inch diameter and 2.5 inches long. Details of test chambers and gas injection equipment are shown in Figure 1.

Chlorine was injected periodically from a cylinder containing 5% Cl_2 gas in dry nitrogen. The gas mixture was sparged into the system through two 30 mm fritter glass discs of medium porosity. Chlorine dissipation rates were found to be slow and chlorine levels could be maintained reasonably constant (±5%) by injecting fresh gas at about 12 hour intervals. Flow rates and injection times were established by analysis of chamber contents.

Experiments with bromine, iodine, and chlorine dioxide were conducted by hanging membranes in buffer solutions contained in three liter jars. The solutions were stirred magnetically and the jars tightly stoppered and wrapped with aluminum foil to prevent chemical loss by volatility and/or photodecomposition. Halogen levels were checked periodically by chemical analysis and augmented, as needed, by addition of small volumes of concentrated stock solutions. Solutions of these chemicals are quite stable when tightly stoppered, refrigerated, and stored in the dark. Bromine and iodine solutions were made up directly from reagent grade chemicals. Chlorine dioxide was prepared from sodium chlorite and hydrochloric acid according to directions provided by Rio Linda Chemical Company [12].

Two chlorine levels were arbitrarily selected for this work. A low level of 3 ppm represents an average chlorine residual applied in water disinfection practice. A high level of 30 ppm, representing a tenfold increase, provides extreme conditions for accelerated testing. Concentrations of the other halogen agents were adjusted so as to correspond to either chlorine level on a molar basis. For example 3 ppm chlorine is approximately equivalent to 7 ppm Br_2, 11 ppm I_2 and 3 ppm ClO_2. No attempt was made to control solution temperature which ranges about $22 \pm 1°C$ in our air conditioned laboratory.

During all membrane exposures, concentrations of halogens and chlorine dioxide were periodically monitored by "wet chemical methods". Halogens were determined by the DPD colorimetric method described in references [13] and [14]. Chlorine dioxide at reasonably high concentrations (>10 ppm) can be determined by direct colorimetry [15]. The intrinsic green color appears to obey Beer's law. At lower concentration levels, this chemical is determined by the DPD method.

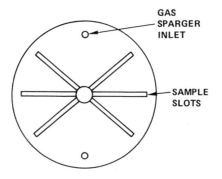

EXPOSURE CHAMBER LID

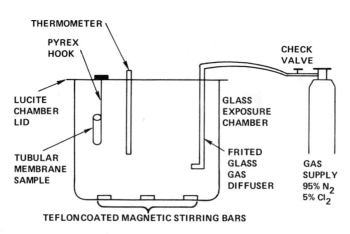

CHLORINE EXPOSURE CHAMBER

Figure 1.   Experimental apparatus for soak tests with chlorine

Assessment of membrane damage was based on performance testing before and after chemical exposure. Testing was conducted in a small flat plate reverse osmosis unit designed to accommodate membrane discs of 45 mm diameter. Feed solution reservoir temperature was maintained at $25 \pm 1°C$ and the brine was continuously recirculated through a filter at the rate of 600 mL/min. Concentration polarization is considered negligible in this cell under these conditions.

Membranes were pre-compacted at 800 psig for approximately one hour, the pressure then being reduced to 600 psig for collection of performance data. At the beginning of this work, control samples were soaked in buffer solutions for times corresponding to membrane exposure. It was subsequently found that control samples were unaffected by buffer solution alone and this procedure was discontinued.

Feed solution used in all experiments contained sodium chloride at a concentration level of 5,000 ppm. Membrane salt rejection is evaluated from conductance measurements of product water and expressed as percent rejection, %R, or desalination ratio, D_r. These units are defined by the following equations in which C_p and C_f are sodium chloride concentrations in feed and product respectively. Note that D_r is very sensitive to concentration changes and expands rapidly as 100% rejection is approached.

$$\%R = \frac{C_f - C_p}{C_f} \times 100 \tag{1}$$

$$D_r = \frac{C_f}{C_p} \tag{2}$$

Product flux was determined from measurements of product volume as a function of time. Flux values determined in mL/hr are converted to gal/ft^2 day (GFD) using the following equation based on a circular membrane area of 15.91 cm^2.

$$GFD = (mL/hr) \times 0.370 \tag{3}$$

Baseline performance data was measured on untreated membranes at 400, 600, and 800 psig in order to assess the relationship between performance and operating pressure. Chemically exposed membranes, however, were run at 600 psig only and performance compared with baseline data at this single pressure.

Results and Discussion

This study was conducted in an effort to learn more about the interaction of halogens with commercial reverse osmosis membranes under a variety of experimental conditions. Membranes used in this work representing several different polymer systems were pro-

vided through the cooperation of manufacturers listed in Table I.
Changes in membrane performance are compared with "baseline data"
(Table II) using untreated membranes with 5,000 ppm sodium chloride
feed.

Table I. Commercial Membranes Studied

UCLA Code	Manufacturer	Mfg. Code	Polymer Type
U-1	Fluid Systems	TFC-RC-100	Poly(ether/urea) (thin film composite)
C-2	Environgenics	CA Blend 72°C cure	CA-CTA 50/50 (homogeneous)
V-1	Hydranautics	γ	Homogeneous CA (coated with vinyl acetate)
A-2	Dupont	Aramid B-9	Homogeneous Aromatic Polyamide
X-2	FilmTec	FT-30	Composition unknown (thin film composite)

Initially all membranes were exposed to 3 ppm chlorine in
buffer solutions at pH levels of 3.0, 5.8, and 8.6 for three weeks.
Both cellulose acetate type membranes C-2 and V-1 were unaffected
by chlorine under these conditions. Continued exposure at higher
chlorine levels did not alter baseline membrane performance. For
example, membrane C-2 exposed to 125 ppm chlorine for 10 days at
pH 3 continued to perform at baseline levels. In subsequent work,
cellulose acetate membranes were also found to be unresponsive to
bromine, iodine, and chlorine dioxide. It can be generally concluded that cellulose acetate type membranes are halogen resistant.
        By contrast, membranes U-1, A-2 and X-2 are all chlorine sen-
sitive, each responding in a unique manner. U-1 is a thin film
composite membrane, the active layer consisting of cross-linked
poly(ether/urea) polymer. A-2 is a homogeneous aromatic polyamide containing certain polyelectrolyte groups. X-2 is a thin film
composite membrane of proprietary composition.
        The pH performance profiles of each membrane after forty hours
exposure to 3.0 ppm chlorine are shown in Figures 2, 3, and 4.
Membrane U-1 shows a typical performance decline with greatest effect at pH 3.0. The decline is progressive (Figure 5) and results
in nearly complete membrane failure after 64 hours of exposure.
        Membrane A-2 appears to "tighten up" on chlorine exposure as
measured by product flux below baseline levels as shown in Figure
3. Membrane tightening continues progressively up to a point after which it is followed by a sharp performance decline. This is

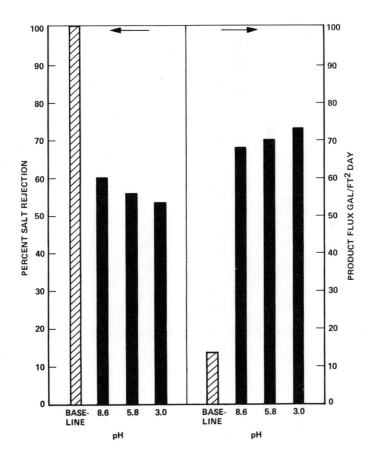

Figure 2. Performance of U-1 membrane after 40-h exposure to 3.0 ppm chlorine at various pH levels

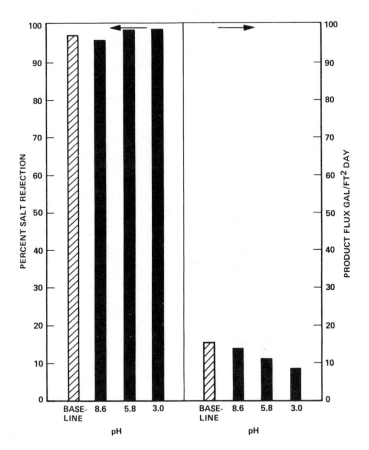

Figure 3. Performance of A-2 membrane after 40-h exopsure to 3.0 ppm chlorine at various pH levels

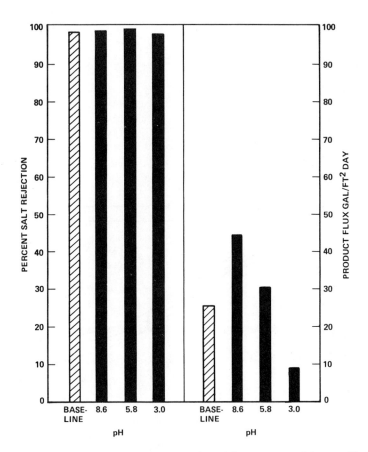

Figure 4. Performance of X-2 membrane after 40-h exposure to 3.0 ppm chlorine at various pH levels

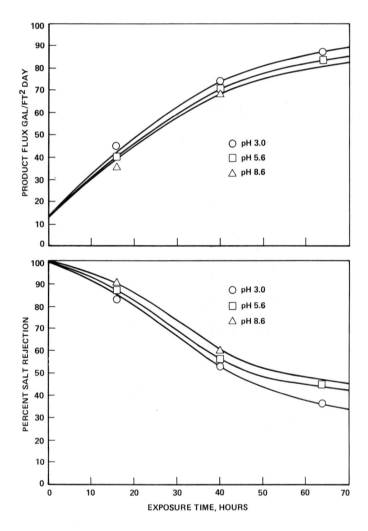

*Figure 5.   Change in flux and salt rejection of U-1 membrane on continued expo-
sure to 3.0 ppm chlorine at various pH levels*

Table II. Commercial Membrane Performance Baseline Data

UCLA Code	Membrane ID	Operating Pressure (psi)	Product Flux (GFD)	Desal.* Ratio (D_r)	% Salt Rejection**
U-1	Fluid Systems TFC-RC-100	400	9.6	437	99.8
		600	13.8	479	99.8
		800	18.4	415	99.8
C-2	Envirogenics CA-CTA Blend 72°C cure	400	12.8	16.2	93.8
		600	19.2	21.6	95.3
		800	25.2	21.8	95.4
V-1	Hydranautics CA coated with vinyl acetate	400	12.6	36.0	97.2
		600	20.2	44.2	97.7
		800	26.1	40.2	97.5
A-2	Dupont B-9	400	10.3	32.5	96.9
		600	15.7	37.0	97.3
		800	21.3	31.3	96.8
X-2	FilmTec FT-30	400	16.2	59.9	98.3
		600	25.8	66.9	98.5
		800	33.3	60.8	98.4

* $D_r = \dfrac{\text{Salt conc. in feed}}{\text{Salt conc. in prod.}}$

** Percent salt rejection based on 5,000 ppm NaCl feed solution.

shown in Figure 6 using 30 ppm chlorine at pH 3.0 in order to amplify this effect.

The performance of membrane X-2 is strongly pH dependent, showing greatest flux change at pH 8.6 and appearing to tighten up at pH 3.0. For some unknown reason, salt rejection remains constant and near baseline for the entire 88 hour exposure period shown in Figure 7.

The next set of experiments were designed to compare chlorine with bromine and iodine in terms of membrane sensitivity. Experiments with A-2 and X-2 were run for forty hours but U-1 was exposed for only 16 hours because of rapid deterioration on exposure to bromine. Concentrations of all halogens were equivalent to 3 ppm Cl_2 on a molar basis. Performance profiles for membranes U-1, A-2 and X-2 are shown in Figures 8, 9, and 10 respectively. Only product flux is reported in this case since it appears to be a more sensitive indicator of performance changes.

In an effort to better interpret these results, a literature review on aqueous halogen chemistry was conducted [16,17]. Halogen molecules react in water solution to produce several chemical species as shown in the following equations where X represents Cl, Br, or I.

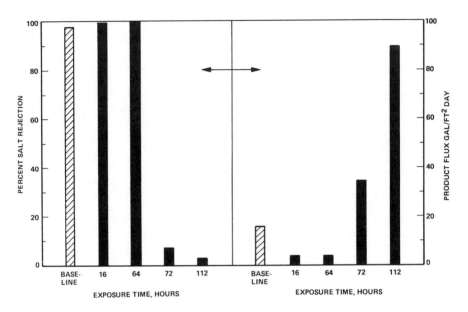

Figure 6.   Change in flux and salt rejection of A-2 membrane on continued exposure to 30 ppm chlorine at pH 3.0

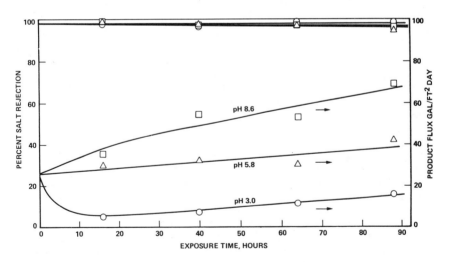

Figure 7.   Change in flux and salt rejection of X-2 membrane on continued exposure to 30 ppm chlorine at various pH levels

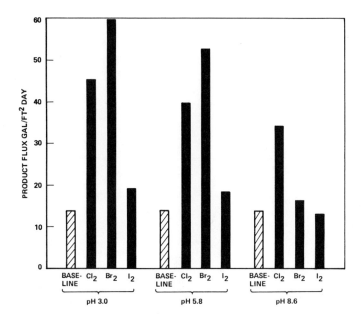

Figure 8. Relative influence of halogens on the performance of U-1 membrane after 16 hour exposure at various pH levels

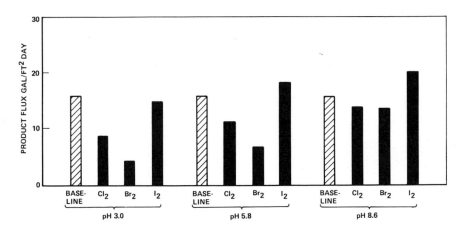

Figure 9. Relative influence of halogens on the performance of A-2 membrane after 40-h exposure at various pH levels

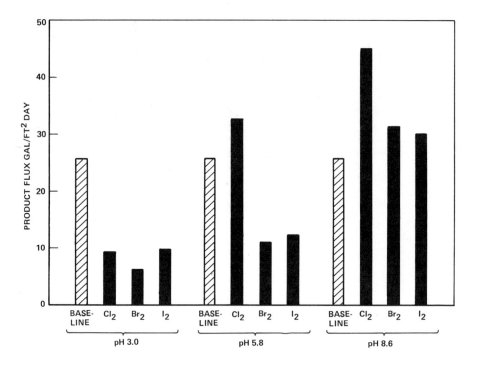

Figure 10.   Relative influence of halogens on the performance of X-2 membrane after 40-h exposure at various pH levels

$$X_2 = H_2O \rightleftharpoons HOX + H^+ + X^- \qquad (4)$$

$$HOX \rightleftharpoons H^+ + OX^- \qquad (5)$$

In basic solution, the following reactions may also occur.

$$X_2 + 2OH^- \rightleftharpoons X^- + OX^- + H_2O \qquad (6)$$

$$3OX^- \rightleftharpoons 2X^- + XO_3^- \qquad (7)$$

Reaction 7 is insignificant for chlorine at room temperature but takes place to a considerable extent for bromine and is nearly complete for iodine.

The distribution of halogen species in aqueous solution depends on pH and equilibrium constants for the above reactions. Table III lists the distribution of species for each halogen at the three pH levels reported in this paper. Derivation of equations for calculation of halogen species concentration are presented in reference [18].

Table III. Fractional Distribution of Halogen Species in Aqueous Solution as a Function of pH*

| | pH | | Mole Percent | |
		X_2	HOX	OX^-
Chlorine	3.0	0.01	99.99	0.0
	5.8	0.0	97.72	2.28
	8.6	0.0	6.36	93.64
Bromine	3.0	69.63	30.37	0.0
	5.8	1.17	98.71	0.12
	8.6		Mostly as BrO_3^-	
Iodine	3.0	99.75	0.25	0.0
	5.8	93.60	6.40	0.0
	8.6		All as IO_3^-	

*Based on a total halogen concentration of 4.23×10^{-5} molar as X_2. This is equivalent to 3.0 ppm Cl_2.

Chemical attack on membrane U-1 is revealed by increasing product flux which is evidently related to breaking chemical bonds within the polymer. Membranes A-2 and X-2 respond to chemical attack by decreased product flux which probably results from halogen addition to these polymers. On this basis, the order of halogen activity below pH 5.8 is $Br_2 > Cl_2 > I_2$. With membrane U-1 at pH 8.6 the order changes to $Cl_2 > Br_2 > I_2$. One may conclude that

chemical attack of all halogens is greater with decreasing pH and
that X_2 and HOX are the most chemically active species. Note that
these species do not exist with bromine and iodine at pH 8.6. Performance data on membrane X-2 at pH 8.6 is difficult to interpret
but may be due to a change in the mechanism of chemical attack as
pH increases.

All three membranes are responsive to attack by halogens.
Chemical interaction evidently proceeds by more than one reaction
mechanism. A possible explanation involves halogen addition as
evidenced by membrane tightening. A second process may result in
chemical bond cleavage which ultimately causes membrane failure.
Halogen attack on membrane U-1 is probably dominated by bond cleavage which is enhanced as pH decreases.

Membranes A-2 and X-2 evidently respond according to more
complicated chemical models. The observed membrane tightening may
result from halogen addition. Subsequent performance decline is
probably related to bond cleavage. With membrane X-2, it appears
that both the extent and mechanism of halogen attack are strongly
pH dependent.

The last series of experiments were conducted with chlorine
dioxide. This interesting chemical is a stronger oxidizing agent
than chlorine and is reported to attack organic compounds by oxidation without halogen addition [19]. As with halogens, cellulose
acetate membranes were found to be unresponsive to chlorine dioxide on long exposure over the usual pH range. This ia a perplex-
ing observation since these same membrane types are severely damaged by ozone [18] and both O_3 and ClO_2 have nearly the same oxidation potential in acid solution.

By contrast, membrane U-1 was so severely damaged by chlorine
dioxide that reproducible experimental data could not be collected.
The response of membranes A-2 and X-2 exposed to 30.0 ppm ClO_2 for
40 hours is illustrated in Figures 11 and 12. Both membranes
show only slight response at pH 3.0 and 5.8 but are severely damaged at pH 8.6. The chemistry of chlorine dioxide in aqueous solution is evidently very pH dependent.

One additional experiment was conducted in an effort to shed
more light on the mechanism of membrane damage. Samples of membrane A-2 were examined by the Beilstein test [20] following exposure. This sensitive qualitative test for organo-halogen species will indicate the incorporation of halogen into the membrane.
Beilstein tests were positive following membrane exposure to chlorine bromine or iodine and negative following exposure to chlorine
dioxide.

Conclusions

The interaction of halogens and chlorine dioxide with reverse
osmosis membranes is dependent on the membrane polymer, the solution pH, and the halogen involved. Cellulose acetate was unresponsive to halogen agents under experimental conditions described

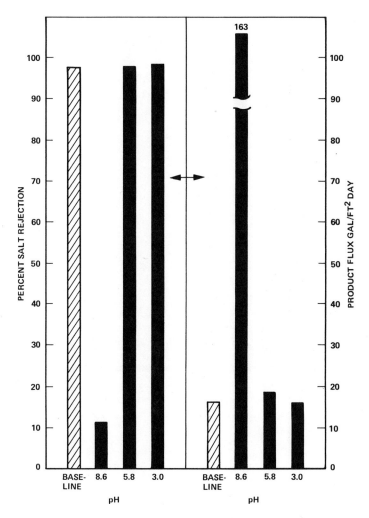

Figure 11. Performance of A-2 membrane after 40-h exposure to 30 ppm chlorine dioxide at various pH levels

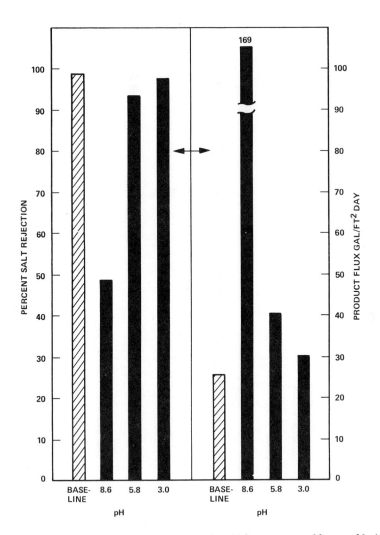

Figure 12.   Performance of X-2 membrane after 40-h exposure to 30 ppm chlorine dioxide at various pH levels

in this paper. All other membranes tested are halogen sensitive, each responding in a characteristic manner.

The most aggressive chemical is chlorine dioxide, producing severe membrane damage at high pH, but being reasonably inert toward membranes A-2 and X-2 at low pH. In general, the other halogens can be arranged in order of reactivity as $Br_2 > Cl_2 > I_2$ at low pH and $Cl_2 > Br_2 > I_2$ at high pH.

The mechanism of membrane attack probably involves several processes such as halogen substitution, halogen addition, and various bond cleavage reactions. The dominant mechanism is related to pH which in turn determines the distribution of halogen species in solution. Membranes exposed to halogens are found to form organo-halogen bonds in the polymer structure. Exposure to chlorine dioxide, however, involves no uptake of chlorine atoms in spite of severe membrane damage.

Further work should be directed at better understanding the nature of halogen-membrane interaction. These efforts may provide guidelines for development of more halogen resistant membranes.

Acknowledgments

The authors wish to acknowledge the support of this research provided by the Office of Water Research and Technology, U.S. Department of the Interior, Washington, D.C., under Grant No. 14-34-0001-7810. Partial support was also provided by the State of California Saline Water Research Funds administered by the Water Resources Center at the University of California, Davis, California. We also express our thanks to the five membrane manufacturers for their splendid cooperation in providing samples for this study.

Literature Cited

1. Vos, K. D., et al., Desalination 5, 157 (1968).
2. Saline Water Conversion Report, pg. 232, U.S. Department of the Interior, Office of Saline Water, 1966.
3. Spatz, D. D., Friedlander, R. H., "Chemical Stability of SEPA Membranes for RO/UF", report from Osmonics, Inc., Hopkins, Minnesota, 1977.
4. Progress Report by Fluid Systems Division of U.O.P. on Contract No. 14-30-0001-3303, to the Office of Water Research and Technology, U.S. Department of the Interior, July 1975.
5. Progress Report by Fluid Systems Division of U.O.P. on Contract No. 14-34-0001-6516, to the Office of Water Research and Technology, U.S. Department of the Interior, March 1976.
6. Special Report from the International Ozone Institute, Environ. Sci. Technol. 11, 26 (1977).
7. Black, A. P., et al., Am. J. Public Health 49, 1060 (1959).
8. Black, A. P., et al., JAWWA, pp. 1401-1421, November (1965).
9. Turby, R. L., Watkins, F., Proc. 7th Ann. Conf., National Water Supply Improvement Assoc., New Orleans, LA, September 1979.

10. Mills, J. F., Schneider, J. A., Ind. Eng. Chem. Prod. Res. Develop. 12, 160 (1973).
11. Perrin, D. D., Dempsey, B., "Buffers for pH and Metal Ion Control", John Wiley and Sons, New York, 1974.
12. Private Communication with Bruce Hicks, Rio Linda Chemical Co., Rio Linda, California, 1979.
13. "Colorimetric Procedures and Chemical Lists for Water and Wastewater Analysis", Hatch Chemical Co., Ames, Iowa, 1971.
14. "Standard Methods for the Examination of Water and Wastewater", 14th ed., American Public Health Assoc., Inc., New York, 1975.
15. Gordon, G., et al., "The Chemistry of Chlorine Dioxide", Prog. in Inorg. Chem., Wiley-Interscience 15, 201 (1972).
16. White, G. C., "Handbook of Chlorination", Van Nostrand Reinhold Co., New York, 1972.
17. Hoehn, R. C., JAWWA 68, 302 (1976).
18. McCutchan, J. W., Glater, J., Final Report to the Membrane Process Division, Office of Water Research and Technology, U.S. Department of the Interior, under Grant No. 14-34-0001-7810, January 1980.
19. Ward, W. J., Proc. 36th Int. Water Conf., Pittsburgh, PA, November 4-6, 1975.
20. Shriner, R. L., et al., "The Systematic Identification of Organic Compounds", John Wiley and Sons, New York, 1964.

RECEIVED December 4, 1980.

High-Flux Cellulose Acetate Membranes

K. W. BÖDDEKER, H. FINKEN, and A. WENZLAFF

GKSS—Forschungszentrum, 2054 Geesthacht, Germany

Three routes to increase the permeate flux of asymmetric cellulose diacetate membranes of the Loeb-Sourirajan type are investigated: increasing the hydrophilicity of the membranes; increasing their compaction stability; employing a swelling agent which allows for higher solvent-to-polymer ratio in the casting solution.

The effect of casting solution composition on flux and rejection of formamide-modified cellulose acetate membranes is shown in Figure 1, illustrating the general capability of this membrane type as function of solvent concentration. Membranes of casting solution composition cellulose diacetate/acetone/formamide 23/52/25 (solvent-to-polymer ratio 2.26) were used as reference membranes in this work.

Increased Hydrophilicity

Effect of Hydrophilic Bentonites. All membrane models imply a direct relation between flux and membrane water content. The gross water content of the membranes can be increased by incorporating pre-gelled hydrophilic bentonites into the membranes. The useful bentonite concentration is limited by the fact that pre-gelation introduces water into the casting solution (1).

Membrane Preparation. The bentonite used, trade-named Bentone EW (Kronos Titan-GmbH, Leverkusen, Germany), is a highly purified magnesium montmorillonite which gels in water. Bentonite addition is by way of a fully swollen gel of 10 g of Bentone EW in 400 g of water to which is added 300 g of acetone to render the aqueous gel compatible with the remainder of the casting solution. 7.1 % of this slurry is introduced into the reference casting solution (see above), resulting in a composition as follows (wt-%): cellulose diacetate/acetone/formamide/water/bentonite 21.4/51.3/23.2/4.0/0.1 (solvent-to-polymer ratio 2.4). A curing time of about three weeks is required before

0097–6156/81/0153–0191$05.00/0

membranes are prepared in the usual manner. Annealing temperatures are somewhat higher than for the reference membrane at the same rejection.

Membrane Properties. The water contents are as follows: without annealing: reference, 67.0; with bentonite, 69.2 wt-%; annealed at 70 °C: reference, 65.8; with bentonite, 68.6 wt-%; annealed at 90 °C: reference, 63.7; with bentonite, 66.3 wt-%. The net gain in water content due to hydrophilic bentonite incorporation is thus of the same order as the water loss on annealing.

The reverse osmosis performance of the two membranes under typical brackish water conditions is shown in Figure 2 (I, reference membrane; III, with bentonite). At a rejection of 85 % the flux is almost doubled (from 2000 to nearly 4000 $1/m^2d$), the effect becoming smaller when going to higher rejections. Maximum brackish water rejection of the bentonite membrane is 97 % as against 98 % for the reference membrane.

The effect of operating pressure on flux for various annealing treatments is shown in Figure 3. As is usually observed the optimum pressure, beyond which the curves flaten out, increases as the membranes become denser. Maximum flux of the untreated membrane at a pressure of 30 bar is around 10 m^3/m^2d (250 gfd) at 20 % brackish water rejection. The optimum operating pressure of annealed bentonite-containing membranes is lowered by about 10 bar, however, the compaction behavior is comparable to that of the reference membrane.

Increased Compaction Stability

Effect of Organophilic Bentonites. Membrane compaction reduces the integral product water output. By implication, membrane stabilization is a means to increase the flux. Stabilization, along with some flux improvement, can be achieved by doping the membranes with organophilic bentonites (2).

Membrane Preparation. The bentonite used, trade-named Tixogel VZ (Süd-Chemie AG, München, Germany) is a quarternary ammonium compound of montmorillonite origin, the ammonium moieties containing hydrocarbon chains, which gels in polar organic solvents. The optimal bentonite concentration, guided by its effect on salt rejection as shown in Figure 4, is 0.1 wt-% of the casting solution. Bentonite addition is in the dry state by thoroughly mixing 1 g of Tixogel VZ with 230 g of cellulose diacetate, then adding acetone followed by formamide according to the reference casting solution composition. Curing time is again three weeks. Annealing temperatures are somewhat lower than for the reference membrane to attain the same rejection. The water content of the doped membrane does not differ from that of the reference membrane.

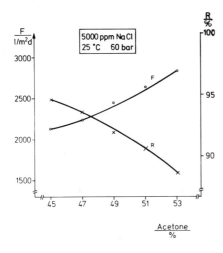

Figure 1. Effect of casting solution composition on flux and rejection of formamide-modified cellulose diacetate membranes

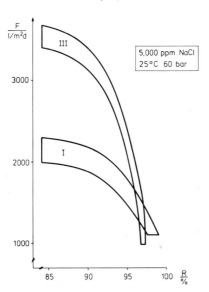

Figure 2. Effect of hydrophilic bentonite incorporation on the reverse osmosis performance of asymmetric cellulose diacetate membranes: I, reference membrane; III, with hydrophilic bentonite.

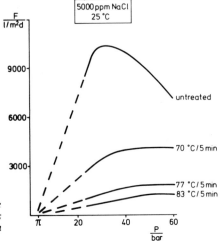

Figure 3. Effect of operating pressure on flux of cellulose diacetate membranes with hydrophilic bentonite incorporation at various annealing levels

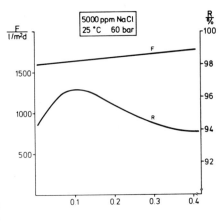

Figure 4. Flux and rejection of cellulose diacetate membranes doped with organophilic bentonite as a function of bentonite concentration

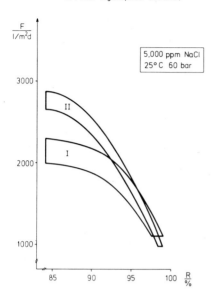

I : Reference membrane.
II : with organophilic additive.

5,000 ppm NaCl
25°C 60 bar

Figure 5. Effect of organophilic bentonite incorporation on the reverse osmosis performance of asymmetric cellulose diacetate membranes: I, reference membrane; II, with organophilic bentonite.

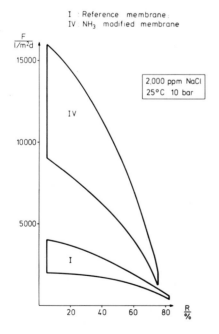

I : Reference membrane.
IV : NH₃ modified membrane

2,000 ppm NaCl
25°C 10 bar

Figure 6. Low-pressure reverse osmosis performance of ammonia-modified cellulose diacetate membranes (IV) compared with formamide-modified reference membranes (I)

Membrane Properties. The reverse osmosis performance of the
bentonite-doped membrane under brackish water conditions is compared to that of the reference membrane in Figure 5 (I, reference
membrane; II, with organophilic bentonite). At low salt rejection
the bentonite membrane again shows a higher initial flux than the
reference membrane, the performance of the two becoming identical
at the high rejection limit.

The objective of employing organophilic bentonite is flux
stabilization. In terms of the membrane compaction slope the sta-
bilizing effect is exemplified by the following figures (brackish
water conditions): reference, -0.10; bentonite-doped, -0.06. In
a field test over 1300 hours on well water of 5200 ppm TDS at a
pressure of 60 bar, starting with an initial flux of 1780 $1/m^2d$
and 95 % rejection, a compaction slope of -0.058 was found; under
the same conditions the reference membrane had a compaction slope
of -0.094.

Increased Solvent-to-Polymer Ratio

Ammonia as Swelling Agent. As is indicated in Figure 1 the
flux of asymmetric cellulose acetate membranes increases with increasing solvent proportion in the casting solution, accompanied
by an unavoidable loss in rejection. By using anhydrous ammonia
as swelling agent in place of formamide, dilute cellulose acetate
solutions are accessible for the preparation of membranes showing
correspondingly high flux values (3).

Membrane Preparation. Dried cellulose diacetate is dissolved
in acetone in the weight ratio of 1 to 3 or 4. Gaseous ammonia is
directed at room temperature over the solution surface in a rotary
evaporator, the ammonia being readily absorbed by the polymer solution. Optimal ammonia concentration is 5 to 6 wt-%, a typical
casting solution composition is cellulose diacetate/acetone/
ammonia 18.8/75.2/6.0 (solvent-to-polymer ratio 4). Casting is
at room temperature. The precipitation bath is maintained at pH 4
through controlled addition of hydrochloric acid to compensate
for the alkaline intake.

Membrane Properties. The performance range of ammonia-modified membranes in low pressure operation is indicated in Figure 6
along with the performance of the reference membrane (I, reference
membrane; IV, ammonia-modified membrane). The lower boundary of
the performance range refers to a solvent-to-polymer ratio of 3,
the upper boundary to a ratio of 4. While the salt rejection towards univalent ions of the ammonia-modified membrane is limited
to below 80 %, the maximum low pressure flux is over 15 m^3/m^2d
(approaching 400 gfd) at a sodium chloride rejection of the order
of 10 %. This membrane thus exhibits the flux capability of an
ultrafiltration membrane while retaining the features of reverse
osmosis membranes, viz. asymmetry and pressure resistance.

Literature Cited

1. Böddeker, K. W.; Kaschemekat, J.; Willamowski, M., Abstract, National Meeting American Chemical Society, 1975, 169, 97.
2. Finken, H., Proc. 7th Int. Symposium Fresh Water from the Sea, 1980, 2, 125.
3. Böddeker, K. W.; Kaschemekat, J.; Woldmann, H., Proc. 4th Int. Symposium Fresh Water from the Sea, 1973, 4, 65.

RECEIVED December 4, 1980.

Highly Anisotropic Cellulose Mixed-Ester Membranes for Microfiltration

R. KESTING, A. MURRAY, K. JACKSON, and J. NEWMAN

Puropore, Inc., 14332 Chambers Road, Tustin, CA 92680

The present study should be seen as a step in the evolution of the colloidal morphology of phase inversion membranes, which conceptually began with dense polymer films and diverged into the two principal branches of *skinned* and *skinless* membranes (Figure 1).

Skinned membranes consist of two layers: a thin dense skin which determines both permeability and permselectivity and a porous substructure which provides physical support for the skin. Such membranes are utilized for the separation of dissolved ions and macromolecules in the processes of *reverse osmosis* and *ultrafiltration,* respectively. Inasmuch as the various classes of skinned membrane which include the *integrally skinned ultragel* of Loeb and Sourirajan *(1),* the *nonintegrally skinned microgel* of Cadotte and Francis *(2),* and the *integrally skinned microgel* of Kesting *(3)* have been reviewed recently *(4, 5, 6),* it need only be noted that the latter two, when deprived of their skins, structurally approximate the second main branch of phase inversion membranes, *viz.* the skinless membranes.

Skinless membranes are the subject of the present treatise. They are utilized in the process of *microfiltration* for the separation of insoluble suspended particles, the most familiar of which are viable microorganisms. Whereas the evolution of skinned membranes has involved such dramatic mutations as the transition from transparent ultragels which require wet storage to opaque wet-dry reversible microgels *(3, 5, 6),* the changes in the colloidal structure of skinless membranes have been more gradual and have taken place entirely within the single class of *skinless microgels.* Although not specifically mentioned by earlier workers, it has become apparent to the present authors that such changes have occurred in the direction of ever increasing *anisotropy, i.e.,* increasing differences in the sizes of pores and cells from one membrane surface to the other. The original skinless microgels such as the graded series developed by Bechhold in 1907 from cellulose nitrate were very similar to the conventional mixed ester membranes of the present. These membranes are *slightly anisotropic* with a degree of anisotropy, DA, (ratio of pore size at the coarser surface to that at the finer surface) of less than 2. A *moderately anisotropic* (DA = 3) *microgel* was reported by Sladek, *et.al.* in 1977 and found to be superior to conventional slightly anisotropic microgels with respect to bacteria recovery in water analyses *(8).* The present study describes a *highly anisotropic* (DA = 5) class of mixed ester *microgel* membrane. Our methodology herein

0097–6156/81/0153–0199$05.75/0

involved the conduction of an experimental survey of representative commercially available slightly anisotropic microfiltration membranes in order to establish their filtration characteristics, as well as their morphological, mechanical and thermal properties, to provide a basis for comparison with our new class of highly anisotropic mixed ester skinless microgel membranes which we have named Tyrann-M/E™ (Patent Pending).

Filtration Characteristics

Air and Water Flow Rates.   The air and water flow rates as functions of differential pressure (corrected for frictional losses in the test system) have been plotted for two noncellulosic 0.45 μM microfilters and for 0.45 μM Tyrann-M/E and conventional slightly anisotropic mixed ester membranes (Figures 2, 3). The flow rates for filtered air and water were found to be independent of which surface of the membrane faced the feed. In every case a linear relationship between pressure and flow rate was observed. The lines tend to be almost but not quite parallel to one another but at considerable displacements along the abscissa. This indicates that whereas all four types respond to pressure in approximately the same manner, there exist substantial differences between their permeabilities, with both mixed ester membranes (at least in the case of the 0.45 μM pore size) exhibiting substantially greater flow rates than both of the noncellulosic types. The air flow rates for Tyrann-M/E are approximately twice those of conventional membranes and three times those of polyamide membranes. It will become apparent later that the reasons for this are related to differences in morphology. The water flow rates for Tyrann-M/E membranes are also greater than those of both conventional and noncellulosic membranes (Figure 3).

Typically, water permeates 0.45 μM Tyrann-M/E membranes at least 50% more rapidly than it does conventional membranes and more than twice the rate at which it permeates the noncellulosic membranes of the same pore size. Air and water flow rates and relative filtration capacities (throughputs) for various 0.1, 0.2, 0.45 and 0.8 μM membranes at 10 psid (corr.) are found in Table I.

Flow Decay.   Perhaps the most important property of a filter is its dirt holding capacity, which affects throughput. This refers to the size of a batch of fluid which can be processed before a membrane becomes plugged by filtered particles thereby terminating or severely diminishing fluid flow. A convenient test of a membrane's filtration capacity is its performance in a *flow decay* experiment in which the product flow rate or permeability is plotted *versus* incremental volumes of filtrate (Figures 4, 5). The solute in this instance was Triton X-400, a cationic surfactant blend whose principal constituents are stearyl dimethyl benzyl ammonium chloride and stearyl alcohol. Since such tests are poorly reproducible in the absolute sense, they are most effectively carried out relative to the performance of a standard membrane exposed to the same solution at the same time. These semiquantitative values indicate that Tyrann-M/E has approximately 1.5 to 4.4 times (depending) upon the pore size) the filtration capacity of conventional membranes. (Table II). It should be clearly understood that Triton X-400 serves only as a model contaminant; the actual throughput for any specific filtration must be determined empirically. Nevertheless the results reported here should serve as a relative indication of what will occur under other test conditions. Relative throughputs were determined at the point where the permeabilities had declined to 20% of that of the initial con-

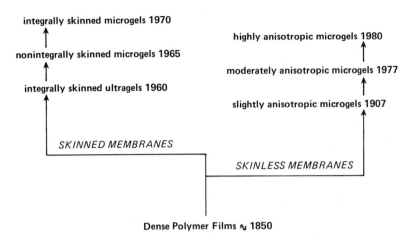

Figure 1. Evolution of the colloidal morphology of phase inversion membranes

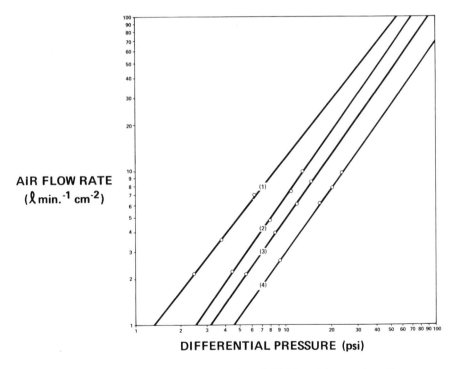

Figure 2. Air flow rate vs. pressure for various 0.45 μM membranes: 1 = Tyrann-M/E; 2 = conventional; 3 = polyamide; 4 = PVF.

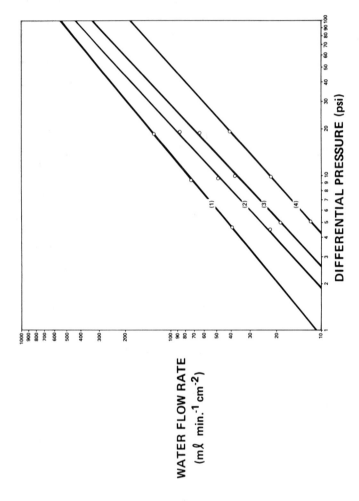

Figure 3.   Water Flow Rate vs. pressure for various 0.45μM membranes: 1 = Tyrann-M/E; 2 = conventional; 3 = polyamide; 4 = PVF.

Table I.   Air and Water* Permeabilities and Filtration
                  Capacities** of Various Microfiltration Membranes

Membrane	Bubble Point (psi)	Air Permeability ($\ell\,min^{-1}cm^{-2}$)		Water Permeability ($m\ell\,min^{-1}cm^{-2}$)		Filtration Capacity (Throughput)**
0.1 μM		*		*		
Tyrann-M/E	106	1.15	3.83	6.60	4.29	1.58
Conventional	185	0.30	1.00	1.54	1.00	1.00
Polyamide	110	0.45	1.50	3.31	2.15	1.16
0.2 μM						
Tyrann-M/E	59	6.28	2.75	39.6	2.54	4.40
Conventional	46	2.28	1.00	15.6	1.00	1.00
Polyamide	57	2.08	0.91	16.0	1.02	1.07
PVF	53	1.37	0.60	7.34	0.47	0.67
0.45 μM						
Tyrann-M/E	35	12.3	1.82	76.3	1.55	2.14
Conventional	32	6.74	1.00	49.1	1.00	1.00
Polyamide	34	4.92	0.73	36.0	0.73	0.50
PVF	30	2.92	0.43	22.2	0.45	0.34
0.8 μM						
Tyrann-M/E	16	40.4	1.64	230	1.95	1.50
Conventional	16	24.5	1.00	118	1.00	1.00

 * Normalized relative to the value for conventional membranes at 10 psid (corr.)
** Normalized relative to the values for conventional membranes after 80% flow
   decay.

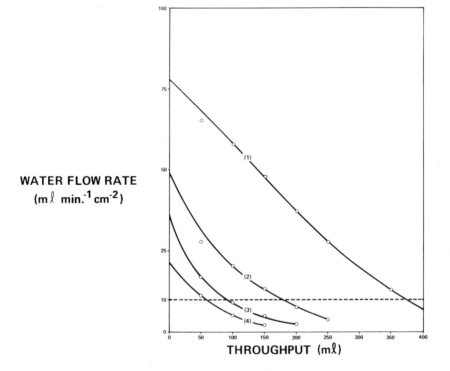

WATER FLOW RATE
$(m\ell\ min.^{-1}\ cm^{-2})$

THROUGHPUT $(m\ell)$

Figure 4.   Flow decay of various $0.45\,\mu M$ membranes with $\sim 0.01\%$ Triton $\times$-400 solution: 1 = Tyrann-M/E; 2 = conventional; 3 = polyamide; 4 = PVF.

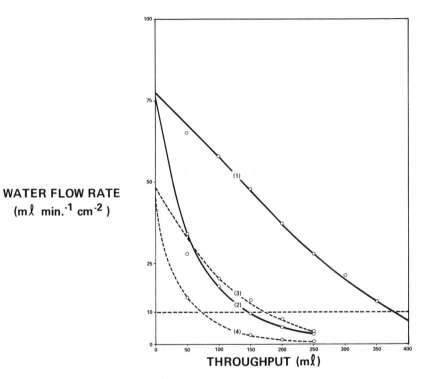

WATER FLOW RATE
(m ℓ min.$^{-1}$ cm^{-2})

THROUGHPUT (mℓ)

Figure 5. Effect of anisotropy on flow decay of 0.45μM Tyrann-M/E and conventional membranes with ~ 0.01% Triton X-400 solutions. Relative pore size adjacent to feed: 1 = Tyrann-M/E, large; 2 = Tyrann-M/E, small; 3 = conventional, large; 4 = conventional, small.

Table II.   Bacterial Retention at Various Challenge Levels for
0.2 and 0.45 ιM Tyrann-M/E and Conventional Membranes

Membrane	Initial Bubble Point (psi)	Challenge Level (CFU/47 mm disk)			Final Bubble Point (psi)	72 hr. Results*		
		1st	2nd	3rd		1st	2nd	3rd
Tyrann-M/E	31.0	2.58×10^7	5.43×10^7	6.90×10^7	34.7	−	−	−
0.45 μM	31.2	↓	↓	↓	36.3	−	−	−
(Lot A00780)	30.8				40.5	−	−	−
Conventional	30.3	2.58×10^7	5.43×10^7	6.90×10^7	53.5	−	−	−
0.45 μM	29.8	↓	↓	↓	42.5	−	−	−
(Lot 191268)	29.8				46.2	−	−	−
Tyrann-M/E	30.1	2.46×10^9	1.23×10^{10}	−	48.0	−	−	
0.45 μM	31.0	↓	↓	−	53.6	−	−	
(Lot A 00780)	30.6			−	>60	−	−	
Conventional	30.5	2.10×10^9	1.05×10^{10}	−	53.8	−	−	
0.45 μM	30.3	↓	↓	−	37.3	−	+**	
(Lot 191268)	39.6			−	54.7	−	−	
0.2 μM	53.0	4.62×10^8	9.24×10^8	1.34×10^9	>70	−	−	−
Tyrann-M/E	48.5	↓	↓	↓	69	−	−	−
(Lot A03680)	48.5				57.4	−	−	−
0.2 μM	53.8	9.84×10^8	1.97×10^9	2.95×10^9	>70	−	−	−
Conventional	52.0	↓	↓	↓	>70	−	−	−
(Lot C8H-								
59206D)	51.8	7.44×10^8	1.49×10^9	2.23×10^9	>70	+	−	−

* − = passed test; + = failed test
** This is considered a questionable failure because the pressure was increased to
40 psi after the membrane plugged at 30 psi.

ventional membrane value. This was the point at which good standard practice required that the conventional membranes be changed. Both mixed ester membranes maintained their positions relative to those of the noncellulosic membranes throughout the test (Figure 4). *Furthermore, the throughput advantage of Tyrann-M/E relative to other microfiltration membranes held true over the entire range of pore sizes and usually was more pronounced, the finer the pore size!* (Table I). Thus, it is feasible to utilize a 0.2 μM Tyrann-M/E filter in place of less anisotropic 0.45 μM filters with little or no throughput penalty. In like manner it is possible that a 0.1 μM Tyrann-M/E filter will match the filtration capacity of some less anisotropic 0.2 μM membranes. In light of the current trend for the removal of ever finer particulate contaminants, the significance of this development is clear. The effect of anisotropy upon the permeability and throughput of "coarse" and "fine" surfaces of conventional- and Tyrann-M/E membranes is depicted in Figure 5. It is apparent that throughputs are maximized by positioning the membranes so that the surface with the larger pores faces the incoming feed solutions. When this is done, the throughput of Tyrann-M/E is much greater than that of both conventional and noncellulosic membranes. However, throughput is greatly diminished when the finer pored surface is in contact with the feed, although it is still roughly equivalent of that for the coarser pored surface of the conventional membranes.

Bacterial Retention.   Inasmuch as the *raison d' être* for microfiltration membranes is their ability to sterilize fluids by interdicting the flow of bacteria and other microbes *via* sieving and absorptive sequestration, bacterial challenges remain the crucially important test of the efficacy of a microfiltration membrane. All of the 0.45 μM Tyrann-M/E membranes repeatedly sustained challenges of 10^3, 10^5, 10^7, 10^9/bacteria/cm^2 (*Serratia marcescens,* ATCC No. 14756) at 30 psid. The test procedure involved culturing of the Bacto-Peptone (B118) broth filtrate for 72 hours at 37°C [9]. The passage of even a single bacterium is sufficient to effect turbidity in the filtrate and constitutes a failure. The 0.2 μM Tyrann-M/E membranes, on the other hand, were challenged with $> 10^8$ bacteria/cm^2 (*Pseudomonas diminuta,* ATCC No. 19146). No bacterial penetration occurred through the Tyrann-M/E membranes. However, occasionally a conventional membrane failed the test. (There is no implication here that conventional membranes are incapable of efficient sterilization with bacterial challenge levels actually encountered in the field. Should, however, additional evidence substantiate the greater sterilization efficiency of Tyrann-M/E relative to conventional membranes, it is possible that this could be attributed to a finer pore structure and perhaps lower void volume of the dense layer fraction of Tyrann-M/E. *Bubble points were taken before sterilization and after completion of the challenge tests* (Table II). The substantial increases in bubble point after undergoing high level bacterial challenges are believed to be the result of pore size reduction as a result of fouling by bacteria. It is significant that the conventional membranes were plugged more readily than the Tyrann-M/E types. Retention tests were also carried out utilizing 0.50 μM monodisperse polystyrene latex spheres. Although some penetration of the surface layer of cells by the latex spheres was apparent in the case of both conventional and Tyrann-M/E membranes, nevertheless, no beads were apparent beyond a depth of approximately 20 μM from the feed surface. However, it cannot be unequivocally stated that no penetration of latex spheres occurred because of the presence of occasional bead-like structures of the same size within the virgin membrane matrix. For this reason he bacterial retention test is considered more meaningful.

Bacteria Recovery.   The initial application of a 0.45 μM Tyrann-M/E will be bacteria recovery in water analyses by the standard fecal coliform membrane filter procedure (10). In this procedure a standard volume of contaminated water is filtered through a membrane. Following filtration the membrane together with the recovered bacteria which remain on its feed surface is placed on a culture medium contained in a Petri dish. The nutrient broth then diffuses upward and nourishes each individual bacterium or colony forming unit (CFU), permitting it to develop into a visible colony. In the standard test employed here, comparisons were made with respect to the recovery of *Escherichia coli* (ATCC No. 11229) on agar spread plates, both surfaces of Tyrann-M/E, and on the gridded surface of conventional 0.45 μM membranes (Table III). (The preliminary data cited here will be augmented in the near future by a complete statistical study which will be the subject of a separate communication.) The results, however, are an indication both of the higher recovery of Tyrann-M/E and of the advantage of positioning its coarse surface adjacent to the incoming feed. When this is done the recovery is 96%. When the CFU are located on the fine surface, recovery declines to 81% which lies within the generally accepted range of values for conventional 0.45 μM membranes. However, for some reason actual recovery by the conventional membranes was only 71%. The higher recovery of bacteria by the coarse side of Tyrann-M/E is significant and is believed to be related to a more efficient "cradling" of the bacteria by virtue of their increased access to the nutrient medium which naturally occurs within larger voids.

Table III.   Comparison of *E Coli* Recovery on Agar Spread
Plates with Recoveries on Various 0.45 μM M/E Membranes

Membrane	CFU* Agar	CFU Membrane	CFU Membrane/ CFU Agar x 100(%)
Tyrann-M/E	46	41	96
(CFU on coarse surface)	44	44	
	45 Avg.	46	
		37	
		48	
		43.2 Avg.	
Conventional	56	43	70.8
	58	35	
	57 Avg.	45	
		42	
		37	
		40.4 Avg.	

*CFU = Colony forming unit.

This interpretation is consistent with that of Sladek *et.al.* who found both that the primary determinant of fecal coliform growth on a membrane filter was the size of the pores adjacent to the feed and that their optimum size was approximately 2.4 μM (8). Sladek's study resulted in the development of a commercial moderately anisotropic membrane with optimum feed surface pores, *but* with fine surface pores of 0.7 μM! The ability of such a large pored membrane to retain all bacteria is questionable and indeed bacterial passage at slightly larger pore sizes was demonstrated. The advantage of 0.45 μM Tyrann-M/E for this application is obvious. It combines 2.4 μM feed side pores which are optimum for recovery with 0.45 μM product side pores which are optimum for retention. Additional advantages of Tyrann-M/E are its lighter background color in the M-FC medium and noninterference of its gridded areas with colony growth.

Bubble Point Constancy.　Although the exact relationship between the bubble point and the "pore size" of a microfiltration membrane is a matter of dispute *(11, 12, 13, 14)*, nevertheless, it remains the quickest and most convenient means for demonstrating the continuing integrity of a membrane filtration system. It is consequently important that the bubble point be both reproducible (within a given range) and constant. It was, therefore, of considerable interest to discover that the bubble points of both conventional and poly(vinylidene fluoride) membranes increased with immersion time in deionized water whereas those of Tyrann-M/E and polyamide remained essentially constant (Figure 6).

Some believe that the increase in the bubble point with time of the conventional membranes is attributable to progressive leaching of the wetting agent. However, the poly(vinylidene fluoride) membrane does not contain an extraneous wetting agent and yet experiences the same behavior. Furthermore, the phenomenon is reversible, *i.e.* when the conventional membrane is removed from water and allowed to dry before reimmersion in fresh water, the bubble point reverts back to the lowest value and once again progressively increases with increasing immersion time. These results are consistent with a reversible swelling (surface swelling would suffice) of conventional and poly(vinylidene fluoride) membranes. The bubble points apparently increase with immersion time because the cell walls imbibe water and occupy progressively more space, thereby occluding a portion of the pore area which was previously available for air passage. Inasmuch as the membrane polymers in Tyrann-M/E are chemically identical to those found in conventional membranes, any difference in behavior between the two are the results either of differences in microstructure and/or the type or concentration of additivies such as wettting agents. Where conventional membranes contain somewhat less than 5% (by weight of polymer) of Triton X-100 or some other surfactant, 0.45 and 0.2 μM Tyrann-M/E contain only 3% glycerol as a humectant. The persistence of frank wetting agents even after aqueous leaching is well known and, in fact, has been utilized by the senior author of the present paper to form liquid membranes at the interface between reverse osmosis membranes and a saline solution interface by intermittent addition of surfactants to a saline feed solution *(15, 16)*. The rate of leaching surfactants from microfiltration membranes has been quantitatively measured in separate studies by Olson *(17)* and Cooney *(18)*. Removal of one surfactant from a single disk 142 mm in diameter required 2.4ℓ of water *(18)*. Glycerol, on the other hand, is not only unobjectionable from a toxicity standpoint, but is much more rapidly and quantitatively removed by aqueous extraction.

Glycerol Extraction.　Although glycerol has been employed as a wetting agent and plasticizer from the earliest days of cellulosic membranes *(19)*, nevertheless, given the present distaste for *any* extractible additive, it was decided to establish quantitatively the extraction of this compound. This was done by passing water through the filter and analyzing the glycerol in the filtrate *(20)*. A single disk 293 mm in diameter was placed in a stainless steel housing of an improved design

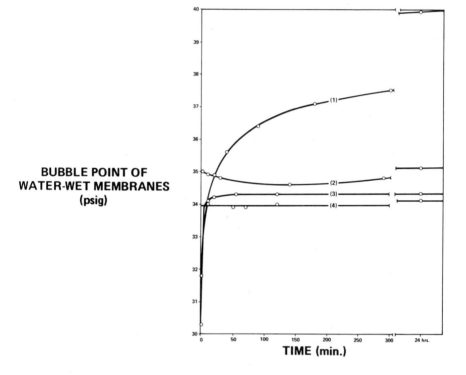

Figure 6.   Bubble point vs. duration of immersion for various 0.45 μM membranes:
1 = conventional; 2 = Tyrann-M/E; 3 = PVF; 4 = polyamide.

which minimized the holdup on the product side of the filter *(21)*. This large disk was chosen both because it contained an amount of glycerol sufficient for analysis ($\sim$0.075 g/disk) and because the information is of practical interest since this is the size which is most commonly utilized for production processing of fluids. One liter of deionized water was passed through the membrane and successive portions of the eluate were collected, concentrated almost to dryness on a hot plate and oxidized by the addition of periodic acid. Potassium iodide was then added and the liberated iodine titrated with sodium thiosulfate solution. The extraction curve demonstrates that the removal of glycerol is both rapid and quantitative (Figure 7). Approximately 90% of the glycerol is extracted by the first 50 ml and 95% by the second 50 ml of water to pass through the membrane. *In other words, the passage of a column of water less than 2 mm in depth through Tyrann-M/E membrane will suffice to purge it of virtually all of its glycerol.* The present authors wish to stress again that we have thoroughly considered the problem of extractible wetting agents in microfiltration membranes. We have chosen glycerol rather than potentially troublesome surfactants because glycerol is not only less objectionable but also is much more readily extracted.

Morphology

Membrane morphology was studied with the aid of scanning electron microscopy (SEM) (Figures 8-12). Considerable variability was found in both gross and fine structure. Both surfaces of each of the two noncellulosic membranes (Figures 8, 9) exhibit a lower effective pore density than do the surfaces of the mixed ester membranes. The noncellulosic membranes also exhibit a number of other structural peculiarities. Although both possess a similar "taffy-like" fine structure, a cross-sectional view of the polyamide membrane (Figure 8) proves that it is comprised of two discrete (but apparently equivalent) layers, whereas the cross-sectional view of the poly(vinylidene fluoride) membrane shows it to be a fiber-reinforced single layer, a feature which increases strength, but often adversely affects permeability and throughput *(16)*. The cross-sectional view shown is that of an unreinforced 0.2 μM poly(vinylidene fluoride) membrane rather than of a fiber reinforced 0.45 μM size, since it is difficult to freeze fracture the latter cleanly (Figure 9). The surface views, however, are of the 0.45 μM membrane. The poly(vinylidene) fluoride) membrane is light tan when dry and becomes almost brown when wet. This appears to be the result of a surface modification which was effected to induce wettability, since the hydrophobic version of this membrane is opaque white. In addition, the cell walls of both noncellulosic membranes are comprised of comparatively massive struts suggestive of low void volume and high resistance which is, of course, consistent with their rather modest flow characteristics. Close inspection of the cross-sectional view of the polyamide membrane shows a separation which occurred between the two layers during preparation of the sample for SEM (Figure 8). Manipulation of additional samples proved that the two layers were separable even at room temperature.

Both surfaces of the conventional membrane are quite similar in appearance, and the cross section is only slightly anisotropic with little difference in pore and cell size from one surface to the other (Figure 10). In contrast, a considerable difference is apparent between the pore sizes at opposite surfaces of the Tyrann-M/E membrane (Figure 11). The structure is highly anisotropic with an approximately five fold difference between the size of the pores at the two surfaces. *Approximately*

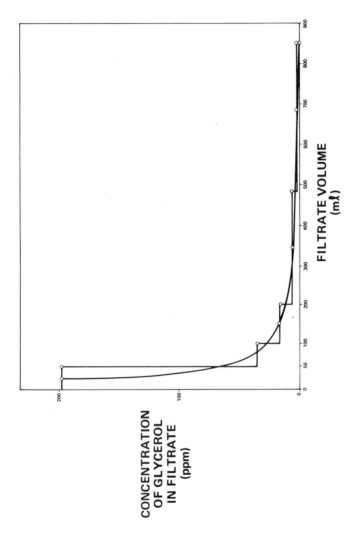

Figure 7. Glycerol extraction curve

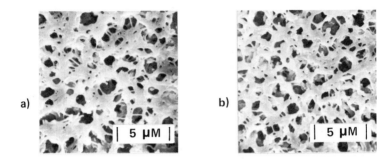

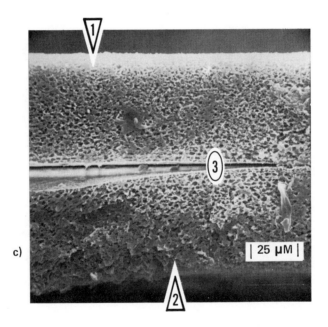

Figure 8. SEM photomicrographs of a 0.45μM polyamide membrane: (a) surface at 1; (b) surface at 2; (c) cross-section with midline separation at 3.

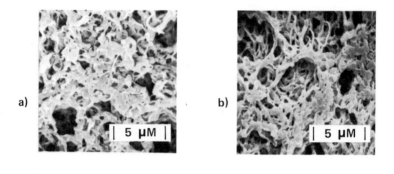

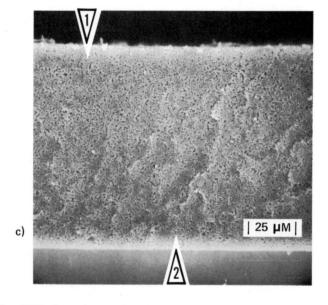

Figure 9.   SEM photomicrographs of the surfaces of a 0.45μM PVF membrane and the cross-section of a 0.2μM PVF membrane: (a) surface at 1; (b) surface at 2; (3) cross-section.

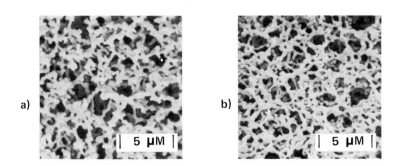

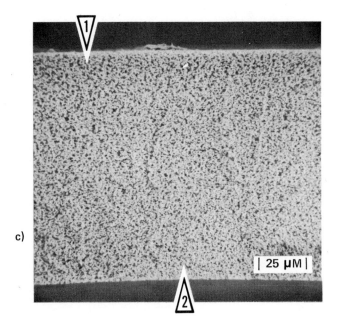

Figure 10. SEM photomicrographs of a 0.45 μM conventional membrane: (a) surface at 1; (b) surface at 2; (c) cross-section.

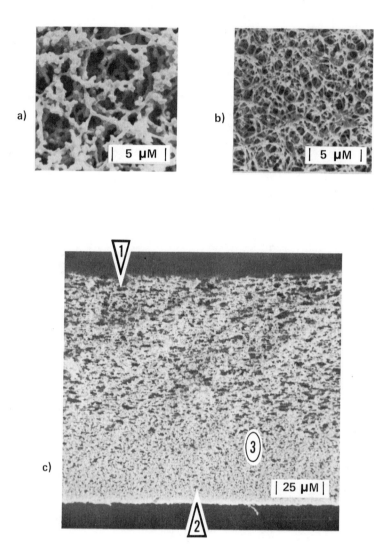

Figure 11.   SEM photomicrographs of a 0.45μM Tyrann-M/E membrane: (a) surface at 1; (b) surface at 2; (c) cross-section with boundary between coarse and fine structures at 3.

the same degree of anisotropy is found over the entire pore size range of Tyrann-M/E microfilters (Figure 12). Cross-sectional views indicate the presence of two integral (and, hence, inseparable) layers, the thicker of which contains the larger cells. This gradation in pore size from one surface to the other confers the filtration capacity of a prefilter/filter combination upon these integral bilayers and is, therefore, responsible for the significantly higher dirt holding capacity of Tyrann-M/E membranes.

While the effects of anisotropy have been considered by earlier workers *(8, 22)*, Tyrann-M/E represents a higher degree of anisotropy than previously obtained for a true phase inversion membrane. However, the advantages of an integral union of bilayers consisting in depth of two-thirds of a coarse structure and one-third of a fine structure were previously recognized for *fibrous* multilayer filter materials *(23)*. Although profound differences obviously exist between the structure of Tyrann-M/E and conventional membranes, they are more closely related to one another than to either of the noncellulosic membranes. (Table IV).

Table IV.   Void and Polymer Volumes for Survey Membranes

Membrane	Specific Gravity of Dense Film (g/cc)	Pore Size (μM)	Void Volume (Porosity) (%)
Tyrann-M/E	1.58	0.1	72.0**
		0.2	74.7
		0.45	79.9
		0.8	84.5
Conventional	1.58	0.1	71.8
		0.2	74.4
		0.45	79.3
		0.8	83.0
Polyamide	1.14	0.1	65.1
		0.2	73.6
		0.45	75.2
Poly(vinylidene fluoride)	1.75	0.2	72.2
		0.45	73.8*(68.1)

* Estimate only since fiber reinforcement made experimentally determined value (in parenthesis) uncertain.
** Preliminary data.

However, subtle differences are apparent between the fine structures of conventional and Tyrann-M/E membranes. In subjective terms the former consists of a structure reminiscent of jumbled jacks whereas the latter resembles a mat of spaghetti. Although there is no proof that in this instance differences in microcrystalline habit are responsible for observable differences in SEM fine structure, it is tempting to speculate that the "jacks" indicate the presence of lamellar microcrystallites and the "spaghetti" structure, a more extended chain type of microcrystallite. Although purely tentative at present, this interpretation is consistent with the greater elasticity, and hence flexibility, of Tyrann-M/E.

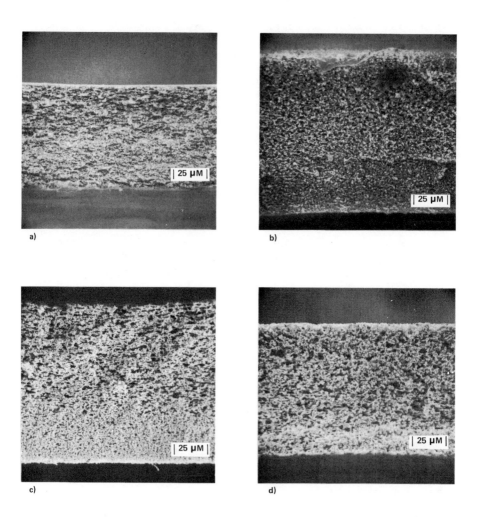

Figure 12.   SEM photomicrographs of cross-sections of Tyrann-M/E membranes:
(a) 0.1μM; (b) 0.2μM; (c) 0.45μM; (d) 0.8μM.

Mechanical and Thermal Properties

Although Tyrann-M/E and even conventional membranes are superior to the new polyamide and poly(vinylidene fluoride) membranes with respect to flow rates and filtration capacities, the latter two are more suitable for filtration of most (but not all) organic solvents and, partially as a result of their lower void volumes (Table IV) exhibit mechanical and thermal properties which are generally superior to those of the cellulosics. It should also be noted that in the special case of fiber-reinforced membranes, the mechanical properties are predominantly functions of the embedded fibers rather than of the membrane structure *per se*.

Considerable differences are apparent between the flexibility and autoclavability of Tyrann-M/E and conventional membranes (Tables V, VI). The former are considerably more flexible. This characteristic flexibility has the advantage that it virtually eliminates breakage in normal handling of flat stock membranes, a nemesis of the conventional M/E types.

A mechanical property which appears to be related to flexibility is elongation at break. Although the quantitative reproducibility of measurements of this property is poor, there appears to exist a threshold value of elongation at break in the machine direction ($\geq 8\%$) below which any membrane cannot be sharply creased without fracturing. Conventional membranes exhibit an elongation at break of approximately 5% and burst into shards when the break point has been reached in contrast to the more elastic Tyrann-M/E membranes which break less catastrophically. It may be that a portion of the flexibility of Tyrann-M/E is due to its spaghetti-like fine structure. It is highly significant that Tyrann-M/E can be creased in the anhydrous condition and that the integrity of the membrane along the fold is maintained as evidenced by the constancy of bubble points after flexing before and after both wet and "dry" autoclaving (Table V). This behavior is in sharp contrast with that of conventional membranes. The latter can *when wet* be bubble pointed along a fold before *(but not after)* wet autoclaving. When dry, however, they cannot be bubble pointed across any fold because of their extreme friability.

Table V.   Effects of Flexing* and Autoclaving** Upon the Bubble
Points of Water-Wet 0.45 μM Membranes

Membrane Type	Membrane Condition	(Initial)	Bubble Point (psi) (Flexed Before Autoclaving)	(Flexed After Autoclaving)
Tyrann-M/E	dry, unrestrained	34.6 ± 0.3	34.5 ± 0.2	34.0 ± 1.0
Tyrann-M/E	wet, restrained	34.7 ± 1.3	34.5 ± 0.3	36.8 ± 0.5
Conventional	dry, unrestrained	35.7 ± 1.1	failed†	failed†
Conventional	wet, restrained	36.1 ± 0.8	35.9 ± 0.8	failed†

* Flexing = a double sharp fold along the diameter of a circular 47 mm disk.
** All samples autoclaved @121°C for 15 min.
† Bubble Point too low to measure owing to catastrophic loss of membrane integrity.

A further peculiarity of conventional M/E membranes is that autoclaving produces uneven shrinkage between machine and transverse directions with the result that a disk which is circular before autoclaving becomes somewhat elliptical after autoclaving (Table VI). Tyrann-M/E, on the other hand, experiences less extensive and more uniform shrinkage and a less severe drop in permeability. The change in bubble points for both membrane types as a result of autoclaving is insignificant. Most of the increase in the bubble points of conventional membranes previously ascribed to autoclaving is now known to be simply a function of swelling and takes place in the absence of autoclaving (Figure 6). Although the origin of the profound differences in mechanical and thermal properties of Tyrann-M/E and conventional membranes is as yet incompletely understood, it may be related to previously noted differences in fine structure.

Table VI.   The Effects of "Dry"* Autoclaving Upon the
                   Diameters, Ellipticities[†] and Air Flow Rates of
                   Various 0.45 μM Membranes

Membranes	Decrease in Diameter After "Dry" Autoclaving** (%)	Ellipticity[†] (%)	Air Flow Rate After "Dry" Autoclaving* (1 min^{-1}cm^{-2}) @10 psid.	Decline in Air Flow Rate After "Dry" Autoclaving* (%)
Tyrann-M/E	3.2 ± 0.4	± 0.1	9.80 ± 0.05	8
Conventional	6.0 ± 1.4	± 1.4	5.05 ± 0.12	18
Polyamide	1.4 ± 0.3	± 0.1	3.65 ± 0.04	2
Poly(vinylidene fluoride)	0.2 ± 0.3	± 0.3	3.40 ± 0.23	0.5

* "Dry" autoclaving, unrestrained, 121°C, 15 min. (Membrane dry when placed in the autoclave).

† Inasmuch as all samples were perfectly round 47 mm disks before "dry" autoclaving, the standard deviation of the measured diameters after autoclaving is a measure of ellipticity, *i.e.* uneven shrinkage in machine and transverse directions.

Conclusions

Tyrann-M/E represents a new highly anisotropic class of microfiltration membrane with permeability and dirt holding characteristics which are superior to those of both noncellulosic and conventional mixed ester membranes and with flexibility and thermal stability which are significantly greater than those of conventional membranes.

Acknowledgements.   The authors wish to acknowledge the contributions of Mr. E.D. Gilley of Puropore's Production Department in machine casting Tyrann-M/E and Mrs. Lois Cunningham, Microbiologist, in conducting the bacterial challenge and recovery tests. We would also like to thank Drs. Ditter, Williams and Morrison and Messers. Cronin, Libby and Norquist for their stimulating discussions and helpful critical evaluations.

Abstract.   This paper treats certain aspects of the morphology of microfiltration membranes of cellulose mixed esters, as well as membranes of polyamide and poly(vinylidene fluoride), and their relationship to filtration characteristics and certain mechanical and thermal properties.

The present authors have developed Tyrann-M/E, a new class of membranes whose gross morphology is characterized by *anisotropy, i.e.,* a gradation of pore and cell size from one surface to the other. Conventional and noncellulosic membranes are only slightly anisotropic, whereas *Tyrann-M/E is highly anisotropic,* consisting of an *integral* bilayer, two-thirds of which is represented by cells approximately five times larger than those found in the remaining one-third. Anisotropy is characteristic of the entire range of Tyrann-M/E microfilters encompassing 0.1, 0.2, 0.45 and 0.8 μM pore sizes. By positioning the membrane such that the larger-pored surface is in contact with the feed solution, both product rate and filtration capacity are substantially greater than those obtained for conventional slightly anisotropic or only moderately anisotropic membranes. That increased throughput has been accomplished without the loss of sterilization efficiency is demonstrated through the successful passage of stringent bacterial challenge tests by 0.2 and 0.45 μM Tyrann-M/E. Its high degree of anisotropy, furthermore, appears to enable 0.45 μM Tyrann-M/E to serve as an efficient "cradle" to maximize bacterial recovery in water analysis applications.

Literature Cited

1. S. Loeb and S. Sourirajan, U.S., 3,133,132, May 12, 1964.
2. J. Cadotte and P. Francis, U.S., 3,580,841, May 25, 1971.
3. R. Kesting, U.S., 3,884,801, May 20, 1975.
4. R. Kesting, *Synthetic Polymeric Membranes,* McGraw-Hill, New York (1971).
5. R. Kesting in *Reverse Osmosis and Synthetic Membranes,* S. Sourirajan, ed., National Research Council, Canada Publ. No. 15627 (1977).
6. R. Kesting, Pure & Appl. Chem., *50,* 633 (1978).
7. H. Bechhold, Biochem. Z, *6,* 379 (1907).
8. K. Sladek, R. Suslavich, B. Sohn and F. Dawson, paper presented at the Symposium on the Recovery of Indicator Organisms Employing Membrane Filters, sponsored by EPA and ASTM (Committee D-10 on Water), 1977.
9. Difco Manual Ninth Edition, P. 256, 1974.
10. *Standard Methods for the Examination of Water and Wastewater Procedure 909 A,* Fourteenth Edition American Public Health Association, Washington, D.C., 1976.
11. T. Meltzer and T. Meyers, Bull. Parenter. Drug Assoc. *25,* 165 (1971).
12. D. Pall, Bull. Parenter. Drug Assoc., *29,* 192 (1975).
13. K. Wallhäusser, Pharm. Ind., *36,* (12) 931 (1974); 37 (1), 10 (1975).
14. A. Baszkin, D. Lyman and T. Meltzer, Pharmaceutical Technology, Jan. 1979.
15. R. Kesting, W. Subcasky and J. Paton, J. Colloid Interface Sci., *28,* 156 (1968).
16. R. Kesting and W. Subcasky, J. Macromol. Sci A3 (1), 151 (1969).
17. W. Olson, R. Briggs, C. Garanchon, M. Ouellet, E. Graf and D. Luckhurst, J. Parenter. Drug Assoc., *34,* (4) (1980).
18. D. Cooney, Anal. Chem., *52,* 1068 (1980).
19. D. Mehta, D. Hauk and T. Meltzer, paper presented at the Second World Filtration Congress, London, England (1979).
20. S. Siggia and G. Hanna, *Quantitative Organic Analysis Via Functional Groups,* Fourth Edition, Wiley-Interscience, New York (1979).
21. Creative Scientific Equipment Corp., Long Beach, California.
22. J. Marshall and T. Meltzer, Bull. Parenter. Drug Assoc., *30,* (5), 214 (1976).
23. D. Pall, R. Estates and C. Keedwell, U.S., 3,353,682, Nov. 21, 1967.

RECEIVED December 4, 1980.

Permeability Properties of Cellulose Triacetate Hollow-Fiber Membranes for One-Pass Seawater Desalination

KAORU FURUKAWA[1], MASAAKI SEKINO, HIROSHI MATSUMOTO, KAZUTO HAMADA, TETSUO UKAI, and HIROHITO MATSUI

Research Center, Toyobo Co., Ltd., 1300-1 Honkatata–cho, Otsu Shiga, 520-02 Japan

RO process for the desalination of seawater was proposed for the first time by Reid in 1953, but no significant advancement was observed until the invention of asymmetric membrane with high water flux by Loeb and Sourirajan in 1960. Since that time, RO process showed remarkable progresses in practical applications in the field of desalination of brackish water for potable and pure water.

On the other hand, the development of seawater desalination, which was the original target of RO process, was delayed because of the insufficient performance of membrane under operating conditions of high pressure and high salt concentration.

For this reason, two pass seawater desalination process have been necessarily employed till quite recently, and the results obtained have been satisfactory to some extent with regard to water quality and practical operation. However, one pass process has advantages over two pass process for simple and compact plant, simple operation, easy maintenance and lower energy consumption.

Although several one pass RO systems have been developed so far, the membrane performances, especially salt rejections have not been satisfactory and were sometimes not stable in long term operation (1) (2). In the use of membranes having insufficient salt rejection, the product water recovery of module is limited to much lower than 30%. Hence two pass process is sometimes employed for high salinity seawater instead of one pass process for high salinity seawater (40,000 ppm TDS) (3). Moreover, with high salinity seawater, water productivity is comparatively low because of its high osmotic pressure. In this case high pressure operation should be advantageous from the stand point of water productivity and salt rejection. However, the conventionally available modules can not be operated under such high

---

[1] Current address: 2-8, Dojimahama 2-chome Kita–ku, Osaka, 530 Japan.

0097–6156/81/0153–0223$05.00/0

pressure as 75 Kg/cm^2G in a practical use because of their insufficient high pressure tolerance.

This may be the reason why there has been little investigation about high pressure desalination.

We have developed one pass seawater desalination module so
called, "Hollosep-High Rejection Type" with excellent salt
rejection in 1978.

Long term experiments of one pass seawater desalination
using our module have been carried out at Chigasaki Laboratory
of Water Reuse Promotion Center under the supervision of Ministry
of International Trade and Industry, Japan (4). A continuous
long term test for 12,000 hours was successfully conducted with
the m-value of 0.02. Another demonstration plant with an 800
m3/D capacity has also been operating over 3,000 hours at the
recovery ratio of 40% using the feed water of F.I. value of
about 4.

Hollosep High Rejection Type is characterized by Cellulose
Tri Acetate (CTA) hollow fiber with dense membrane structure and
high salt rejection, and also by the module configuration favorable for uniform flow of feed water through hollow fiber layers
(5). These features suggest that Hollosep may be operated under
the conditions of higher recovery ratio compared to conventional
conditions.

The purpose of the present work is to evaluate the applicability and merit of high pressure desalination process by the
use of Hollosep-High Rejection Type.

I am going to speak of an experimental study of the membrane
permeability under high pressure of the CTA hollow fiber for one
pass seawater desalination, "Hollosep-High Rejection Type". The
module performance has been simulated for high pressure operating
range by simplified module model based on the data of the hollow
fiber, and examined the agreement with the actual module performance. Furthermore, we will discuss later on the result of
operating cost study under high pressure operation.

Experimental

1) Preparation of Hollow Fiber Membrane. CTA (Cellulose
Tri-Acetate) hollow fiber membranes were prepared by apinning a
dope solution of CTA followed by soaking and anealing.

2) Module Fabrication. The bundle of several thousands of
hollow fibers is fabricated into an element and assembled to a
module. Hollow fibers in an element are arranged in a mutually
crossed configuration without any kind of supporting materials
between hollow fiber layers. This module configuration contributes to uniform flow of feed water, small pressure drop,
minimizing concentration polarization and extending the allow-
ance of fouling index of feed water, up to F.I. = 4. Tube sheet
part of the element is fabricated by the use of improved epoxy
resin with resistance against high pressure and high temperature.

The construction of Hollosep is shown in Figure 1.
The specifications of the modules are shown in Table 1.

3) <u>Measurements of RO Performance.</u> RO performances were measured by the simple apparatus, as shown in Figure 2. The water flux and salt rejection of the hollow fiber membranes under operating pressure in the range of 50 to 120 Kg/cm^{2}G were determined using the feed water of 3.5% NaCl, at 25°C and at product water recovery ratio of less than 1%, after an elapsed time of 2 hrs.

The RO performance of module was evaluated under operating conditions of pressures in the range of 40 to 75 Kg/cm^{2}G, NaCl concentration of feed water in the range of 3.5 to 5.0% and product water recovery ratio of 30 to 60%.

4) <u>Simulation of Module Performance.</u> The module performance over the wide range of operating conditions was calculated by a simplified module model on the basis of the data of the hollow fibers.

The simplified module model and the calculation scheme will be shown later in Figure 7 to 8 and Table 3.

Results and Discussions

1) <u>Characteristics of Hollow Fiber Membrane.</u> A microscopic view of hollow fiber membrane of Hollosep is shown in Figure 3.

Characteristics of the hollow fiber membrane is shown in Table 2. The outer diameter and wall thickness of this hollow fiber membrane is fairly thick compared with those of other hollow fibers for seawater desalination. Salt rejection of hollow fiber membrane is high enough to be applied to one pass seawater desalination.

Resistance of the hollow fiber membrane against high pressure was evaluated by measuring water flux rate and salt rejection under operating pressure of up to 120 Kg/cm^{2}G in 3.5% NaCl feed water. The data obtained were analyzed in terms of pure water permeability A and solute transport parameter $D_{AM}/K\delta$ given by Kimura-Sourirajan's equation (6). The results are shown in Figure 5. Membrane performance remained almost unchanged up to the pressure of 100 Kg/cm^{2}G. The result may suggest that this hollow fiber membrane is well resistant against high pressure and can be practically operated under appreciably high pressure.

2) <u>Characteristics of Module, "Hollosep-High Rejection Type"</u> RO performance of the module Hollosep-High Rejection Type is compared with various kinds of modules reported so far in terms of A and $D_{AM}/K\delta$ value. The results are shown in Figure 5.

The A value of Hollosep is lower by a facter of less than 10 compared to that of flat sheet membranes, whereas the $D_{AM}/K\delta$ value of Hollosep is quite low by a factor of 100 than that of

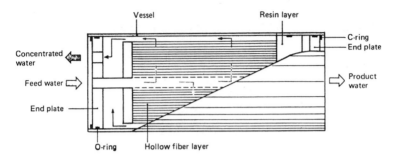

Figure 1.   Construction of hollosep

Figure 2. Schematic view of reverse osmosis test loop: (1) hollow fiber membrane; (2) pressure vessel; (3) feed water; (4) filter; (5) pressure pump; (6) relief valve.

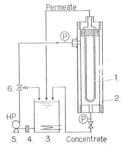

Figure 3.   Microscopic view of hollow fiber of hollosep—high-rejection type

TABLE 1. SPECIFICATION OF HOLLOSEP

MODEL		HR5350S	HR8350	HR8650
SIZE DIAMETER	MM	140	305	305
LENGTH	MM	1220	1330	2640
PRODUCT FLUX	M^3/D	>3.5	>10	>20
SALT REJECTION	%	99.2	99.2	99.2
TEST CONDITION				
FEED WATER	PPM	35000	35000	35000
PRESSURE	KG/CM^2G	55	55	55
TEMPERATURE	°C	25	25	25
RECOVERY	%	30	30	30

TABLE 2. CHARACTERISTICS OF THE HOLLOW FIBER OF
HOLLOSEP-HIGH REJECTION TYPE

Hollow Fiber Dimension :
    OD.   165 μ
    ID.   70 μ

Reverse Osmosis Performance of Hollow Fiber :
    Flux Rate   50 ℓ/m^2 Day
    Salt Rejection 99.7 %

(Test Conditions)
    Feed Water   35,000 ppm NaCl
    Pressure   55 Kg/cm^2G
    Temperature   25 °C
    Recovery   <5 %

flat sheet membranes and the lowest of three hollow fiber
membrane for one pass seawater desalination. These permeability
characteristics of Hollosep, coupled with specially crossed
configuration of hollow fibers in the module, may contribute to
low concentration polarization and high salt rejection of the
module.

The results may suggest that Hollosep can be operated under
the conditions of high salt concentration and high recovery
ratio. A long term performance test of the module at high
pressure of 75 Kg/cm^{2}G was carried out during the period of more
than one month, as shown in Figure 6. The observed compaction
factor was lower than 0.03. Although the recovery ratio was
raised from 30 to 60% at the end of this test, the module performance was scarcely changed.

3) Simulation of Module Performance by Simplified Module
Model. If a simple module model be made available, it
becomes convenient to perform a primary plant design work and
also to obtain primary figure for operating conditions.

In the case of Hollosep, it may be possible to employ a
simplified module model bacause of its low concentration
polarization, uniform feed water flow and low pressure drop.

Assuming that the concentration polarization, pressure drop
and back mixing are negligible, module model can be expressed
simply in terms of the transport equation and the material
balance of each component.

The scheme of a simplified module model is shown in Figures
7 through 8 and Table 3. As shown in Figure 7, the membrane
area of the module are divided into n pieces of sections (in the
case of Hollosep, n pieces of hollow fiber layers).

Feed water (C_F, Q_F) is allowed to enter into the module
from its left side. Permeated water at each membrane section is
expressed simply by Solution Diffusion model (Eq (1), (2) in
Table 3) Concentrated water (C_B, Q_B) is discharged from the
right side of the module. Summation of product water at each
membrane section results in total product water (C_P, Q_P). At
each membrane section, material balance is taken on each
component (Eq (7), (8) in Table 3).

Calculation flow chart is schematically shown in Figure 8.
A typical module performances under various operating conditions
are shown in Figure 9 and 10, where the results calculated by
the simplified module model are compared with the experimental
data obtained with actual module.

As shown in Figure 9, in the case of 3.5% NaCl solution
calculated values are in fair agreement with the experimental
results in a wide range of operating conditions. In the test
of various salt concentration at constant pressure of 75 Kg/cm^{2}G,
as shown in Figure 10, considerably good agreement was observed
at a recovery ratio of 30%. However, some deviation is observed
in the range of higher salt concentration and higher recovery
ratio.

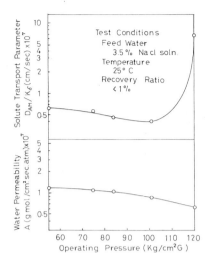

Figure 4. *Applied pressure vs.* A *and* D_{AM}/K *value of the hollow fiber of hollo-sep—high-rejection type*

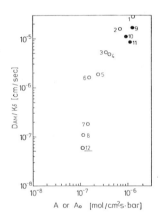

Figure 5. *Membrane performances of various commercial RO modules: (1) DDS, #995; (2) Toray, 1st stage; (3) Toyobo, 2nd stage; (4) DDS, #999; (5) du Pont, B-9; (6) Toyobo, 1st stage; (7) du Pont, B-10; (8) Dow, one pass; (9) ROGA-4000; (10) ROGA-4100 ST; (11) ROGA-4160 HR; (12) Toyobo, one-pass Hollosep HR-8350*

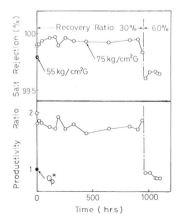

Figure 6. *Performance of hollosep—high-rejection type module HR-5350-SH. Feed water, 3.5% NaCl solution; temperature: 25°C.*

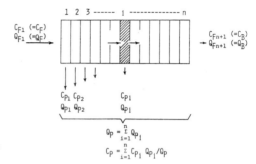

Figure 7.   Simplified module model

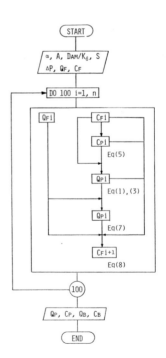

Figure 8.   Calculation flow chart

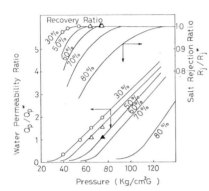

Figure 9. Applied pressure vs. module performance at various recovery ratio: Feed water, 3.5% NaCl solution; temperature, 25°C; Q_p^* = product water at 55 kg/cm² g; 30% recovery; (——), calculated curve.

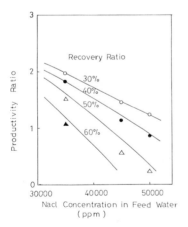

Figure 10. Salt concentration vs. module performance at various recovery ratio: pressure, 75 kg/cm² g; (——), calculated curve.

TABLE 3   PRODUCT WATER QUALITY AND MATERIAL BALANCE

TRANSPORT EQUATION

$$J_{wi} = A [\Delta P - \alpha(C_{Fi} - C_{pi})] \qquad (1)$$

$$J_{Si} = (D_{AM}/K_\delta)(C_{Fi} - C_{pi}) \qquad (2)$$

WHERE

$$Q_{pi} = (J_{wi} + J_{Si}) S_i \qquad (3)$$

$$C_{pi} = J_{Si} S_i / Q_{pi} \qquad (4)$$

SOLUTE CONCENTRATION IN PERMEATE SOLUTION IS DERIVED FROM E$_q$ (1) (4)

$$C_{pi} = (-a_1 + \sqrt{a_1^2 - 4a_0 a_2})/2a_2 \qquad (5)$$

WHERE

$$a_0 = -(D_{AM}/K_\delta) C_{Fi}$$

$$a_1 = A \Delta P - \alpha AC_{Fi} + (D_{AK}/K_\delta)(1 + C_{Fi}) \qquad (6)$$

$$a_2 = \alpha A - (D_{AM}/K_\delta)$$

MATERIAL BALANCES ARE

$$Q_{Fi} = Q_{Fi+1} + Q_{pi} \qquad (7)$$

$$C_{Fi} Q_{Fi} = C_{Fi+1} Q_{Fi+1} + C_{pi} Q_{pi} \qquad (8)$$

TABLE 4   HIGH PRESSURE SEAWATER DESALINATION
— PRODUCTIVITY AND ENERGY CONSUMPTION —

FEED WATER   : 4.2% NaCl SOLN.
TEMPERATURE   : 30°C
RO MODULE   : HOLLOSEP HR 8350
                (IMPROVED RESIN)

CASE		A	B	C	D	E	F
OPERATING	PRESS (KG/CM^{2}G)	55	55	55	75	75	75
CONDITION	RECOVERY (%)	20	30	40	20	30	40
PRODUCT	PRODUCTIVITY RATIO*	0.90	0.72	0.45	2.02	1.80	1.59
WATER	SALT PASSAGE RATIO*	1.39	1.87	3.39	0.63	0.72	0.90
ELECTRIC POWER (KWH/M^3)		10.8	7.3	5.4	14.8	9.8	7.4

* REFERENCE
FEED WATER   : 3.5% NaCl SOLN.
TEMPERATURE   : 25°C
PRESSURE   : 55 KG/CM^{2}G
RECOVERY   : 30%

TABLE 5   HIGH PRESSURE SEAWATER DESALINATION
— OPERATING COST EVALUATION —

CASE		A	B	C	D	E	F
OPERATING	PRESS (KG/CM^{2}G)	55	55	55	75	75	75
CONDITION	RECOVERY (%)	20	30	40	20	30	40
OPERATING COST ($/M^3)	ELECTRIC POWER	0.52	0.35	0.26	0.71	0.47	0.35
	MEMBRANE REPLACEMENT	0.31	0.39	0.63	0.15	0.16	0.19
	CHEMICALS & FILTERS	0.05	0.03	0.02	0.05	0.03	0.02
	TOTAL COST	0.88	0.77	0.91	0.91	0.66	0.56

@ 4.8$/KWH
EXCHANGE RATE : US$1 = ¥250

This deviation may be attributable to concentration polarization caused by a decrease in the flow velocity of the feed water in the above conditions.

The simplified module model can be sufficiently applicable to a wide range of practical operating conditions, in spite of its limitation in very severe operating condition mentioned above.

4) Operating Cost Evaluation under High Pressure. It seems reasonable that operation under higher pressure may cause an increase in water productivity of module.

On the other hand the operation under higher pressure may cause a rise in the power cost of high pressure pumps and also may require an improvement in resistance against higher pressure of the vessel of module, accompanied with a rise in its production cost. Moreover, in general, the compaction of hollow fibers and also deterioration of epoxy resin used in the tube sheet will be accelerated and this may arose trouble in the module However, in the case of the module Hollosep-High Rejection Type, the resistances against high pressure are improved in both hollow fiber membranes and epoxy resin.

Module performance and energy consumption were estimated in the case for the desalination of 4.2% salinity seawater under high pressure of 75 Kg/cm^{2}G at different recovery ratios. The results are shown in Table 4.

Operating cost was evaluated in each case including membrane (element) replacement. (Depreciations Taxes, insurances, and labors expences are not included here). Estimated operating cost per product water is shown in Table 5. Based on these results it may be said that the operation under higher pressure is appreciably advantageous for desalination of high salinity seawater. A continuous long term test on this subject using large sized modules is now under consideration.

Conclusion

1) RO performance of the CTA hollow fiber membrane used in Hollosep was measured under higher pressure and analysed in terms of A and $D_{AM}/K\delta$ value. These values remained almost unchanged under operating pressure of up to 100 Kg/cm^{2}G. Moreover, long term performance test of the module at high pressure of 75 Kg/cm^{2}G was satisfactorily carried out with compaction factor less than 0.03.

2) Module performance calculated by the simplified module model based on the permeability of hollow fiber membrane was in fair agreement with actual module over the wide range of operating conditions.

3) Operating cost was studied in the case of high salinity seawater by the use of Hollosep, we may conclude that the operation under higher pressure is advantageous for lowering operating cost.

References

1) C.F. Macgowan, D. Ammons, H. Mahon, E. Wagener and
T. Davis, Proceedings of the 5th International Symposium on
Fresh Water from the Sea, Vol 4, (1976) 385-396.
2) H. Ohya, Proceedings of the 6th International Symposium
on Fresh Water from the Sea, Vol 3, (1978) 341-350.
3) C.E. Hickman, I. Jamjoon, A.B. Riedinger and R.E. Seaton,
Desalination, 30 (1979) 259-281.
4) Y. Kunisada, H. Kaneda, M. Hirai and Y. Murayama,
Desalination, 30 (1979) 334-345.
5) T. Ukai, Y. Nimura, K. Hamada and H. Matsui, Desalination, 32 (1980) 169-178.
6) S. Kimura and S. Sourirajan, A.I.Ch.E., 13 (No 3)
(1967) 497-505.

RECEIVED December 4, 1980.

The Effect of Phosphoric Acid as a Casting Dope Ingredient on Reverse-Osmosis Membrane Properties

B. KUNST and Z. VAJNAHT

Institute of Physical Chemistry, University of Zagreb,
41001 Zagreb, P.O.B. 177, Yugoslavia

Since Loeb and Sourirajan's discovery (1) of a workable asymmetric reverse osmosis membrane, a lot of work has been done in order to elucidate and control the formation, structure and properties of a "skin", the surface layer of an asymmetric membrane.

Physical structure of the skin seems to be well defined and described (2,3,4) in the case of very tight asymmetric membranes, i.e. membranes giving higher than 98% sodium chloride rejections. The skin structure of the asymmetric membranes having solute rejections in the 70-95% range is not so well known. Variations in the skin structure and consequently in the membrane performance in such a case can be attributed to specific effects in the membrane formation process due to different materials (polymer, additive) and different preparation procedures used.

It has been shown (5,6,7) that a membrane casting dope is a strongly structurized polymer solution, and that the morphology of the membrane surface layer can be correlated to the structure of the casting solution. The latter paramater affects the nature and details of the phase inversion process occuring in the upper part of the cast solution, in an incipient skin. Thus the solution structure is one of the factors responsible for the skin properties, and consequently for the performance of the ultimately formed asymmetric membrane.

In the case of cellulose acetate (CA) casting dopes the solution structurization is mainly due to hydrogen bonding between polymer molecules and additives (swelling agents) in the solution. Therefore, a choice of a proper additive is an important step in the casting dope formulation.

The aim of this study is to investigate the ability of ortho-phosphoric acid to function as the pore-producing additive for the preparation of CA reverse osmosis membranes. Ortho-phosphoric acid (PA) is known to be a strongly hydrogen bonded liquid, and it has been claimed (8) to be a promising additive for the asymmetric CA membrane formation. To our knowledge, there has not been a thorough study on the problem.

0097–6156/81/0153–0235$05.00/0

Experimental

Eastman cellulose acetate E-398-3 and reagent-grade acetone and phosphoric acid, Merck, Darmstadt, W. Germany were employed for the casting dope preparations.

Two series of the casting solutions listed in Tables 1 and 2 were prepared.

The viscosities of the membrane casting dopes were measured by a Hoeppler viscometer as previously described (6). The solution densities were obtained by the modified Gibson and Loeffler (9) dilatometer. From these data the solution viscosities at different temperatures were calculated. The activation energies of viscous flow obtained from the $\log\eta$-1/T plots were corrected by the corresponding values of the solvents used.

Table 1. Effect of Concentration of Phosphoric Acid Used as Additive on the Casting Solution Properties

Solution type	H_3PO_4, wt.%	ΔE_v cal/mole
501	30	6.510
502	50	6.930
503	75	7.470
504	85	7.490
505	90	
506	95	8.490

Casting dope composition: CA   17%
                           acetone 68%
                           additive 15%

Table 2. Effect of Casting Solution Composition on the Casting Solution and Membrane Properties

Solution & membrane type	Casting solution composition, wt.%			ΔE_v cal/mol	NaCl rejection of membranes as-cast f, %
	CA	acetone	additive (85 wt.% H_3PO_4)		
510	17	78	5	7.140	51,2
511	17	73	10	7.310	16,0
512	17	70	13		15,4
513	17	69	14	7.450	15,1
504	17	68	15	7.490	9,8
514	17	66	17	7.910	7.8

Porous asymmetric CA membranes were prepared from all the solutions listed in Tables 1 and 2. Temperature of the casting solutions was 25°C except in one case which is later thoroughly discussed. The glass plate on which the solution was cast was kept at the same temperature as the casting dope. Temperature of the casting atmosphere was 20-25°C and the relative humidity was 60-65%. If not otherwise specified the evaporation period was as short as possible, i.e. the cast solution was immersed immediately into a gelation bath consisting of ice-cold water.

The reverse osmosis membranes were tested in the standard experimental set-up (10). The experiments were carried out at three different pressures: 17.4, 40.8 and 102 bars; the corresponding sodium chloride concentrations were 3500 ppm, 5000 ppm and 29000 ppm. Before the reverse osmosis runs, membranes were thermally shrunk for 10 minutes in water and subsequently pressurized at 15-20% higher pressures than those used during the reverse osmosis experiments. A feed flow rate of 400 ml/min was used giving a mass transfer coefficient $k \simeq 40 \times 10^{-4}$ cm/s on the high pressure side of the membrane.

The solute separation f, defined as

$$f = \frac{ppm_{NaCl} \text{ in feed} - ppm_{NaCl} \text{ in product}}{ppm_{NaCl} \text{ in feed}}$$

was determined in each experiment. The solute concentrations in feed and product solutions were measured by the conductivity bridge.

Results

Casting Solution Composition Effects

These have been investigated on both the casting solution structure and the asymmetric membrane properties. Two relevant parameters have been examined: 1. The PA concentration in the fixed amount of additive, i.e. the additive quality, and 2. the additive content in the casting dope.

In Table 1 a series of solutions of various PA concentrations in the additive together with the corresponding values of the activation energy of viscous flow, ΔE_v, are listed. When plotted against the increasing PA concentration in additive (Figure 1) the ΔE_v values show a systematic although not a regular increase. Following the rise at low PA concentrations the curve levels off between 75 and 85 wt.% PA and eventually turns sharply upward. The shape of the presented curve seems to be significant because an increase of the ΔE_v values is known (6,11) to indicate the enlargement of the supermolecular aggregation within the membrane casting dope.

The reverse osmosis results for membranes cast from the solutions listed in Table 1 are given in Figure 2. The shrinkage

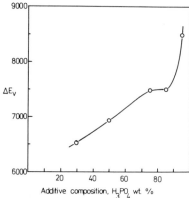

Figure 1. Effect of phosphoric acid concentration in additive on the activation energy of viscous flow of casting solutions

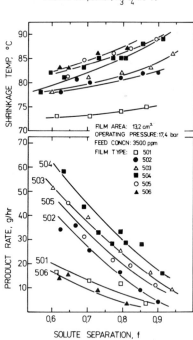

Figure 2. Shrinkage temperature profiles and membrane performances in relation to the additive composition

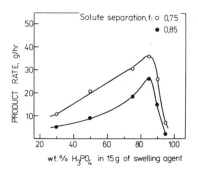

Figure 3. Membrane fluxes in relation to additive composition at two typical levels of solute rejection

temperature profiles of the membranes, i.e. shrinkage temperature versus solute separation curves (upper part of the Figure) are seen to shift upwards with the increasing PA content in the additive.

The membrane performances (lower part of Figure 2) do not change accordingly. The films made by using the most diluted acid (Batch 501) show rather poor performance; more concentrated acid improves the membrane performance (films 502, 503 and 504) and the higher acid concentrations in the additive have a negative effect. This is very well illustrated in Figure 3 which gives the membrane flux in relation to the PA content in the additive for the two chosen values of solute rejection. Both curves exhibit maxima at approximately 85 wt.% PA pointing to the acid content that produces the asymmetric membranes of optimal performance.

Table 2 lists the casting solution dopes investigated with the goal to find the best additive to solvent ratio. Again, the ΔE_V values determined show a slow but steady increase and a faster rise at the highest additive content.

These results are consistent with the reverse osmosis data shown in Figure 4. The shrinking temperature profiles of the membranes regularly shift toward higher temperatures with an increased additive content. The corresponding membrane performances show a typical optimum at 14 wt.% of additive (513-type films) and a sudden drop of the performance at higher additive content.

Effect of Casting Solution Temperature

To elucidate this effect a series of membranes was prepared from the most promising casting dope (Batch 513) that has been cooled down to $0°C$. The results presented in Figure 5 show that in this way a shift of the shrinkage temperature profile toward lower temperatures followed by the better membrane performance has been obtained. Such a result seems to be rather unexpected, and it will be discussed later.

Discussion

The foregoing results have shown that the observed phenomena in the membrane casting solutions and in the asymmetric membranes cast therefrom are closely related. This has been previously explained by the refined concept of asymmetric membrane formation (5). According to this in the membrane casting dope a long-range dynamic polymer network exists prior to the phase inversion. When the latter process is triggered it takes place within the existing network. The dimensions of aggregates that form the network and their crosslinking density affect the size and number of droplets of the newly formed phase in the "skin-to-be", and eventually the porosity of the membrane's skin.

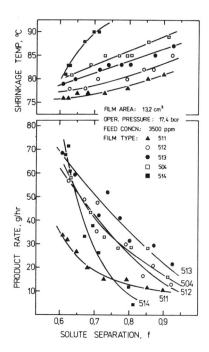

*Figure 4.   Shrinkage temperature profiles
and membrane performances in relation
to the casting solution composition*

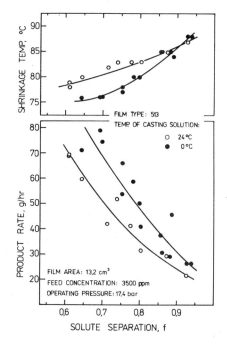

*Figure 5.   Shrinkage temperature profiles
and membrane performances of Batch-
513 films at two different temperatures of
casting solutions*

According to this the observed enlargement of the supermolecular aggregates within a casting dope caused by an increase
of PA content in the additive (Figure 1) should be followed by the
appearance of bigger pores in the skin of the asymmetric membrane
(12,13). This is really the case here, and it is shown by the
shift of the shrinkage temperature profiles of the membranes
toward higher temperatures. The relative positions of membrane
shrinkage temperature profiles is known (12,14) to be an indirect
measure of the membrane's skin porosity. Higher located shrinkage
temperature curve points to the presence of relatively bigger
pores in the skin layer of membranes in the as-cast conditions,
and such findings are illustrated in the upper part of Figure 2.

Further, the observed changes in trends of both the ΔE_v
curve (Figure 1) and the membrane performance data (Figure 3)
that happen in the same range of PA concentrations, lead to the
conclusion that a certain stable level of supermolecular
organization reached in the membrane casting dope creates
conditions for the membranes with optimal skin properties to be
formed.

In order to explain the specific role of PA in the membrane
casting dope one has to take into consideration the structure of
PA. The molecule of PA forms (15,16) a tetrahedral PO_4 group
which is linked to the other molecules by hydrogen bonds. In
86 wt.% PA two PO_4 groups are connected by one hydrogen bond
(Figure 6) enabling formation of a chainlike structure of PA.
The other two hydroxyls in each PO_4 group of the chain link it
with water or some other proton acceptor molecules in the solution.
In a diluted PA there are less direct PO_4–H–PO_4 connections, with
more water molecules inserted between PO_4 groups, which means
that dilution hinders the formation of long PA chains. In a more
concentrated PA double hydrogen bonds between PO_4 groups appear
(17) leaving less free hydroxyls for the side linkages of PA chain
with other molecules in the solution.

Such structural properties of PA give us a key for the
interpretation of the presented data.

The optimally structurized casting dope contains the
additive composed of 85 wt.% PA. As mentioned above such additive
is made up of PA chains which form optimally long intermolecular
bridges among CA molecules. A tridimensional structure in the
casting dope exists and its strength is enhanced by the "side"
hydrogen bonding of hydroxyls not engaged in PA chains formation.
Such additional crosslinking of CA molecules densifies the
tridimensional network in the casting dope, the effect of which
does not change remarkably the size of the aggregates. This
might be the reason why the ΔE_v values remain nearly the same
when the additives containing 75-85 wt.% of PA are used. The
optimally sized and densified network in the casting dope
accommodates the phase inversion process in the upper layer of the
cast solution and represent one of the parameters that control
the eventual porosity of the skin.

The less concentrated PA as the additive in a casting dope does not make long enough crosslinks among CA molecules, so the effective size of dynamic polymer aggregates in the solution prior to the phase inversion is too small - the ΔE_v values are lower. The highly concentrated PA as the additive has a detrimental effect due to lost ability of such an acid to create a dense intermolecular network with CA molecules. In this case PA cannot even break CA-CA links - the ΔE_v values are therefore high, and it acts more as a nonsolvent than as a pore-producing substance.

The effect of the solvent to additive ratio in the casting solution has a well-known trend similar to those for the magnesium perchlorate- and formamide-base casting dopes (12,13). A low additive content in the casting solution produces smaller aggregates due to a dominant dissolving action of acetone. This is reflected in the relatively small effective pores in the membrane's skin and inadequate membrane productivity. By increasing the amount of additive supermolecular aggregates become larger and the resultant asymmetric membranes better. After an optimum in the additive's content has been reached (14 wt.%), further addition of the pore-producing agent leads to the steep drop in the membrane performance which is typical (5) for the films cast from the solutions approaching the phase separation boundary. In the case of the PA-based solutions containing 17 wt.% of CA, the phase separation line is at approximately 18 wt.% of additive, confirming the observed deviations of both the shrinkage temperature profile and the membrane performance curve of the Batch-514 type films from those for the other membranes. There is obviously an extensive ordering in this solution which manifests by the relatively high ΔE_v value measured.

A remarkable change in both the shrinkage temperature profile and the membrane performance caused by cooling the most promising casting dope (Batch 513) points to the formation of more numerous and relatively smaller pores in the membrane's skin as compared with the films made at room temperature. The smaller pores in the skin and their precursors, droplets of the inverse phase in the upper layer of the cast solution are the result of changes in the structure of supermolecular network in the solution. Less intensive thermal motion existing in the solution at lower temperature cannot break too many of the hydrogen bonds which densify the kinetic entities. This means that supermolecular structures in the solution remain pretty dense, and as such influence the creation of smaller and more numerous droplets, that eventually transform into smaller and numerous pores in the skin.

The offered interpretation of the presented results seems to be strongly supported by the most significant feature of the produced membranes - their surprisingly good performances at higher operating pressures. Figure 7 compares the performances of the 513-type membranes cast from the solution cooled down to

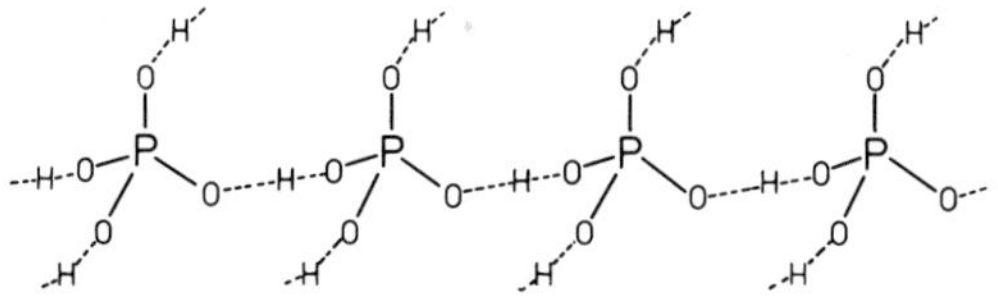

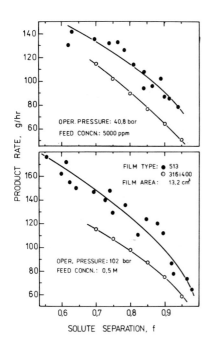

Figure 6.   Schematic of the structure of 86% o-phosphoric acid

Figure 7.   Comparative performances of PA-, MPC-, and F-based cellulose acetate membranes at medium and high operating pressures

0°C with those of the standard magnesium perchlorate- and forma-
mide-based asymmetric films at 40,8 and 102 bars, respectively.
The improvement in performance is evident, and if expressed
numerically (Table 3) it amounts to at least 30%.

Table 3. Comparison of Membrane Productivities

Operating pressure, bar	Flux, m^3/m^2 day		Productivity improvement, %
	Membranes 316 & 400	Membranes 513	
$17,4^a$	0,522	0,544	4,4
$40,8^b$	1,175	1,647	40,2
$102^{\ c}$	1,358	1,773	30,6

The flux values have not been corrected for the concentration
polarization, which is greater for more productive membranes.

[a] Feed concentration: 3500 ppm NaCl

[b] Feed concentration: 5000 ppm NaCl

[c] Feed concentration: 0.5 M NaCl

Such a significant gain in membrane productivity at higher
operating pressures can be attributed to an increased mechanical
strength of the upper membrane layer, which is caused by the
densely crosslinked tridimensional polymer network in it.

Summary

Highly productive cellulose acetate reverse osmosis membranes
have been prepared from the casting dopes containing phosphoric
acid as a pore-producing additive. Phosphoric acid is shown to
influence the supermolecular structurization of the casting dope.
The effect is attributed to a chainlike structure of phosphoric
acid which is capable of linking polymer molecules by hydrogen
bonds in a complex tridimensional network. A correlation between
the solution structurization and the membrane performance has
been confirmed. A significant improvement in the membrane
performance at higher operating pressures has been found.

This work has been supported by the Office of Water Research
and Technology, U.S. Department of the Interior, under Contract
No. 14-01-0001-1427, and by the Research Fund of Croatia,
Yugoslavia.

Literature Cited

1. Loeb, S.; Sourirajan, S. University of California at Los Angeles Engineering Report, 1961, No. 60-60.
2. Schultz, R.; Asunmaa, S. Recent Progr. Surface Sci. 1970, 3, 293.
3. Kesting, R.E. J. Appl. Polym. Sci. 1973, 17, 1771.
4. Panar, M.; Hoehn, H.H.; Hebert, R.R. Macromolecules 1973, 6 777.
5. Kunst, B.; Skevin, D.; Dezelic G.; Petres, J.J. J. Appl. Polym. Sci. 1976, 20, 1339.
6. Kunst, B.; Vajnaht, Z. J. Appl. Polym. Sci. 1977, 21, 2505.
7. Kunst, B.; Vajnaht, Z. Proc. 6th Intern. Symp. on Fresh Water from the Sea, Las Palmas, Spain, 1978, 3, 219.
8. King, W.M.; Cantor, P.Q. U.S. Patent 3,444,286 (May 13, 1969).
9. Gibson, R.E.; Loeffler, O.H. J. Am. Chem. Soc. 1939, 61, 2515.
10. Sourirajan, S. "Reverse Osmosis"; Logos Press, London and Academic Press, New York; 1970, p.26.
11. Tager, A.A.; Dreval, V.E. Russ. Chem. Rev. 1967, 36, 361.
12. Kunst, B.; Sourirajan, S. J. Appl. Polym. Sci. 1970, 14, 2559.
13. Pilon, R.; Kunst, B.; Sourirajan, S. J. Appl. Polym. Sci. 1971, 15, 1317.
14. Kunst, B.; Sourirajan, S. J. Appl. Polym. Sci. 1970, 14, 1983.
15. Van Wazer, J.R. "Phosphorus and Its Compounds", New York, Interscience Publishers; vol. 1 Chemistry; 1958, p.487.
16. Cotton, F.A.; Wilkinson, G. "Advanced Inorganic Chemistry" New York, Interscience Publishers 1962, p.397.
17. Simon, A.; Weist, M. Z. anorg. allgem. Chem. 1952, 268, 301.

RECEIVED December 4, 1980.

Electron Microscopy of Cellulose Acetate Reverse-Osmotic Membranes by Means of the Improved Replication Method

MASARU KATOH

Nissei Sangyo Co., Ltd., S. I. Center, Mori Bldg. 17, Minato-ku, Tokyo, 105 Japan

SHO SUZUKI

Science University of Tokyo, Department of Chemistry, Faculty of Science,
Kagurazaka, Shinjuku-ku, Tokyo, 162 Japan

The diameters of the pores of the surface layer of Loeb-Sourirajan-type cellulose acetate membranes have been reported by several authors (1-6). The reported values of the diameters cover the range between 10 Å and 60 Å. For electron microscopic observations, the replication method must be used. In order to obtain the excellently contrasted images the surface of the sample is shadowed with heavy metals in vacuum. In many cases the Pt-Pd alloy has been used as a pre-shadowing metal. But the resolution of the Pt-Pd replica is at the level of about 50 Å, since the size of the evaporated particles is between 20 Å and 40 Å (7, 8, 9). If the pore sizes are in the range of the above-mentioned level, we cannot observe them.

By means of the more advanced replication technique using tungsten as a pre-shadowing metal, the electron microscopic observation of both the pores and the morphological changes caused by annealing steps are reported in the present paper.

Experimental procedures

All experiments were conducted with a Hitachi H-500 type electron microscope, both operated at 100-kV and observed at the magnification of 100,000 and 200,000.

Preparation of the membranes. The membranes are prepared by means of the Manjikian's method (10). The three kinds of membranes, unannealed, 50°C- and 85°C-annealed ones, are ready for electron microscopic observations.

Samples for electron microscopy. The membranes are treated by freez-drying of the same method as reported by Riley, Merten, Gardner (11). The samples immersed in isopentane are cooled in liquid nitrogen and then dehydrated in vacuum.

Shadowing techniques. The principles of the present method is shown schematically in Figure 1. The evaporation source is a

0097-6156/81/0153-0247$05.00/0

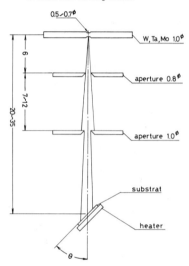

Figure 1.   Schematic of evaporating arrangement (in millimeters)

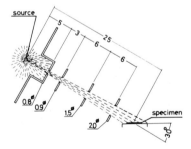

Figure 2.   Use of apertures for shadowing (in millimeters)

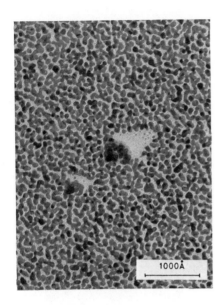

1000Å

Figure 3.   Electron micrograph of evaporated Pt–Pd alloy particles. Carbon particles are shadowed (×150,000).

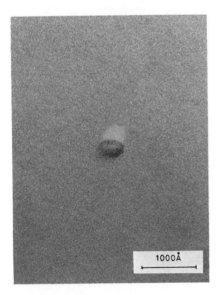

1000Å

Figure 4.   Electron micrograph of evaporated W particles. A carbon particle is shadowed (×150,000).

Figure 5. Electron micrograph of the W preshadowed carbon replica of the surface of an unannealed Loeb–Sourirajan-type cellulose acetate membrane (×140,-000)

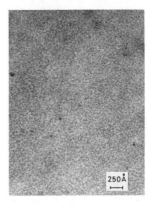

Figure 6. Electron micrograph of the W preshadowed carbon replica of the surface of a membrane annealed for 5 min at 50°C (×140,000)

Figure 7. Electron micrograph of the W preshadowed carbon replica of the surface of a membrane annealed for 5 min at 85°C (×140,000)

a notched-wire, or a tungsten wire of 50 mm in length and 1.0 mm
in diameter, and its middle portion is slimed about 0.7 mm in
diameter. The wire is set in an ordinary vacuum evaporator of
electron microscopy, and an electric power of about 10 V and 60 –
100 A is applied to it instantly. As shown in Figure 2, two more
aperture plates having the hole of 0.8 and 1.5 mm in diameter are
set between the source and substrate to prevent thermal radiation
effect from the evaporation source and to improve shadowing quality. With this apparatus, we prepare the one step replica, and use
tungsten as the pre-shadowing metal. We have compared the resolution of the tungsten shadowed replica with that of the Pt–Pd
alloy one. The shadowing angle is 30° and the thickness of carbon
film is about 100 Å and that of both W metal and Pt–Pd alloy are
30 Å.

Results and discussion

Figures 3 and 4 show the highly magnified electron micrographs of both evaporated tungsten and Pt–Pd alloy. The size of
Pt–Pd alloy evaporated particles is at the level of about 50 –
100 Å and that of tungsten, about 3 – 5 Å. So the resolution of
the tungsten pre-shadowed replica may be at the level of about
15 – 20 Å.

By means of the one step replica with tungsten as pre-shadowing metal, the electron micrograph of the surface of an unannealed
membrane is shown in Figure 5. In the micrograph we can find the
pores whose sizes range between 10 and 27 Å. The greater part of
them is between 15 – 25 Å. The surface appears just like crater
and there are also observed some wave-like features, the sizes of
which are at the level of 100 – 500 Å. The pores exist uniformly
on the surface.

Figure 6 shows the surface of the 50°C annealed membrane,
where we can observe the existence of cavities, the sizes of
which are between 25 and 50 Å. Upon annealing, the fine pores as
observed in the unannealed one disappeared and the cavities (25 –
50 Å) were dispersed uniformly on the surface. The features of
the surface are very different from those of the unannealed one.

In the micrograph of the surface of the 85°C annealed
membrane (Figure 7), the wave-like features are observed, and the
sizes of the wave range between 25 and 75 Å. Its appearance
resembles that of the unannealed one, but the number of pores is
samller than the unannealed one. The pore sizes are at the level
about 20 Å, and the number of pores is not so many.

As the effects of an annealing step on the properties of
cellulose acetate membranes, the increase of crystallinity by
means of the X-ray diffraction method (12, 13) and the changes of
pore sizes by the BET adsorption method (5) have been reported.

In our present observations with the unannealed membrane,
we can ascertain the existence of a number of pores, which are at
the level of about 10 – 30 Å. Then with the 50°C annealing step,

the features of the surface markedly change and such pores as observed in the unannealed one, can not be observed. The 85°C annealed surface is subjected once again to the reorientation of molecules, and it is considered that the glass transition may occur (12, 13). The surface becomes comparatively smooth and the pores of about 15 Å, is very small in number. The decrease in the number of pores is attributed to the shrinkage of pores. The pores cannot be observed under the present resolution of the electron micrograph, and we miss the existence of such small pores.

It should be noted that in our micrograph, in which the higher resolution replica method is used, the semispheres of about 200 Å in diameter can not be observed (6, 14).

It is concluded that the pore sizes of the Loeb-Sourirajan-type membrane are under the level of 10 - 15 Å. The remarkable transition of the features of the membrane surface by the annealing step is observed.

Literature Cited

1. Banks, W., Sharples, A. J. appl. Chem., 1966, 16 28.
2. Glueckauf, E.; Russell, P.J. Desalination. 1970, 8, 351.
3. Meares, P. Eur. Polym. J., 1966, 2, 241.
4. Agrawal, J.P.: Sourirajan, S. J. Appl. Polym. Sci. 1970, 14, 1303.
5. Ohya, H.; Konuma, H.; Negishi, Y. J. Appl. Polym. Sci. 1977, 21, 2515.
6. Schultz, R. D.; Asunmaa, S.K. Recent Progr. Surface Sci. 1970, 3, 291.
7. Bradley, D.E. Nature, 1958, 181, 875.
8. Katoh, M.; Nakazuka, H. J. Electron Microsc., 1977, 26, 219.
9. Katoh, M. Private communication.
10. Manjikian, S.; Loeb, S.; McCutchan, J.W. Proc. 1st Intern. Symp. Water Desalination, U.S. Dept. Interior, Office of Saline Water, Wash., D. C. 1965, 2, 159.
11. Riley, R.L.; Merten, U.; Gardner, J.O. Desalination, 1966, 1, 30.
12. Strathmann H.; Scheible, P. Kolloid-Z. u. Z. Polymere, 1971, 246, 669.
13. Strathmann H.; Scheible, P.; Baker, R.W. J. Appl. Polym. Sci. 1971, 15, 811.
14. Kesting, R.E. J. Appl. Polym. Sci., 1973, 17, 1771.

RECEIVED January 2, 1981.

Asymptotic Solute Rejection in Reverse Osmosis

SUN–TAK HWANG

Chemical and Materials Engineering, The University of Iowa, Iowa City, IA 52242

WOLFGANG PUSCH

Max-Planck-Institut für Biophysik, Kennedy–Allee 70,
6000 Frankfurt am Main 70, West Germany

In the literature, there are many transport theories describing both salt and water movement across a reverse osmosis membrane. Many theories require specific models but only a few deal with phenomenological equations. Here a brief summary of various theories will be presented showing the relationships between the salt rejection and the volume flux.

The solution–diffusion model ($\underline{1}$) assumes that water and salt diffuse independently across the membrane and allows no convective salt transport. The reciprocal salt rejection, $1/r$, is linearly related to the reciprocal volume flux, $1/q$:

$$\frac{1}{r} = 1 + \frac{K_s D_s}{d} \cdot \frac{1}{q} \tag{1}$$

where K_s is the salt distribution coefficient, D_s is the salt diffusivity and d is the membrane thickness.

The finely-porous membrane model ($\underline{2,3}$) assumes that a substantial amount of salt is transported by convective flow through the narrow pores of the membrane. Integrating the Nernst–Planck equation for salt transport ($\underline{3}$) and using the appropriate boundary conditions, the following relationship is obtained between the salt rejection and the volume flux:

$$\frac{1}{1 - r} = \frac{1}{1 - r_\infty} - \frac{r_\infty}{1 - r_\infty} \exp \left[-q(1 - r_\infty)d/P_s\right] \tag{2}$$

where r_∞ is the asymptotic salt rejection and P_s is the salt permeability.

Katchalsky and Curran ($\underline{4}$) formulated the nonequilibrium thermodynamic equations for the transport of material through a discontinuous membrane. However, there was a difficulty in their expressions, as they required the "average concentration" in the membrane. In order to overcome this difficulty of evaluating the

0097–6156/81/0153–0253$05.00/0

average concentration and the concept of discontinuity, Spiegler
and Kedem (5) introduced a continuous membrane model. This model
consists of alternating thin layers of membranes and solutions
under local equilibrium. Thus, Spiegler and Kedem were able to
convert the difference equations derived by Katchalsky and Curran
into a set of differential equations. Then, upon integration
across the membrane, they arrived at the same final expression
for the salt flux as in the finely-porous membrane model. The
salt rejection is related to the volume flux exactly in the same
manner:

$$\frac{1}{1 - r} = \frac{1}{1 - \sigma} - \frac{\sigma}{1 - \sigma} \exp \left[-q(1 - \sigma)d/P_s\right] \tag{3}$$

where σ is the reflection coefficient. It is apparent that $r = \sigma$
when q becomes infinitely large, that is, $r_\infty = \sigma$. Therefore,
Eq. (3) is identical to Eq. (2).

In a recent study, Pusch (6) derived a linear relationship
between the reciprocal salt rejection and the reciprocal volume
flux based on the model-independent nonequilibrium thermodynamic
expressions:

$$\frac{1}{r} = \frac{1}{r_\infty} + \frac{P_s}{r_\infty d} \cdot \frac{1}{q} \tag{4}$$

This is an excellent model from the viewpoint of determining the
transport coefficients from experimental data. A simple least
squares fit gives r_∞ from the intercept and $P_\infty/r_\infty d$ from the slope.
The only weakness is in the approximation of the mean salt con-
centration $\tilde{c}_s \simeq \tilde{c}_\infty \simeq c'$. This will be discussed again later.

Volumetric Transport

As summarized above, there are many transport models and flow
mechanisms describing reverse osmosis. Each requires some
specific assumptions regarding membrane structure. In general,
membranes could be continuous or discontinuous and porous or non-
porous and homogeneous or non-homogeneous. One must be reasonably sure about the membrane structure before he analyzes a particular set of experimental data based on one of the above
theories. Since this is difficult, in many cases, it would be
desirable to develop a model-independent phenomenological theory
which can interpret the experimental data.

In the following discussion, a purely phenomenological theory
will be presented for the tranport of salt and total volume.
Hence, it does not assume any particular membrane structure or
transport mechanism. However, the membrane is assumed to be continuous in the sense that any physical quantity may be differentiated or integrated throughout the membrane. In an analogous
manner to the regular treatment of transport phenomena (7), the

transport of salt and total volume across a membrane can be treated phenomenologically without resorting to a specific transport mechanism.

The molar flux of salt with respect to stationary coordinates or a laboratory observer is

$$\phi_s = C_s v_s \tag{5}$$

where C_s is the salt concentration in the membrane and v_s is the salt velocity relative to stationary coordinates. It should be noted that this flux ϕ_s is not a diffusive flux, which is relative motion with respect to some average velocity. Two frequently used average velocities are mass average velocity and molar average velocity. Here, we will introduce a volume average velocity $v^\dagger$ (8):

$$v^\dagger \equiv \sum_i C_i \bar{V}_i v_i = \sum_i \phi_i \bar{V}_i \tag{6}$$

where $\bar{V}_i$ is the partial molar volume of the ith species. Here i represents s for salt, w for water, and M for membrane. Using this reference frame, the molar flux of salt can be divided into two terms:

$$\phi_s = C_s v_s = C_s (v_s - v^\dagger) + C_s v^\dagger \tag{7}$$

The first term on the right-hand side is the diffusive flux relative to the volume average velocity. The second term represents a contribution due to bulk flow. It should be emphasized here that the separation of the total flux into two contributions is always possible regardless of the actual transport mechanism through the membrane. In other words, Eq. (7) is purely phenomenological and does not require any specific transport model.

If the diffusive flux is expressed according to Fick's diffusion equation:

$$C_s (v_s - v^\dagger) = -D_s \frac{dC_s}{dx} \tag{8}$$

then, Eq. (7) becomes:

$$\phi_s = -D_s \frac{dC_s}{dx} + C_s v^\dagger \tag{9}$$

In reverse osmosis, the total volume flux is frequently used.

$$q = \phi_w \bar{V}_w + \phi_s \bar{V}_s \tag{10}$$

Comparing Eqs. (6) and (10), the following identity is obtained (note that the membrane flux ϕ_M is zero):

$$v^{\dagger} = q \tag{11}$$

which means that the total volume flux is actually the volume average velocity. Substituting this identity relationship into Eq. (9), the Nernst-Planck type equation is obtained:

$$\phi_s = -D_s \frac{dC_s}{dx} + C_s q \tag{12}$$

However, a distinction should be made in that Eq. (12) is purely phenomenological and does not require any transport mechanism model while the Nermst-Planck equation used in the previous finely-porous membrane model requires a specific pore model. Another difference is that the salt concentration in Eq. (12) is that in the membrane while the quantity appearing in the Nernst-Planck equation refers to the salt concentration in the membrane pores.

The generalized equation of motion can be written as (9):

$$\frac{\partial C_i}{\partial t} + \nabla \cdot C_i \vec{v}_i = R_i \tag{13}$$

where R_i is the molar rate of production of the ith species per unit volume, and is zero in a reverse osmosis system. If the partial molar volume can be assumed to be constant, multiplying through by $\bar{V}_i$ and summing over all species, the following equation results:

$$\frac{\partial \sum_i C_i \bar{V}_i}{\partial t} + \nabla \cdot \sum_i C_i \vec{v}_i \bar{V}_i = 0 \tag{14}$$

At the steady state the first term drops out and substituting Eq. (6) into the above equation, the equation of continuity becomes:

$$\nabla \cdot \vec{v}^{\dagger} = 0 \tag{15}$$

When this is applied to the one dimensional reverse osmosis system Eqs. (11) and (15) yield:

$$\frac{dq}{dx} = 0 \tag{16}$$

Thus, it becomes apparent that the total volume flux remains constant throughout the membrane at steady state. It is also obvious that the molar salt flux is constant at steady state.

Therefore, the diffusivity is the only variable coefficient in Eq. (12), which can be integrated as follows:

$$\int_{C_s'}^{C_s} \frac{dC_s}{q\,C_s - \phi_s} = \int_0^x \frac{dx}{D_s} \tag{17}$$

Defining the average diffusivity, $\bar{D}_s$:

$$\frac{1}{\bar{D}_s} \equiv \frac{\int_0^d \frac{dx}{D_s}}{\int_0^d dx} \tag{18}$$

Eq. (17) yields:

$$C_s - \frac{\phi_s}{q} = \left(C_s' - \frac{\phi_s}{q}\right) \exp(qx/\bar{D}_s) \tag{19}$$

This equation describes precisely how the salt concentration varies in the membrane as a function of position.

Homogeneous Membrane

When the membrane is homogeneous, the salt distribution coefficients are assumed to be identical at both sides of the membrane. The salt distribution coefficient is denoted as K_s, which relates the salt concentration in the membrane to the salt concentration in the bulk:

$$K_s = \frac{C_s'}{c_s'} = \frac{C_s''}{c_s''} \tag{20}$$

Here, single prime refers to the feed side (high pressure) and double prime refers to the product side (low pressure) and the lower case c's refer to the bulk concentrations. Even if the membrane is homogeneous, it is possible to have a variable diffusivity, which may be a function of salt concentration.

The boundary condition on the low pressure side of a reverse osmosis cell requires that the salt and water fluxes through the membrane determine the bulk salt concentration on the low pressure side. Thus, the following relationship results:

$$\frac{C''_s}{C''_w} = \frac{\phi_s}{\phi_w} \tag{21}$$

In addition, for a dilute solution the following approximations may be used:

$$c_w \bar{V}_w \simeq 1 \quad , \qquad q \simeq \bar{V}_w \phi_w \tag{22}$$

Therefore, the boundary condition given by Eq. (21) can be rewritten as:

$$C''_s \simeq \frac{\phi_s}{q} \tag{23}$$

Introducing the salt rejection, r:

$$r = 1 - \frac{C''_s}{C'_s} = 1 - \frac{\phi_s}{q C'_s} \tag{24}$$

and by combining Eq. (20) and Eq. (19) with the substitutions $x = d$ and $C_s = C''_s$, the following relationship results:

$$\frac{1}{1 - r} = \frac{1}{K_s} + \left(1 - \frac{1}{K_s}\right) \exp(-qd/\bar{D}_s) \tag{25}$$

If the asymptotic salt rejection, r_∞, is introduced when the volume flux becomes infinite, Eq. (25) gives:

$$K_s = 1 - r_\infty \tag{26}$$

The diffusivity may be replaced by the permeability defined by:

$$P_s = K_s \bar{D}_s = (1 - r_\infty) \bar{D}_s \tag{27}$$

Substituting Eqs. (26) and (27) into Eq. (25), the salt rejection can be expressed as follows:

$$\frac{1}{1 - r} = \frac{1}{1 - r_\infty} - \left(\frac{r_\infty}{1 - r_\infty}\right) \exp[-q(1 - r_\infty)d/P_s] \tag{28}$$

This is identical to the Spiegler-Kedem relationship, Eq. (2), and that of finely-porous membrane model, Eq. (3), with $\sigma = r_\infty$. However, it should be noted that Eq. (28) is derived phenomenologically without any assumptions on the transport mechanism.

When the volume flux is small, Eq. (28) can be approximated as:

$$\frac{1}{r} \simeq 1 + \frac{P_s}{r_\infty d} \cdot \frac{1}{q} \tag{29}$$

This equation may be compared with Eq. (1), the solution-diffusion model, and Eq. (4), the Pusch equation. Therefore, it is easily seen that when $1/r$ is plotted against $1/q$, it should give an almost straight-line for large values of $1/q$ with a slope of $r_\infty d/P_s$. The curve of Eq. (28) will deviate from this straight-line only for small values of $1/q$. This fact is illustrated in Figure 1 for $r_\infty = 0.8$. For the sake of comparison, Eq. (4) is plotted as well. As shown in the figure, the two equations give almost the same linear relationship between $1/r$ and $1/q$. When q becomes very large, Eq. (28) deviates slightly from the straight line but both equations give the same value of the asymptotic salt rejection, r_∞.

The mean salt concentration $\bar{C}_s$ can be calculated from Eq. (19) using the following definition:

$$\bar{C}_s \equiv \frac{\int_0^d C_s \, dx}{\int_0^d dx} \tag{30}$$

If the mean solution concentration, which is a fictitious quantity, is defined as:

$$\tilde{c}_s \equiv \frac{\bar{C}_s}{K_s} \tag{31}$$

and after some calculations, the following relationship results:

$$\frac{\tilde{c}_s}{c_s'} = \frac{(1 - \bar{D}_s r_\infty/qd) \exp(qd/\bar{D}_s) + \bar{D}_s r_\infty/qd}{\exp(qd/\bar{D}_s) - r_\infty} \tag{32}$$

The ratio of the mean solution concentration to the feed salt concentration is plotted in Figure 2 as a function of volume flux. Two extreme cases will be of interest. First, when $qd/\bar{D}_s \to \infty$, the right-hand side of Eq. (32) approaches unity. This means that for all values of r_∞, the mean solution concentration becomes the feed salt concentration as the volume flux becomes infinite. The second case is when $qd/\bar{D}_s$ is very small. In this case Eq. (32) becomes indeterminant. Hence, L'Hospital's Theorem must be applied to find the limiting value. It gives two different limiting values depending on the value of r_∞. When $r_\infty = 1$ exactly, $\tilde{c}_s/c'$ approaches 0.5 as $qd/\bar{D}$ becomes zero, but for all other values of r_∞, $\tilde{c}_s/c'_s$ asymptotically approaches unity. These asymptotic trends are shown in Figure 2.

Homogeneous Double Layer Membrane

In order to gain some understanding of the behavior of an asymmetric membrane, let's consider a composite membrane consisting of two homogeneous membranes laminated together as shown in Figure 3. The same model has been studied recently by Henkens et al. (10). The first layer solution is:

$$C_s = \frac{\phi_s}{q} + \left(C'_s - \frac{\phi_s}{q}\right) \exp(qx/\bar{D}_1) \tag{33}$$

and the second layer solution is:

$$C_s = \frac{\phi_s}{q} + \left(C^j_s - \frac{\phi_s}{q}\right) \exp[q(x - d_1)/\bar{D}_2] \tag{34}$$

where $\bar{D}_1$ and $\bar{D}_2$ are the average diffusivities of salt in the first and second layers, respectively. The boundary conditions are as follows:

$$
\begin{array}{llll}
x = 0 \; ; & C_s = C'_s & \left.\rule{0pt}{20pt}\right\} & \text{first layer} \\
x = d_1 \; ; & C_s = C^i_s &
\end{array}
$$

$$
\begin{array}{llll}
x = d_1 \; ; & C_s = C^j_s & \left.\rule{0pt}{20pt}\right\} & \text{second layer} \\
x = d_2 \; ; & C_s = C''_s &
\end{array}
$$

$$C^j_s = a \, C^i_s \; , \qquad \text{where} \quad a = \text{distribution coefficient}$$

When the two solutions are combined using the appropriate boundary conditions, the following relationship is obtained:

$$C''_s - a\frac{\phi_s}{q} = a\left(C'_s - \frac{\phi_s}{q}\right) \exp[qd_1/\bar{D}_1 + q(d_2 - d_1)/\bar{D}_2] \tag{35}$$

Using the relationships

$$C'_s = K'_s \, c'_s \qquad \text{and} \qquad C''_s = K''_s \, c''_s \tag{36}$$

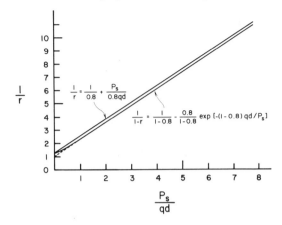

Figure 1.   Comparison of two salt rejection equations

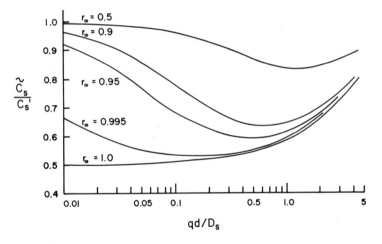

Figure 2.   Mean salt concentration

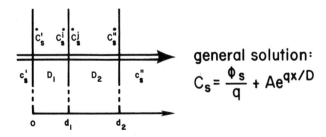

Figure 3.   Homogeneous double-layer membrane

and the definition of salt rejection

$$r = 1 - \frac{c_s''}{c_s'} = 1 - \frac{\phi_s}{qc_s'} \tag{37}$$

the following relationship is obtained:

$$\frac{1}{1-r} = \frac{1}{K_s'} + \left(\frac{K_s''}{aK_s'} - \frac{1}{K_s'}\right)\!\bigg/\exp[qd_1/\bar{D}_1 + q(d_2 - d_1)/\bar{D}_2] \tag{38}$$

If $r_{1\infty}$ and $r_{2\infty}$ are introduced according to Eq. (26)

$$K_s' = 1 - r_{1\infty} \qquad \text{and} \qquad K_s'' = 1 - r_{2\infty} \tag{39}$$

for the first and second layers, respectively, Eq. (38) can be rewritten as:

$$\frac{1}{1-r} = \frac{1}{1-r_{1\infty}} + \left(\frac{1-r_{2\infty}}{a(1-r_{1\infty})} - \frac{1}{1-r_{1\infty}}\right)\!\bigg/\exp[qd_1/\bar{D}_1 + q(d_2 - d_1)/\bar{D}_3]$$

$$\tag{40}$$

when $q \rightarrow \infty$, the overall salt rejection r becomes $r_{1\infty}$. This means that the overall asymptotic salt rejection for the double layer membrane is determined only by the first layer.

Non-homogeneous Membrane

For a non-homogeneous membrane, both the diffusivity and salt distribution coefficient may vary as a function of position across the membrane. However, the steady-state conditions require that the molar salt flux and the total volume flux remain constant throughout the membrane. Therefore, the integrated expression, Eq. (19) is still applicable to the non-homogeneous membrane system. Following the same scheme as for the case of the homogeneous membrane with the modified salt distribution coefficients:

$$K_s' = \frac{C_s'}{c_s'} \qquad \text{and} \qquad K_s'' = \frac{C_s''}{c_s''} \tag{41}$$

the expression for the salt rejection becomes:

$$\frac{1}{1-r} = \frac{1}{1-r_\infty'} + \left(\frac{1-r_\infty''}{1-r_\infty'} - \frac{1}{1-r_\infty'}\right)\exp[-qd/\bar{D}_s] \tag{42}$$

When $q \to \infty$, it is apparent that

$$r_\infty = r'_\infty \qquad (43)$$

which means that the overall asymptotic salt rejection is determined by the top layer of the membrane. This conclusion is consistent with the result obtained for the double layer model from Eq. (40).

Another interesting case is when $qd/\bar{D}_s \to 0$. The salt rejection at this limiting condition becomes

$$r_0 = \frac{r'_\infty - r''_\infty}{1 - r''_\infty} \qquad (44)$$

which is non-zero in general.

Reversed Membrane

If an asymmetric membrane is reversed, and the reverse osmosis experiments are carried out, the degree of salt rejection will be quite different from the results obtained for the normal experiments. In this case, the salt rejection is given by:

$$\frac{1}{1 - r} = \frac{1}{1 - r''_\infty} + \left(\frac{1 - r'_\infty}{1 - r''_\infty} - \frac{1}{1 - r''_\infty} \right) \exp[-qd/\bar{D}_s] \qquad (45)$$

Thus, the asymptotic salt rejection is determined by the other side's surface rejection:

$$r_\infty = r''_\infty \qquad (46)$$

Also, the limiting salt rejection when the volume flux becomes zero is

$$r_0 = \frac{r''_\infty - r'_\infty}{1 - r'_\infty} \qquad (47)$$

Essentially, the same results will be obtained from the homogeneous double layer theory if the subscripts 1 and 2 are exchanged in Eq. (40).

Conclusion

An exact mathematical relationship is obtained between the salt rejection and total volume flux in reverse osmosis based on a purely phenomenological theory assuming constant salt permeability. This approach does not require a specific membrane model;

while, the results still agree with the finely-porous membrane
model and the Spiegler-Kedem model. It also shows that there are
essentially no distinctions made between the present results and
the ones obtained by Pusch when experimental data are correlated.
Furthermore, the calculations justify the assumption introduced
by Pusch that $\tilde{c}_s = \tilde{c}_\infty = c_s'$ at the two extreme cases when $q \to 0$
and $q \to \infty$.

The present study shows that the asymptotic salt rejection,
r_∞, is determined by the top skin layer of a membrane. This is a
result of the steady-state mass balance and the boundary conditions. Although there are no experimental data to support this,
it has been shown theoretically that the asymptotic salt rejection
is identical to the reflection coefficient for the homogeneous
membrane, $r_\infty = \sigma$.

Finally, it should be mentioned that it is very difficult to
accurately measure the values of r_∞ when it is close to unity. On
the other hand, when the value of r_∞ is low, membrane compaction
will take place. In spite of these difficulties, experiments are
currently being conducted to test the present theory at the
Max-Planck-Institut für Biophysik in Frankfurt, Germany.

Acknowledgment

The authors are grateful to Professor R. Schlögl for his
interest in this work. The financial support by the "Bundes-
minister für Forschung und Technologie," Bonn, Germany, is
greatly appreciated.

Nomenclature

a   = salt distribution coefficient between two contiguous
      membranes

C_s = salt concentration in the membrane

c_s = salt concentration in the bulk

$\tilde{c}_s$ = mean solution concentration

D_s = salt diffusivity

$\bar{D}_s$ = average salt diffusivity

d   = membrane thickness

K_s = salt distribution coefficient between the bulk and the
      membrane

P_s = salt permeability

q   = total volume flux

R   = molar rate of production per unit volume

r   = salt rejection

r_∞ = asymptotic salt rejection at $q \to \infty$

t   = time

$\bar{V}$ = partial molar volume

v   = velocity

$v^\dagger$ = volume average velocity

x   = dimension across membrane

Greek letters

σ = reflection coefficient

ϕ = molar flux relative to stationary coordinates

Superscripts

'   = feed side

"   = product side

—   = average

Subscripts

i   = ith species

s   = salt (solute)

w   = water (solvent)

1,2 = layers

Literature Cited

1. Lonsdale, H.K.; Merten, U.: Riley, R.L.; Vos, K.D.;
    Westmoreland, J.C., Reverse Osmosis for Water Desalination,
    OSW Res. & Develop. Prog. Rept. No. 111, May 1964.

2. Schmid, G., Z. Elektrochem., 1950, 54, 424.

3. Schlögl, R., _Ber. Bunsenges. Physik. Chem._, 1966, 70, 400.

4. Katchalsky, A.; Curran, P.F., "Nonequilibrium Thermodynamics," Harvard Univ. Press, Cambridge, MA., 1965, p. 124.

5. Spiegler, K.S.; Kedem, O., _Desalination_, 1966, _1_, 311.

6. Pusch, W., _Ber. Bunsenges. Physik. Chem._, 1977, _81_, 269.

7. Bird, R.B.; Stewart, W.E.; Lightfoot, E.N., "Transport Phenomena," Wiley, New York, N.Y., 1960, p. 500.

8. _ibid_, p. 518.

9. _ibid_, p. 556.

10. Henkens, W.C.M.; Eijsermans, J.C.; Smith, J.A.M., _J. Membrane Sci._, 1979, _5_, 149.

RECEIVED December 4, 1980.

Ultrastructure of Asymmetric and Composite Membranes

ISRAEL CABASSO[1]

Gulf South Research Institute, P.O. Box 26518, New Orleans, LA 70186

The development of the Loeb-Sourirajan asymmetric cellulose acetate membrane (1) has been followed by numerous attempts to obtain a similar membrane configuration from virtually any available polymer. The presumably simplistic structure of this cellulose acetate membrane - a dense, ultrathin skin resting on a porous structure - has been investigated by transmission and scanning electron microscopy since the 1960s (2,3). The discovery of macrovoids (4), a nodular intermediate layer, and a bottom skin have contributed to the question of the mechanism by which a polymer solution is coagulated to yield an asymmetric membrane.

A few empirical and theoretical studies to postulate a general set of rules for the fabrication of asymmetric membranes by phase inversion mechanism (in which the polymer solution is coagulated within a nonsolvent bath) have been attempted. Thus, for example, from the literature which described the formation of asymmetric membranes, Klein and Smith (5) compiled working rules in the early 1970s regarding the requirements of a casting solution:

1. The casting composition solubility parameters (δ_t) should be near the solubility boundary facing the quench medium.
2. A volatile solvent component should be such that its loss will move the composition out of the solubility area, rather than into it.
3. The solids content at the solution boundary must be high in order to cause a rapid transition from solution to gel.
4. All components of the system should be miscible with the quench medium (nonsolvent).

The above set of rules - though accurately descriptive of earlier casting procedures - has led to serious misconceptions pertaining to the formation of anisotropic membranes, and therefore, misconceptions in the formulation of new polymeric casting solutions. It is evident that the polymer solution concentration progressively increases at the surface layer during the evaporation period, and

[1] Current address: Chemistry Department, State University of New York, Syracuse, NY 13210

0097-6156/81/0153-0267$06.25/0

formation of the pellicle is visible to the naked eye. Yet it was proven that for many dope mixtures (including that of cellulose acetate), the evaporation period is not necessary and the anisotropic structure is formed in situ upon quenching (6,7). (This is also shown in the wet-spinning of hollow fiber membranes, which are spun directly into the coagulation bath.)

Some casting compositions in which one of the solvent components (e.g., chloroform) is immiscible with the coagulating medium (water) were recently reported to be very effective (8). In order to bring the casting formulation closer to the solubility boundary, numerous formulations cited in the literature employ a so-called "swelling agent" (9), which simply designates a nonsolvent for the polymer, which dissolves in the polymer better than in the coagulant. The swelling agent concept is perhaps the most obscure and misleading item in the short history of the anisotropic membrane. The fact is that such membranes can be cast from a single solvent [e.g., dimethylformamide for polysulfone and poly(vinylidene fluoride), and dioxane for derivatives of polyphenylene oxide.] In analyzing the myriad formulations conceived for cellulose acetate membranes, apart from the addition of a "swelling agent" (by the general definition given above), it is hard to recognize a common feature among them.

On the other hand, careful observation of the gelation process clearly indicates that the entire morphological structure of a polymeric membrane is often affected by the difference in specific gravity between the cast solution and the coagulation liquid. This aspect has been overlooked in the past when variables for dope mixture formulation were considered in the casting process. If this element is taken into account when evaluating known casting formulations, one may conclude that the introduction of components (additives, swelling agents, or solvents) with relatively high specific gravities (> 1) [e.g., dioxane (7), chloroform (8), phosphoric acid (10), and formamide (11)] seems to be very effective in the preparation of these membranes. This leads us to the conclusion that the specific gravity of the solution mixture as well as the chemical properties of the materials in which a polymer candidate is dissolved is of utmost importance in shaping membrane morphology. This aspect of membrane fabrication has been investigated in the course of the present study and will be discussed in this manuscript.

The structure of the so-called "composite" membranes used in reverse osmosis is also much more complex than the conventional, simplistic description of the ultrathin semipermeable film deposited on and supported by a porous substrate. Most of these membranes which exhibit high flux and separation are composed of an anisotropic, porous substrate topped by an anisotropic, ultrathin permselective dense layer which is either highly crosslinked, or exhibits a progressively decreased hydrophilicity toward the surface. The basic difference between the conventional anisotropic (asymmetric) membrane and the thin film composite is that the latter might be composed of two or more different polymers which exist in the membrane as separate layers. The structural differences among the membranes described above were analyzed by electron microscopy techniques and are discussed in the following sections.

Experimental

The relationship among the casting solution compositions, the specific gravities of the components, and the coagulation mechanisms were studied employing the experimental set-up shown in Figure 1. A polymer solution was cast (thickness of 250-300 μm) on a glass slide 8 x 4 cm in size and then submerged to a depth of 7 cm in the coagulation bath (water), as shown in Figure 2. The mode of solvent dissipation from the cast layer was detected by a schlieren pattern. The schlieren photographs were taken with a camera set up perpendicular to the long side of the slide. A black-ruled background was used to detect convection flows in the coagulation bath. In the experiments described herein, the polymer solution was cast on the slide and then instantaniously submerged (slid into the bath at a 45° angle) so as to eliminate turbulance; this part of the experiment (casting and submersion) took 1 to 4 seconds. The light source and flashlight were adjusted so that the photographs could be taken with a shutter speed of 1/60 second. Selected polymers and solvents used in this experiment are listed in Table 1. In general, all observations of coagulations conducted with the materials specified in Table 1 indicate a definite linkage between specific gravities of the components (the polymer solution, solvent mixture, and coagulation liquid) and the phase-inversion mechanism. Only a few typical examples will be discussed briefly here.

The results shown in Figures 2-7 are summarized in Table II.

TABLE I.   SOLVENTS AND POLYMERS

Material	Specific Gravity (ρ)	Molar Volume (V)	Solubility Parameters		
			(δ_d)	(δ_p)	(δ_h)
1,4-dioxane	1.03	85.7	9.3	0.9	3.6
tetrahydrofuran (THF)	0.89	81.7	8.2	2.8	3.9
acetone	0.79	74.0	7.6	5.1	3.4
water	1.00	18.0	7.6	7.8	20.7
dimethylformamide (DMF)	0.94	77.0	8.5	6.7	5.5
formamide	1.13	39.8	8.4	12.8	9.3
cellulose acetate (visc. 3)	1.31				
polysulfone (3500)	1.24				
M-polyphenylene oxide	$\sim$ 1.1				

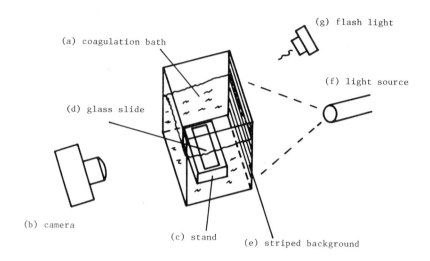

Figure 1. Experimental set-up for schlieren detection in a coagulant bath

Figure 2. Detection of solvent (acetone) convection flows in a water coagulating bath; (a) surface of cellulose acetate (20 wt % in acetone); (b) acetone convection flow upward; (c) accumulation of acetone on the surface of the coagulation bath. Elapsed time = 45 s.

TABLE II.   COAGULATION MODES OF CASTING SOLUTIONS (Figures 2-7)

Figure Designation	Polymer (wt%)	Solvent	Elapsed* Time	Membrane Structure
Figures 2,3	cellulose acetate (20)	acetone	< 4 s	dense
Figure 4	cellulose acetate (20)	tetrahydro-furan (THF)	< 4 s	dense
Figure 5	polysulfone (15)	THF	< 4 s	dense
Figure 6	polystyrene (15)	THF	< 4 s	dense and fragmented
Figure 7	polysulfone (15)	dioxane	none	porous
-----	cellulose acetate (20)	dioxane	none	porous
-----	cellulose acetate (20)	acetone/ formamide (1/1)	15 min	porous

*
time interval between submersion and appearance of schlieren pattern.

All the polymer solutions that were prepared from very low specific gravity solvents exhibited rapid depletion of solvent, once submerged in the aqueous bath.

Figures 2-5 exhibit a convection flow (upward) from the surface of the nascent membrane that lasts until more than 80 wt% of the solvent is depleted from the cast layer. The heavy accumulation of the solvents (which are highly water miscible in nature) on the top of the coagulating bath is clearly shown in Figures 2 and 4. As for Figure 6, the whole casting layer fragmented into slices of dense polystyrene ($\rho \simeq 1$); the solvent depletion was instantaneous. A typical case for all the casting solutions with high specific gravity solvent mixtures is shown in Figure 7. With this type of response, schlieren patterns could be detected only by brief stirring in the vicinity of the nascent membrane surface, and even then only after an elapsed time of more than 500 seconds. Experiments were carried out with solutions of cellulose acetate in acetone and acetone/formamide (Table III) (Figures 2 and 3). The gradual increase in the formamide fraction to solution increased the elapsed time before schlieren patterns appeared. For the solution composition formamide/acetone (40/60), slow convection flow appeared suddenly after 650 seconds, but the formation of the pellicle at the nascent membrane interface could be clearly seen 15 seconds after submersion in the water bath. Such pellicles could not be discerned for solutions cast from THF or pure acetone.

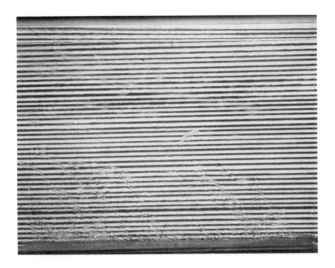

Figure 3.   Acetone convection flows from the surface of cast cellulose acetate solution.   Elapsed time = 10 s (see Table II).

Figure 4.   THF convection flow pattern in a water coagulating bath from cellulose acetate (20 wt % in THF).   Elapsed time = 45 s.

*Figure 5.   THF convection flow from the surface of polysulfone (15 wt % in THF).
Elapsed time = 20 s.*

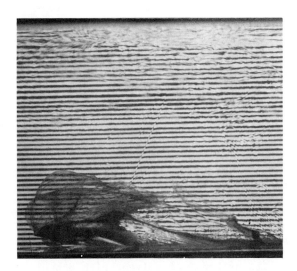

*Figure 6.   Coagulation of polystyrene (15 wt % in THF) in water.   Elapsed time
= 10 s.*

TABLE III.   EFFECT OF FORMAMIDE ON COAGULATION

Sample Number	Cellulose Acetate (wt%)	Formamide/ Acetone (ratio)	Solvent Specific Gravity (ρ_s)	Solvent Depletion* beginning (sec)	end (sec)
302	20	0/100	.79	< 10	$\gtrsim$ 126
296	16.6	20/80	.86	40	$\sim$ 190
A-314	15	30/70	.89	62	$\gtrsim$ 350
A-307	13.3	40/60	.92	650	
A-300	20	33/47	.93	> 734	
A-298	25	35/40	.95	> 730	
A-294	25	35/40	.95	> 740	

*
As evidenced by schlieren pattern

The scanning electron microscopy micrographs shown in the body of this manuscript were taken by AMR-1000 and Jeol C-35 instruments. All specimens were gold-palladium coated. To obtain the cross-section morphologies, the membranes were fragmented in liquid nitrogen.

Discussion

Dope Composition and Coagulation Process. The formation of a porous membrane by the coagulation of a polymer solution in a non-solvent bath has been discussed by various investigators and a criteria for the diffusion-controlled formation of the porous structure was attempted recently by Cohen, et al. (12). The model employed by these investigators assumes that the coagulation bath is well stirred, so that the existing solvent does not remain in the vicinity of the interface (and the composition of the coagulant at the film boundary is at all times that of the original bath). While one can employ such an assumption in order to make use of coagulation models (especially in order to avoid a boundary prob-lem), the problem in reality is that convection flows of solvent and solvent-nonsolvent mixtures through the cast layer interface (Figure 2) (and within the nascent membrane) prevail concurrently with the diffusive exchange of solvent with nonsolvent.

In a typical case, when a polymer solution is cast on a glass plate or release paper and then submerged in a coagulant bath, the cast surface (its interfacial zone facing the coagulant) undergoes a series of transitions which, in general, will be results of one or a combination of the following three mechanisms:

Coagulant

Case A.   Case B.   Case C.
Exchange   Solvent Out   Coagulant In

Cast Layer

Each of the three mechanisms yield different micro- and macro-
structures. The occurrence depends largely on the differences in
the specific gravities of the components. The exchange mechanism
can be considered as a pure diffusion problem - that controls
gelation via stepwise phase inversion - only when the specific
gravities of the polymer solution (ρ_p), its solvent mixture (ρ_s),
and the coagulant (ρ_c) are equal ($\rho_p = \rho_s = \rho_c$) and if the heat
of mixing (ΔH^M) and hydrostatic pressure of the coagulant above the
nascent solid phase are minimal. If these conditions are not met,
convection flows of the liquid components often dominate the coagulation process. For example, if a polymer with high specific gravity (such as cellulose acetate, $\rho_p \simeq 1.3$) is cast from its solution
in acetone ($\rho_s \simeq 0.788$) and is coagulated in an aqueous bath, the
gelation process is represented by a general Case B behavior - the
solvent is mobilized from the interface in a convection-type flow
to the upper levels of the coagulant bath (Figure 2), while the
nascent coagulant at the interface is contracting inward toward
the bottom (i.e., the casting plate). What is seen in Figures 3 and
4 is quite similar to rapid evaporation of solvent, which is char-
actized by its relatively high vapour pressure. The progressive
increase in polymer concentration and the subsequent solidification
does not necessarily yield a porous structure.

   Conversely, in most observed cases where solidification occurs
as a result of continued depletion of solvent (as described in
Case B), the highly concentrated polymer layer solidifies as a
relatively dense, amorphous, plasticized film. Water diffusion
into this highly plasticized layer becomes prevalent (Case A) at
a stage where the contraction has gone "too far" to yield even a
microporous membrane structure.

   The schlieren experiments employing solutions with THF and
dioxane as solvents proved that at least two different coagulation
mechanisms exist in an unstirred bath. It is evident that Case B
applied for the THF solution, while Case A applied for the dioxane
solution. The depletion and removal of the THF from the cast layer
interface via convection flow (rather than diffusive exchange with
water molecules) is instantaneous, and the rapid accumulation of
the solvent on the surface of the aqueous coagulation bath is
notable. As for the dioxane solution (Figure 7), schlieren patterns
could not be observed even after 1000 seconds - even when phase

separation was completed. The fact that a schlieren pattern appeared
upon gentle stirring of the region close to the interface proves
that a concentrated layer of dioxane/water solution is gradually
accumulated at the nascent membrane interface and that diffusive
exchange (Case A) dominates the coagulation mechanism.

Both solvents are cyclic ethers with about the same molar
volume and solubility parameters, with THF the more polar of the
two (Table I). However, no logical connection can be established
between the gross morphological differences that are produced upon
coagulation of the 15 wt% polymer solution in water and the chemical
properties of these two solvents. Yet, the differences in the
specific gravities does indeed predict the behavior that is displayed
in Figures 4, 5 and 7), and consequently, significant differences
in the membrane structures. Examining the classic problem of cellulose acetate/acetone, an identical coagulation response to that
shown by THF is observed (Figures 2 and 3). The instant depletion
and removal of the acetone-rich layer (in the coagulation bath)
follows a solidification of the cellulose acetate into a dense,
tight semi-isotropic membrane. It was therefore of interest to
examine the role of formamide as a necessary component (11) in
the fabrication of asymmetric and porous cellulose acetate membranes.
A phase diagram of cellulose acetate/formamide and acetone is shown
in Figure 8.

The nine formulations that produce Loeb/Sourirajan-type membranes are shown and were all taken from the literature (7, 11, 13).
The solid line represents the phase boundary. A related solubility
parameter diagram (5) indicates that formamide is also somewhat
of a swelling agent for the polymer; therefore, coagulation and its
morphological outcome are commonly viewed to be largely a result
of specific chemical interaction which determines the state of
existence of the macromolecular chains in the casting solution.
However, many other solvents which exhibit a range of interaction
- with cellulose acetate - similar to that reflected through the
solubility parameters of formamide (Table I) do not yield the desired
porous structure. (One must remember that the as-cast cellulose
acetate reverse osmosis membranes, though anisotropic, are still
porous, and densification of the skin is a result of a subsequent
annealing in most instances.) Examining the specific gravities of
solution formulations presented in Figure 8, each specific gravity
of the solvent mixture is within the range of 0.9 to 1, indicating
that as concentration of the polymer in solution increases from
17 wt% to 32 wt%, a slight decrease in the specific gravity of the
solvent mixture is allowed.

The series of coagulation experiments employing cellulose
acetate solutions in various acetone/formamide mixtures (Table III)
indicates that the contribution of formamide to the cast solution's
specific gravity greatly influences the rate and coagulation
mechanism of the cast solution. What seems to be an important
point in the formulation of cellulose acetate anisotropic membranes
is that the compositions that bring the casting solution sufficiently
close to the gelation point are also those that bring the specific
gravity of the mixture close to that of the coagulant. Therefore,
these two variables are synergistic. Skin formation occurs at the

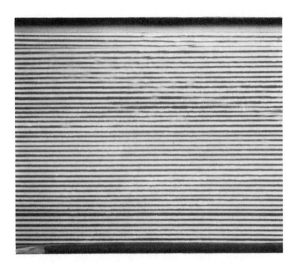

Figure 7.   Coagulation of polysulfone (15 wt % in dioxane). Schlieren patterns were not detected. (This was the case for any coagulation of a polymer solution with a high specific gravity solvent.) Elapsed time = 45 s.

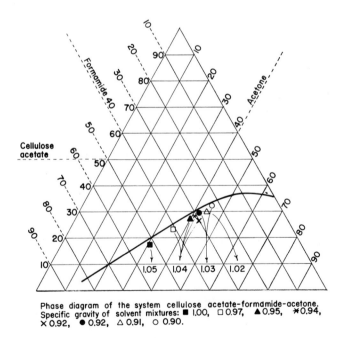

Phase diagram of the system cellulose acetate-formamide-acetone. Specific gravity of solvent mixtures: ■ 1.00, □ 0.97, ▲ 0.95, ✳ 0.94, ✕ 0.92, ● 0.92, △ 0.91, ○ 0.90.

Figure 8.   Phase diagram of the system in cellulose acetate–formamide–acetone

interface where the polymer solution is in direct contact with the coagulant. Subsequent liquid-liquid phase separation with nucleation and growth of the polymer-rich or polymer-poor phase is predominantly controlled by diffusive exchange (Case A). The formation of the initial skin layer (as observed for the ratio 40/60 formamide/acetone in Table III) acts further as a limiting barrier through which the exchange of solvent for nonsolvent is controlled. Acetone, however, can be replaced by dioxane to produce a very effective anisotropic cellulose acetate membrane and the whole problem of adjusting the specific gravity is thus eliminated.

Phase separation controlled by diffusion exchange often results in a skin which is composed of a micellar assembly of nodules, as will be discussed below. When extremely hydrophobic polymers (e.g., modified-PPO) are cast from dioxane into water ($\rho_s \simeq \rho_p \simeq \rho_c$), a dense polymer layer is formed at the solution's interface that somewhat resembles the type of layer formed by interfacial polymerization. There is almost no inward contraction of the interfacial skin, and the coagulation process is controlled by diffusion through the dense, interfacial thin film. These result in an anisotropic membrane with a very fine "coral" structure (Figures 9 and 10). The skin, which has a lateral orientation, is not an integral extension of the porous matrix and tends to crack easily.

Relationship Between Nodular and Rejecting Layers. Nodular formation was conceived by Maier and Scheuerman (14) and was shown to exist in the skin structure of anisotropic cellulose acetate membranes by Schultz and Asunmaa (3), who ion etched the skin to discover an assembly of close-packed, ~ 188 Å in diameter spheres. Kesting (15) has identified this kind of micellar structure in dry cellulose ester reverse osmosis membranes, and Panar, et al. (16) has identified their existance in the polyamide derivatives. Our work has shown that nodules exist in most polymeric membranes cast into a nonsolvent bath, where gelation at the interface is caused by initial depletion of solvent, as shown in Case B, which follows restricted inward contraction of the interfacial zone. This leads to a dispersed phase of micelles within a continuous phase (designated as "polymer-poor phase") composed of a mixture of solvents, coagulant, and a dissolved fraction of the polymer. The formation of such a skin is delineated in the scheme shown in Figure 11.

In casting processes, the nodular layer may fuse to yield a dense amorphous layer when the solvent moves rapidly (by diffusion and convection) from the lower, as-yet uncoagulated zone, to the interface.

The development of anisotropic membranes based on a hydrophobic polymer matrix (e.g., polysulfone derivatives or phosphonylated-PPO) which does not collapse upon drying, made possible a more thorough investigation into the origin and role of the nodular layer. It is now clear that if the nodular layer extends to the interface without fusion, the membrane is open to solute permeation. Solute separation would then be dependent upon the serriedness of the nodules

Figure 9.   Cross-section of a modified-PPO hydrophobic membrane exhibiting a very fine coral structure

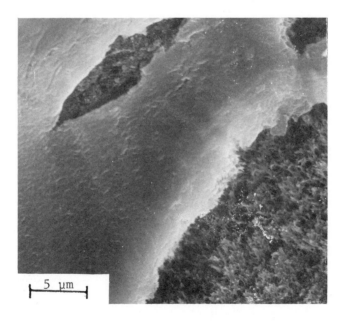

Figure 10.   Torn surface of a modified-PPO anisotropic membrane (also shown in Figure 9) after exposure to lateral stress

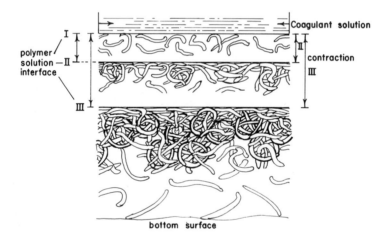

Figure 11. Initial mechanisms of phase inversion: (I) polymer solution interface at zero time; (II) initial depletion of solvent, inward contraction, and formation of the nodular layer; (III) end of contraction and establishment of the nodular layer.

and the spatial cross-section of the solute species. This is a
typical situation for many ultrafiltration membranes.

Where solute dimensions are in the range of sodium and chloride
ions, as for a reverse osmosis membrane, the nodules' packing density
should be much higher than, for example, that shown in Figure 12.
This implies that the selective layer of reverse osmosis membranes
may have a different origin from that of the micelles. Such a case
is clearly identified by examination of the skin structure of
cellulose acetate/poly(bromophenylene oxide phosphonate) alloy
membranes (17), which exhibit a high flux and high salt separation
(Figure 13). The skin rests on an assembly of giant spheres (up to
1 μm in diameter) and is certainly originated by a different coagulation mechanism than that of the spheres.

The nodular layer is one of three compacting zones in reverse
osmosis membranes. Exposure to elevated hydraulic pressure gradually increases the serriedness of this layer. The nodular
zones shown in Figures 12 and 13 are not fused, and the spaces
between spheres are filled with amorphous polymer deposits from the
polymer-poor phase in which the micelles were dispersed during
coagulation. Upon exposure to elevated hydraulic pressure, the
nodules may fuse into the rejecting layer with time (in reverse
osmosis, this phenomenon is highly dependent on the polymer's
hydrophilicity). For example, a high salt separation membrane
(phosphonylated-PPO) exhibited extensive compaction of the skin zone
after exposure to 13.6 atm pressure (200 psi) for five months in a
reverse osmosis operation; this compaction of the skin zone is
shown in Figure 14. This seems to be contrary to the conventional
belief that the skin thickens as a function of pressure and time
(through fusing with the matrix immdiately below). The micrographs show, rather, densification of the tested skin, which
results in an apparent skin that is thinner by half than its
untested counterpart. Further microscopic analysis (18) detects
numerous nodules imbedded in the lower section of the skin - only
partially fused to become an integral part of the amorphous layer
shown as an apparent skin in Figure 14B. This implies that the
rejecting layer does indeed thicken at the expense of the nodular
layer.

At this pressure range ($\sim$ 13.6 atm), the compaction and densification of the skin's nodular zone notably surpasses that of the
adjacent macrovoids shown in the photomicrograph, the reason being
that the polymer density around such macrovoids is very high.
Their collapse pressure is several orders of magnitude greater
than that of macrovoids which are located farther below the nodular
zone, as will be discussed below.

Bottom Skin. The origin of the bottom skin is different from
that of the surface skin. The bottom surface of the membrane is
usually an integral extension of the highly porous substructure,
and as such, should display the same configuration (Figure 15A).
However, many dope formulations yield a highly structured, dense

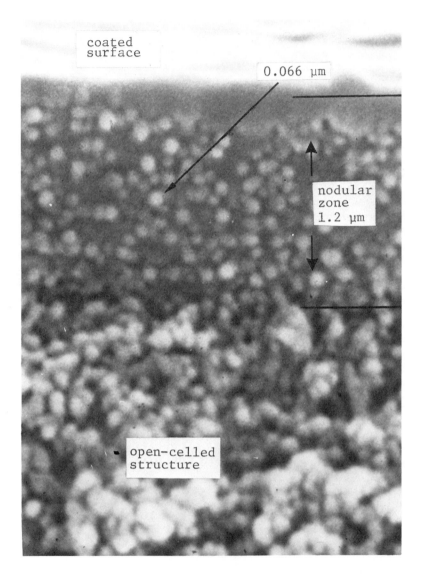

Figure 12.   Cross-section of the surface zone of a polysulfone hollow fiber (spun from DMF directly into water while conducting nitrogen through the lumen)

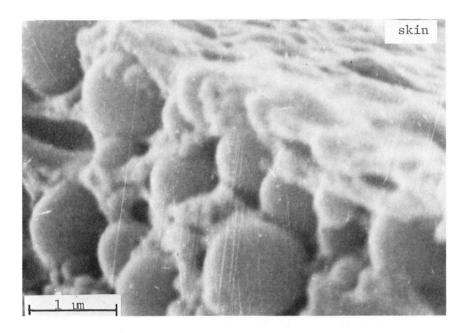

Figure 13. Cross-section of the skin zone of a reverse osmosis membrane consisting of cellulose acetate–poly(bromophenylene oxide phosphonate)

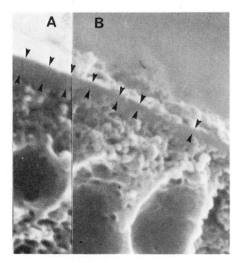

Figure 14. A phosphonylated-PPO reverse osmosis membrane before (A) and after (B) testing for 5 months under a pressure of 13.6 atm

skin that may or may not be porous (Figure 15B). Bottom skin formation is largely due to the interaction between the casting surface
and the components of the dope mixture. Different surfaces would
yield diversified bottom skin structures. For example, by employing polyphosphonates which exhibit a varied degree of adherence to
the casting surface (e.g., glass), one may obtain skin layers with
a wide range of characteristics (19).

It is important to note that bottom skin formation is not
limited to the case where the dope mixture is cast on a solid
surface. In the wet-spinning of hollow fiber membranes, a gas
(e.g., dry nitrogen) is conducted through the inner orifice (the
fiber lumen) while the nascent fiber is coagulated externally
by an aqueous solution. These fibers often exhibit an internal
skin similar to the bottom skin of flat sheet membranes, even though
the lumen does not contact any solid surface. The gas pressure
applied in the lumen (or in flat sheet membranes, the hydrostatic
pressure applied by the coagulant) may affect the formation of a
tight bottom skin. This subject is still open to further investigation. The existance of a bottom skin contributes to the
membrane's resistance and if this skin is not porous, membrane
productivity is greatly impeded.

Macrovoids. The formation of macrovoids has been discussed
in detail in previous publications (20). In short, they are
almost exclusively a result of coagulant penetration through the
nascent membrane interface during the first stages of coagulation
following the submersion of the cast layer (or the spun extrudate)
in the coagulating bath. In Figure 16, a reverse osmosis membrane
is shown containing three types (distinguished by location in the
membrane morphology) of macrovoids: a. large macrovoids that
extend through most of the membrane's substructure, b. medium-sized
macrovoids that extend through one-third of the membrane, and
c. small macrovoids situated near the membrane's nodular layer.

The membrane shown in Figure 16A has a salt rejecting skin
($\sim$ 95%), and operates satisfactorily at low hydraulic pressures
- up to 10 atm ($\sim$ 147 psi). However, a gradual increase in the
pressure causes a nonuniform collapse of the macrovoids (Figure 16B).
The collapse of the large and medium-sized macrovoids causes lateral
tension at the membrane surface, which then yields to the acting
forces. What was originally a flat surface now has a "mountainous"
topography. Since a highly permselective skin does have minimal
capacity for elongation, the membrane permselectivity is reduced
substantially by macrovoid collapse. It is important to note
once again that the small macrovoids adjacent to the membrane surface neither collapse nor burst. A membrane's failure progresses
from bottom to top, and at points of high lateral tension, longitudinal cracks extending to the rejecting layer can be identified.

The finely porous morphology of the membrane shown in Figure 16
is characteristic of a dope mixture containing a combination of
solvents with individual specific gravities in the same order of

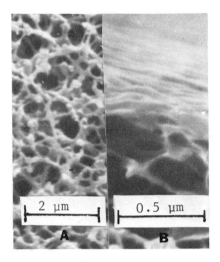

Figure 15. Bottom surfaces: (A) phosphonylated-PPO reverse osmosis membrane; (B) interior skin at lumen of the polysulfone hollow fiber shown in Figure 12.

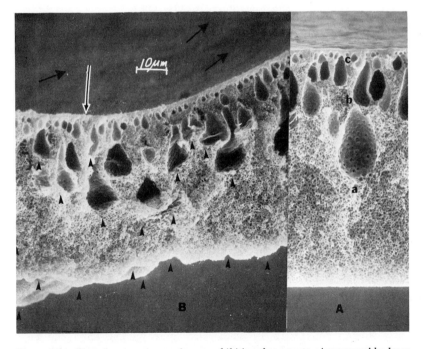

Figure 16. Reverse osmosis membrane exhibiting three types of macrovoids: large (a), medium (b), and small (c). (A) Before testing and (B) after exposure to 13.6 atm hydraulic pressure. A longitudinal crack in the skin is designated by the perpendicular arrow.

magnitude as that of the coagulant (e.g., a mixture of dioxane/
acetic acid with water as coagulant). The texture of the porous
structure might drastically change if the polymer is cast from a
solvent mixture containing a component with a very low specific
gravity (e.g., acetone). The porous substructure may be almost
entirely composed of longitudinal macrovoids (Figure 17). Since
the walls of these voids are rather dense, the structure maintains
a relatively high resistance to compaction, and as shown in
Figure 17B, the region below the skin is kept utterly intact after
several weeks of reverse osmosis testing at a working pressure of
13.6 atm (200 psi). This type of substructure stems from the use
of low specific gravity solvents in the dope mixture - in the
present case, acetone/acetic acid/phosphonylated-PPO (37.5/37.5/25).
The rapid depletion of the acetone from the cast layer into the
coagulating medium (i.e., water, which intrudes substantially into
this dope formulation) causes the substructure to coagulate around
and over the coagulant intrusions in a mechanism similar to that
described in the preceding section for the formation of dense
membranes. A notable feature of the membrane shown in Figure 17
is the absence of a nodular layer in the vicinity of the permselective skin, although further microscopic examination detects
imbedded spheres in the macrovoid walls (18).

Composite Membranes. A general scheme showing the cross-section
of a composite membrane [or what is often called a thin film composite membrane (21)] is shown in Figure 18. The skin zone consists
of a rejecting layer and a hydrophilic, crosslinked gel layer. The
support most commonly used is an anisotropic porous membrane
(e.g., polysulfone). The rejecting layer can be deposited by dip
coating (Figure 12) or in situ polymerization of monomers which
yield an extremely tight, permselective barrier.
The large variety of composite membranes reported in the
literature are not necessarily represented by the structure shown
in Figure 18. Nevertheless, the membranes which have materialized
as commercially feasible, operating reverse osmosis units (e.g.,
PA-300, NS-100, which are crosslinked polyamide derivatives -
ultrathin film depositions on porous polysulfone supports) are
accurately represented by this scheme. In comparing the Loeb-
Sourirajan type of membrane to the composite membrane, one may
be puzzled by the function of the gel layer shown in the scheme.
An early generation of composite membranes, developed by Riley,
et al. (21), was based on cellulose triacetate (CTA) cast in an
ultrathin coat from chloroform on the finely porous surface of a
cellulose nitrate/cellulose acetate substrate. These membranes did
not reflect a need for a hydrophilic-gel intermediate layer. Yet,
this membrane substrate is much more hydrophilic than the rejecting
CTA layer, and high flux as well as high separation were concurrently obtained. This is not the case if the porous substrate
is highly hydrophobic. A rejecting layer deposited on such a surface would yield an extremely poor productivity due to the loss of

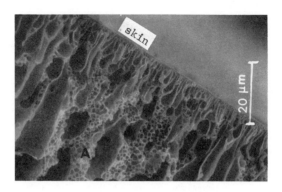

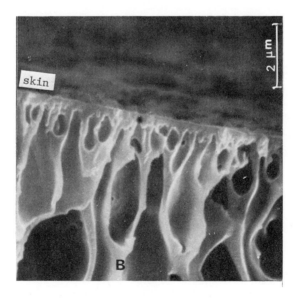

Figure 17.   Cross-section of a reverse osmosis membrane with dense-walled macro-voids

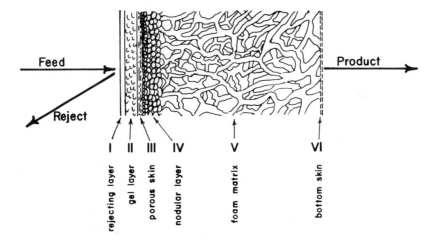

Figure 18.   Cross-section scheme of a composite reverse osmosis membrane

effective surface area; a "gutter layer" is then needed in order to channel the permeated water into the pores to maintain productivity. This is the main function for this intermediate layer. A second function is to serve as a "cushion" between the rigid, uneven support surface and the highly crosslinked permselective deposit, which has a minimal capacity to absorb lateral stresses.

In most cases where crosslinked polyamide derivatives (22) are deposited on a polysulfone substrate, the fabrication process consists of serval stages that can be summarized as: 1) coating the substrate with a hydrophilic polyamine derivative. 2) chemically crosslinking the surface zone of the coated layer by employing a crosslinking agent. 3) inducing thermal (self) crosslinking of the polyamine layer beneath the chemically crosslinked surface (i.e., thus producing a gel layer). It was shown that if the chemical crosslinking (23) is allowed to proceed through the entire coated layer - thus yielding a highly crosslinked, dense layer on top of the hydrophobic substrate - the performance of the membrane is reduced to the degree of nonproductivity.

In the Loeb-Sourirajan type of membrane, the skin and substructure are of the same polymer. Since the substructure extends from the skin, the necessity of producing a layer is totally eliminated; and from a mechanical viewpoint, the nodular layer serves as a supporting element "assisting" the skin to absorb minor lateral stress.

Conclusion

Thorough analysis and evaluation of membrane morphology is mandatory for the understanding of transport phenomena in membranes, and especially for those with rather complex structures, as described in the present manuscript. Each single membrane can be viewed perhaps as a "black box" when operating in a certain well-defined system. Yet, any deduction on transport mechanism that is based solely on transport data is highly speculative. For example, the presence of a double skin, macrovoids, the densification of the nodular layer, and other items described herein cannot be predicted by the analysis of transport data. But they can be identified, and can be very supportive to "whoever dares to look into the black box."

Acknowledgements

The author would like to acknowledge the support of the Office of Water Research and Technology, U.S. Department of the Interior. Credit is due also for experimental work carried out by Mr. C.S. Eyer, Mr. R. LeBoeuf, and Mrs. B. Zimny. Special appreciation is expressed to Ms. A. Echols for her assistance in preparation of this manuscript.

Literature Cited

1.   Loeb, S; Sourirajan, S; Adv. Chem. Ser., 1962, 38, 117.

2.   Riley, R.L.; Gardner, J.O.; Merten, U.; Science, 1964, 143, 801.

3.   Schultz, R; Asunmaa, S; Recent Progr. Surface Sci., 1970, 3, 293.

4.   Frommer, M.A.; Lancet, D; "Reverse Osmosis Membrane Research," Lonsdale, H.K. and Podall, H.E., Eds., Plenum Press, New York, 1972; pp. 85-110.

5.   Klein, E; Smith, J.K.; "Reverse Osmosis Membrane Research," Lonsdale, H.K. and Podall, H.E., Eds., Plenum Press, New York, 1972; pp. 61-84.

6.   Sarboulouki, M.N.; Polym. Letts. Ed., 1973, 11, 753.

7.   Sirkar, K.K.; Agarwal, N.K.; Pandu, G; J. Appl. Polym. Sci., 1978, 22, 1919.

8.   Aptel, P; Cabasso, I; J. Appl. Polym. Sci., 1980, 25, 1969.

9.   Kesting, R.E.; "Permeability of Plastic Films and Coatings," Hopfenberg, H.B., Ed., Plenum Press, New York, 1974; pp. 402.

10. Kunst, B; Vajnaht, Z.; presentation in Synthetic Membrane Symposium (A.C.S.) Second Chem. Cong. of the North American Cont., Las Vegas, Nevada, August 24, 1980.

11. Manjikian, S; Ind. Eng. Chem. Prod. Rev., 1967, 6, 23.

12. Cohen, C; Tanny, G.B.; Prager, S; J. Polym. Sci., (Physics Ed.) 1979, 17, 477.

13. Fahey, P.M.; Grethlein, H.E.; Desalination, 1979, 9, 297.

14. Maier, K.H., Scheuermann, E.A.; Kolloid Z., 1960, 171, 122.

15. Kesting, R.E.; J. Appl. Polym. Sci., 1973, 17, 1771.

16. Panar, M; Hoehn, H.; Hebert, R; Macromolecules, 1973, 6, 777.

17. Cabasso, I; Tran, C.N.; J. Appl. Polym. Sci., 1979, 23, 2967.

18. Cabasso, I; unpublished results.

19. Cabasso, I; "Study of Novel Polymers and Alloys in Asymmetric and Composite Membranes," U.S. Dept. of Interior, OWRT Research and Development Report, Feb. 26, 1979.

20.   Cabasso, I; "Ultrafiltration," Cooper, A, Ed., Plenum Press, New York, 1980; pp. 47.

21.   Riley, R.L.; Hightower, G.R.; Lyons, C.R.; Tagami, M; "Permeability of Plastic Films and Coatings," Hopfenberg, H.B., Ed., Plenum Press, New York, 1974; pp. 375.

22.   Rozelle, L.T.; Cadotte, J.E.; Cobian, K.E.; Kopp, C.V. Jr; "Reverse Osmosis and Synthetic Membranes, Sourirajan, S., Ed., National Res. Cons., Canada, 1977; pp. 249.

23.   Cabasso, I; Tamvakis, A.P.; J. Appl. Polym. Sci., 1979, 23, 1509.

RECEIVED January 5, 1981.

Reverse-Osmosis Research in India:
Scope and Potentialities

D. J. MEHTA and A. V. RAO

Central Salt and Marine Chemicals Research Institute, Bhavnagar 364002, India

The supply of good-quality potable water to the community is a measure of the degree of civilization which a society can reach, and it is the civic responsibility of those in power to ensure a continued supply of good-quality potable water to the masses. There are many large areas in our country which are deficient in potable water. The most extensive arid and semi-arid regions are in the western and north-western parts and in the central Deccan Plateau of India where drinking water problems due to salinity are acute. Most of the regions along the coastal belt also do not have good quality drinking water resources. India, receives an average rainfall of 93.5×10^{11} M^3 with roughly 30 per cent of it as ground water which should prove sufficient to meet the requirements of the people for agriculture, industry and drinking purposes. However, due to the vastness and topography of the country and the scattered intensity of the rain-fall pattern, the task of finding and transporting good quality water to the people in the isolated and remote areas of the vast arid and semi-arid regions of the country is, in itself, a stupendous and formidable one. It is precisely in this background that this Institute has embarked upon a systematic research programme on the desalination of brackish and sea water. Intensive research and development studies on the distillation processes during sixties led to the development of proto-type plants based on flash distillation, humidification-dehumidification and solar distillation. The main concern in all the distillation processes with the sole exception of solar-distillation is that the energy cost is so incredibly large that it forbids their adoptability to meet the drinking water needs of the community.

0097–6156/81/0153–0293$05.00/0
© 1981 American Chemical Society

The successful development of asymmetric cellulose
acetate membranes by Loeb and Sourirajan in the early
sixties, at the University of California, Los Angeles, has been primarily responsible for the rapid
development of Reverse Osmosis (RO) technology for
brackish/sea water desalination. Reverse Osmosis
approaches a reversible process when the pressure
barely exceeds the osmotic pressure and hence the
energy costs are quite low. The energy requirement
to purify one litre of water by RO is only 0.003 KW
as against 0.7 KW required just to supply the vapo-
risation energy to change the phase of one litre of
water from liquid to vapour by evaporation. Thus
RO has an inherent capability to convert brackish
water to potable water at economic cost and thus
contribute effectively to the health and prosperity
of all humanity.
     The promise of a bright future for RO made possi-
ble by the intense pursuit of Loeb and Sourirajan has
inspired a small group of research workers in this
Laboratory to initiate R&D efforts in this new and
developing science, in the late sixties. The work
of Loeb and Sourirajan has been and continues to be
the fountain head of all the inspiration and encouragement and has become a guiding torch in our pursuit of R&D efforts to develop a suitable indigenous
technology for brackish/sea water desalination. The
present paper describes, at length, the various R&D
activities in Reverse Osmosis at the Central Salt
and Marine Chemicals Research Institute, in particular. An attempt is also made to project the R&D
achievements of other research organizations in the
country.

Development of Cellulosic Polymers:

     Systematic investigations were carried out for
the preparation of cellulose acetate of D.S. 2.65 and
other mixed esters which included cellulose acetate-
propionate, cellulose acetate-butyrate, cellulose
acetate-benzoate and cellulose acetate-methacrylate.
The experimental conditions were optimised for maximum yield of the ester. Flat osmotic membranes were
developed from these esters and characterised for
their osmotic and transport properties. The membranes were evaluated in a reverse osmosis laboratory
test-cell using 5000 ppm sodium chloride solution
at 40 bars pressure. Table 1 presents the typical
performance data of these membranes.
     Of these esters, CA-Methacrylate was found to

TABLE I

CHARACTERISATION AND PERFORMANCE OF CA MIXED ESTERS

Name of the Ester	% Substitution	Mole weight	Tensile strength psi.	% S.R.	Product water flux gfd.
CA,D.S. 2.5 (Commercial)	acetyl 39.7-39.9	30000-60000	1200	90-92	10-12
CA,D.S. 2.65	acetyl 41.6-41.7	40000-60000	1700	95-96	11-15
CA-Propionate	acetyl 10-15 Propionyl 30-35	30000-50000	1300	93-94	12-13
CA-Butyrate	acetyl, 10-15 Butyl, 35-40	30000-50000	1400	93-94	12-13
CA-Benzoate	acetyl, 15-20 Benzyl, 20-25	40000-60000	1700	93-95	15-20
CA-Methacrylate	acetyl, 40-42 Methacry- 7-12 lyl	50000-55000	1500	90-92	15-18

possess fairly high rejection for urea and boric
acid; 55 and 50 per cent respectively as compared to
20 per cent or less for CA membranes. It was also
observed earlier that CA-PMMA blend membrane also
gave 75-80 per cent urea   and 60 per cent boric
acid rejection (1). Thus it seems reasonable to
assume that introduction of methacrylate group in
CA molecule alters the chemical nature of the surface of CA membrane and thus improves its rejection
efficiency for urea and boric acid.

Tubular membranes of 8' long were prepared from
blend composition consisting of CA and PMMA and performance data for one month operation was collected.
These datas show high product water flux (18-20 gfd.)
with low flux decline slope. However, it was observed that these membranes initially showed "fountains"
which disappeared in about 30 minutes time. This
was attributed to the peculiar membrane rheology and
orientation of PMMA molecule with respect to CA molecule. This needed further study for confirmation.

Development of Non-Cellulosic Polymers:

Synthesis of Polysulfone: The intermediates required
in the synthesis of polysulfone namely (i) chloro-
benzene sulfonyl chloride and (ii) dichloro diphenyl
sulfone were prepared by the reaction of chloroben-
zene with chlorosulfonic acid under controlled conditions. These were characterised by the melting point
determination and elemental analysis. Poly sulfone
was obtained by the condensation of sulfone with
bis-phenol-A sodium salt in Dimethlsulfoxide. The
polymer thus obtained was characterised by (i) elemental analysis, (ii) softening point and (iii) reduced viscosity. Membranes prepared from the labo-
ratory-synthesised product gave 25 gfd water flux
at 50 psig. When tested with 0.5 per cent dextran
solution these films gave more than 98 per cent
dextran rejection with 10 gfd product-water flux
at 50 psig. thus showing promise of its use in
ultrafiltration applications.

PAN.PMMA and Copolymer of AN/MMA: Conditions were
optimised for homo-polymerisation of acrylonitrile
and methyl methacrylate monomers and copolymerisa-
tion of AN/MMA. The characteristics of these
polymers are given in Table II.

TABLE II

CHARACTERISTICS OF ACRYLIC POLYMERS

Name of the polymer	Mole weight	Softening point °C	% Nitrogen
Poly(acrylonitrile)	130,000 to 135,000	245 to 260	23.0 to 23.1
Poly(Methylmethacrylate)	600,000 to 700,000	280	-
AN/MMA co-polymer	153,000 to 150,000	-	1.85

Flat membranes from these polymers were tested for desalination and found to be of low salt rejecting type. However, the copolymer was found to possess more than 90 per cent rejection for 1 per cent dextran solution with 10.0 gfd water flux at 200 psi thus indicating the possibility of application of these membranes in ultrafiltration and hemodialysis.

Reverse Osmosis in Water Desalination and Rural Development:

Reverse osmosis desalination plants consisting of 8' long tubular membranes prepared from commercial CA of D.S. 2.5 were set up for supply of drinking water and boiler feed water at two different locations. Table III gives typical performance data of the RO plant set up in a village to supply drinking water to the village people. The plant was operated for over six months.

TABLE III

PERFORMANCE DATA OF RO PLANT OF 3000 gal/day CAPACITY (Operating conditions : Feed rate, 3 gal/min; Operating pressure, 600 psi; Feed salinity, 5000 ppm

Solvent flux (gfd)	Salt rejection %	Recovery %	Feed temp. °C
8-9	80-85	50-55	25-28

The performance data of the RO plant set up and operated for 21 days in a textile mill in north India
for the supply of boiler feed water are given in
Table IV

TABLE IV

PERFORMANCE DATA OF RO PLANT OF 2,500 Gal/Day
CAPACITY FOR SUPPLY OF BOILER FEED WATER.

Feed water salinity : 2850 ppm
Feed flow rate   : 3 gal/min.
Operating Pressure   : 600 psi

Solvent flux (gfd)	Salt rejection %	Recovery %	Remarks
8.5	95-97	52	The plant was opera-ted without any pre-treatment.

It was observed that the plant gave a trouble-
free service during the 21 day period. However, flu-
shing of the membranes with feed water was resorted
to only once after 15 days of continuous operation.
After 21 days, the plant showed signs of decline in
salt rejection which dropped to 88 per cent. At this
stage the membranes were flushed with oxalic acid.
The fouling of the membranes was observed to be somewhat rapid. At the end of the continuous operation,
the plant was shut down and the slimy material collected from within the membranes was analysed (Table V)

TABLE V

ANALYSIS OF SLIME COLLECTED FROM WITHIN THE RO MEMBRA-
NES.

Constituents	% by weight
Fe as Fe_2O_3	1.21
Al as Al_2O_3, 1 H_2O	20.50
Ca as $CaSO_4$, 2 H_2O	8.70
Insolubles	5.51
Organic matter	63.50

The organic matter was assumed to be due to (i) oil contamination from the piston pump and (ii) the presence of large quantity of microorganism in the feed water (106000 per ml). The analysis indicated that exhaustive pretreatment consisting of sand filter, acid dosing, chlorination and SHMP dosing is essential for prolonged successful operation of the RO plant on natural well waters. Based on the performance of 500 gal/day capacity RO spiral plant which was operated continuously for 30 days (2) a 2500 gal/day capacity plant was designed and fabricated to be set up in a village "Arnej" 120 km. from Bhavnagar. The plant was run continuously round-the-clock for 3 months in the institute processing 1200 ppm bore well water. The feed water was filtered in a sand filter and the pH was adjusted to 5.5 by acid dosing before it entered the spiral modules. The performance of the plant at the start was 7 gfd flux with 85 per cent S.R. which gradually declined to about 75 per cent when the modules were cleaned thoroughly and the operation was continued further.

Reverse Osmosis/Ultrafiltration in Industry:

Exploratory studies were also undertaken to examine the technical feasibility of application of RO/UF in industrial processes such as waste treatment for recovery of chemicals and/or reuse of water, and in pollution control. Some of the typical problems which were investigated earlier have already been reported (3). Other applications which were studied further are briefly described here:

(i) Concentration of Vitamin B-12: Exploratory experiments on the concentration of Vit.B-12 using cellulose acetate membranes were carried out. Flat membranes having an area of about 5 sq. inches are used in an UF test kit. The effect of parameters like polymer solution composition, evaporation time and shrinkage temperature were studied for the tailor making of the membranes. The commercial requirement for the concentration is hiking of concentration from 20 mg/l to 10 g/l. The feasibility of the process was assessed by experiments in three stages (i) 19 mg/l to 122 mg/l (ii) 96 mg/l to 0.75 g/l and (iii) 1.03 g/l to 10.5 g/l all at 85 psig. The flux ranged from 4.2-5.6 gfd, and is independent of feed concentration and the rejection varied from 98.6 to 99.5 per cent, indicating technical feasibility of concentration, without the attendant decrease in flux due to the increased feed concentra-

tion. Improvements of the membranes for better flux
are under way.

(ii) <u>Concentration of Skim Milk and Whole Milk</u>: A few
trials on concentration of skim milk and whole milk
respectively to 5 and 3.5 times were carried out at
an operating pressure of 65 psig with cellulose acetate membranes. The permeates in both the cases were
extremely clear and the fluxes were about 6 and 3 gfd
for skim milk and whole milk respectively.

(iii) <u>Treatment of Cutting Oil Waste Emulsion</u>: Clear
permeate, low in oil content and BOD was obtained during ultrafiltration of cutting-oil waste at 35 psig
operating pressure with cellulose acetate membranes
at a flux of about 6-8 gfd.

Further experiments are continued on large scale
to establish the economic feasibility of RO/UF for the
concentration of these substances on a commercial level

<u>Economics of Desalination by RO</u>:

The cost of a 10 m^3/day tubular RO plant is estimated at Rs.8,500/m^3 and the water cost is Rs.10/m^3.
For the same capacity with spiral configuration the
cost is calculated to be Rs.6,000/m^3 with a water cost
of Rs.6/m^3. For capacities of over 100 m^3 per day,
the treatment cost is expected to be brought down to
an acceptable level of Rs.5/m^3. Table VI shows projected cost for tubular RO plants of different capacities.

<u>R&D activities of other Research Organizations in
Reverse Osmosis</u>:

(a)   At Bhabha Atomic Research Centre (BARC) (<u>4</u>),
Bombay, studies on reverse osmosis primarily aim at
developing the technology on a commercial scale for
the desalination of brackish water and sea water. A
10 m^3/day pilot plant based on cellulose acetate membranes (tubular module) was designed and fabricated
in the mid-seventies. The support tubes used were
of aluminium. The plant is still in operation with
about 10-20 gfd flux and 90-98 per cent rejection
for a feed containing 5,000 ppm dissolved salts. Presently, development work is going on to replace Al.
tubes with FRP porous tubes to improve the economics,
reliability and to overcome corrosion problems. Membrane life has been found to be about one year. Enough
operational data have been collected to design large
capacity R.O. plants. Besides this, development of

TABLE VI

COST ESTIMATES FOR REVERSE OSMOSIS PLANTS OF DIFFERENT CAPACITIES RANGING FROM 10 m³ TO 500 m³

Raw water TDS - 5000 ppm; Product water TDS 700 to 1000 ppm

Plant capacity, m³/day	1	2	3	4	5	6
	10	25	50	125	250	500
Capital Investment:						
1. Modules and Membranes	33,000	67,000	1,33,000	3,31,000	6,58,000	13,04,000
2. Pump	17,000	20,000	32,000	60,000	1,20,000	2,25,000
3. Subsidiary cost(erection assembly & miscellaneous)	13,000	8,000	15,000	39,000	78,000	1,53,000
4. Pre-treatment assembly	22,000	40,000	80,000	1,00,000	1,15,000	3,20,000
Total	85,000	1,35,000	2,60,000	5,30,000	10,00,000	20,00,000

OPERATING COST PER M³

Cost of Power Rs.0.20/kwh; Labour charges @ Rs.500/month per person 3 persons for 1 & 2, 5 persons for 3 & 4 and 6 persons for 5 & 6

Plant capacity, m³/day	10	25	50	125	250	500
1. Energy cost	1.15	1.15	1.15	1.15	1.15	1.15
2. Labour and supervision	5.00	2.00	1.00	0.66	0.33	0.20
3. Maintenance (2% of CI)	0.38	0.26	0.24	0.23	0.23	0.22
4. Depreciation						
a) On plant 8%	0.70	0.81	0.80	0.79	0.79	0.78
b) On pump 12%	0.50	0.32	0.26	0.19	0.19	0.18
c) On membrane 200%	1.70	1.86	1.86	1.86	1.86	1.86
d) Chemical pretreatment	0.32	0.31	0.30	0.32	0.35	0.31
Cost of product water per m³	Rs. 9.75	6.71	5.50	5.20	4.90	4.70

compact modules which can be fabricated by small scale
industries is in progress.

(b)   At defence laboratory, Jodhpur (4) suitable flat
and tubular semi-permeable membranes yielding high
flow rate and salt rejection have been developed. A
pilot plant of capacity 5,000 lpd based on flat type
membranes has been completed. A similar capacity
plant based on tubular type membranes has also been
developed.

(c)   NEERI, Nagpur (4) is engaged in research and
development work related to use of reverse osmosis
process for treatment of waste waters. Preliminary
field studies have been conducted utilising small
R.O. units. It is planned to scale up these studies
and also extend its application towards conversion
of brackish waters.

Present Status and Future Perspective:

        The emphasis in RO is more on the improvement
of the quality and life of the membranes. Investigations are in progress to improve upon the performance of CA membranes by introducing elaborate pretreatment methods and modifying the membrane structure
either chemically or by admixture of the casting solution with certain additives. In the future programme,
development of non-cellulosic polymers such as aromatic polyamides, PBIL etc. and CTA fibres and ultrathin films in the composite membrane are given due
consideration. Fabrication and setting up of spiral
plants in villages in a phased programme will be
carried out to meet the needs of rural communities
with population of 1 to 2 thousand. More stress is
given to the development of Hollow fine fibre technology and adequate finances are allocated for the
same. Work is also initiated to fabricate one mobile
unit of 10 m^3/day for demonstration of the process in
the villages and also treat different quality feed
waters.

Conclusion:

        The economics of Reverse Osmosis Process will be
highly favourable provided the desalination industry
is taken up in a big way bringing down the capital
investment. Water management and distribution particularly the water supply in the rural areas must be
given top priority and should be under the direct
control of central and federal government agencies;
and in this endeavour reverse osmosis has a potential

role to play in bringing relief to the section of the people who are afflicated with brackish water problems and thereby projecting the advantages and benefits of R&D efforts to the society.

ABSTRACT

Reverse Osmosis has emerged as a major breakthrough in the realm of water desalination. Its simplicity of operation and lower capital costs as compared to other desalination techniques are its attractive features. Research work carried out in this Institute in the early seventies to develop useful osmotic membranes from the indigenously available commercial cellulose acetate resulted in membranes with fairly satisfactory performance of 7 to 8 gfd. flux and 85 to 90 per cent salt rejection. The studies on solution-structure and evaporation rate led to the modified composition of membranes which gave 12 to 15 gfd. flux and 93 to 95 per cent S.R. Cellulose acetate mixed esters were then prepared and membranes developed from these esters, in general, gave fairly high salt rejection (95 to 96 per cent) with moderate water flux (8-12 g f d). Blend compositions of CA-CTA and CA-PMMA were developed which gave high product water flux of 20-30 gfd. and salt rejection of 90-97 per cent. The paper describes the Research and Development efforts and projects the relevance of RO in as much as its ability to meet the drinking water needs of the rural community and unfolds the unlimited industrial potentialities.

Literature Cited:

1. Narola, B.J.; Chandorikar, M.V.; Rao, A.V. Paper presented at 2nd Symposium on "Synthetic Membranes in Science and Industry", Tubingen, September 17-19, 1979.

2. Mehta, D.J.; Rao, A.V.; Govindan, K.P. Desalination, 1979, 30, 325.

3. Mehta, D.J.; Pandya, V.P.; Rao, A.V. Desalination, 1977, 20, 403.

4. Thomas, K.T. CSMCRI Silver Jubilee Souvenir, 1979, 37.

RECEIVED December 4, 1980.

Thin-Film Composite Reverse-Osmosis Membranes: Origin, Development, and Recent Advances

JOHN E. CADOTTE and ROBERT J. PETERSEN

FilmTec Corporation, 15305 Minnetonka Boulevard, Minnetonka, MN 55343

The original Loeb-Sourirajan membrane consisted of an asymmetric film having an ultrathin, dense, surface barrier layer integrally supported by a thick, porous, spongy underlayer. An approach to the improvement of such membranes was to separately fabricate these two layers, each maximized for performance, then join them together as laminates. The final laminates would serve as high-performance thin-film composite reverse osmosis membranes. The origin and development of this concept, as carried out at North Star Research and Development Institute and more recently at FilmTec Corporation by the authors, will be briefly described, followed by a description of recent membrane advances in this area. Examples reviewed are ultrathin cellulose acetate membranes, the invention of microporous polysulfone support films, and the development of NS-100 and NS-200 membranes. Two new membranes of this type, designated as NS-300 and FT-30, will be described. Both are chlorine-resistant, non-polysaccharide thin-film composite membranes. The NS-300 membrane has brackish water desalination characteristics, very high fluxes, and potential applications in brackish and waste water treatment processes. The FT-30 membrane possesses high flux and seawater rejection characteristics, and is finding use in single-pass seawater desalination for potable water production.

The origin of thin-film-composite reverse osmosis membranes began with a newly formed research institute and one of its first employees, Peter S. Francis. North Star Research and Development Institute was formed in Minneapolis during 1963 to fill a need for a nonprofit contract research institute in the Upper Midwest. Francis was given the mission of developing the chemistry division through support, in part, by federal research contracts. At this time the initial discoveries by Reid and Breton (1) on the desalination capability of dense cellulose acetate membranes and by Loeb and Sourirajan (2) on asymmetric cellulose acetate membranes had recently been published. Francis speculated that improved membrane performance could be achieved, if the ultrathin, dense barrier layer and the porous substructure of the asymmetric

membrane were separately fabricated, then laminated together.
Each of these two layers could then be individually optimized
for maximum performance.

In 1964 Francis fabricated the first thin-film-composite
cellulose acetate reverse osmosis membrane. The ultrathin barrier layer was made by float-casting a liquid film of cellulose
acetate solution in cyclohexanone onto a water surface (3).
Migration of the cyclohexanone from the organic phase into the
aqueous phase left behind a floating skin of cellulose acetate
on the water. The ultrathin polymer film could be laminated to
a support layer by sliding an appropriate microporous support
film under the water surface and bringing it underneath the
floating film. The thickness of the dense barrier film could be
controlled to within ± 15 percent over the range of 200 to 5,000
angstroms. This achievement led to an initial research contract
with the Office of Saline Water, U.S. Department of the Interior,
which eventually expanded into a 13 year, broadly based membrane
research effort at North Star (now merged into Midwest Research
Institute).

The first thin-film-composite membranes used microporous
cellulose acetate films as porous supports for the barrier layer
membranes (3). These support layers were asymmetric Loeb-
Sourirajan membranes themselves, but were cast under conditions
that promoted porosity and high water flux, in excess of 250 gallons per square foot per day (gfd). These composite membranes
behaved well except for a problem of low flux, which was about
2-3 gfd at 1500 psi pressure in simulated seawater tests. This
was traced to both compaction and relatively low surface porosity
in the asymmetric cellulosic support layer despite its initially
high flux. Better results were achieved using Millipore VSWP
microfiltration membranes as porous supports; resulting fluxes
rose to about 5 gfd (4). These were also cellulosic in nature,
however, and compaction appeared to be a problem in wet, long
term, high pressure tests.

In 1966, Cadotte developed a method for casting microporous
support film from polysulfone, polycarbonate, and polyphenylene
oxide plastics (4). Of these, polysulfone (Union Carbide Corporation, Udel P-3500) proved to have the best combination of compaction resistance and surface microporosity. Use of the microporous
sheet as a support for ultrathin cellulose acetate membranes
produced fluxes of 10 to 15 gfd, an increase of about five-fold
over that of the original microporous asymmetric cellulose acetate support. Since that time, microporous polysulfone has been
widely adopted as the material of choice for the support film in
composite membranes, while finding use itself in many ultrafiltration processes.

A significant advance was made in the art of thin-film-composite membranes by Cadotte in 1970 with the advent of the NS-100
membrane (5). This reverse osmosis membrane contained an ultrathin aryl-alkyl polyurea formed insitu on a microporous polysul-

fone support. This membrane was fully noncellulosic, having no cellulose ester polymers in either the barrier zone or the porous support zone. Two important characteristics that resulted were nonbiodegradability and no compaction under sustained high pressure. The membrane, furthermore, demonstrated single-pass seawater desalination qualities. Most thin-film-composite membranes since that time have been noncellulosic.

Preparative Routes to Thin-Film-Composite Membranes

A schematic diagram of a typical, commercial quality thin-film-composite membrane is presented in Figure 1. The microporous polysulfone support film is cast on a woven or non-woven fiber backing material, usually made from polyester fibers. The polysulfone support is approximately 50 μm (two mils) in thickness and about half of it penetrates into the polyester backing material. This polyester web-polysulfone structure is usually employed without drying for application of the reagents used to form the thin barrier layer. After deposition of the barrier layer, the composite membrane is subsequently dried and/or heat-cured to complete the membrane preparation. In instances where the thin barrier layer is not integrally attached to the support surface, drying may form an adequate bond. Generally it is preferred that the thin barrier layer should be well bonded to the support surface to prevent damage or delamination during use.

Table 1 lists five approaches that have been used for forming the barrier layer of a composite membrane. The first method listed is the forming of the ultrathin membrane separately on a different surface such as by float-casting on water or by slowly withdrawing a clean, flat glass plate from a dilute solution of the polymer (the Carnell-Cassidy technique) (6,7,8). This ultrathin film is then transferred to a microporous support film. Adhesion between the thin barrier film and the support surface was sometimes a problem in this approach. This method has been used mostly for cellulose acetate composite membranes, although it is a general method that can be used with many polymers. For the remaining methods listed in Table 1 the thin barrier layer is formed in situ, i.e., directly on the support surface. Methods B and C, involving dip-coating of the porous support in a solution of a polymer or a reactive monomer, appear to be a logical and simple approach for forming thin-film-composite membranes. However, few successful reverse osmosis membranes have been made by these techniques. One problem has been the limited solvent resistance of polysulfone support film. Only water, lower alcohols and aliphatic hydrocarbon solvents can be used as solvents. A second problem with Methods B and C is that the coating solution must be dilute to produce a thin barrier layer. Dilute, low viscosity solutions tend to migrate upon drying to produce defective or discontinuous coatings.

Lonsdale and coworkers (9) have fabricated cellulosic thin-

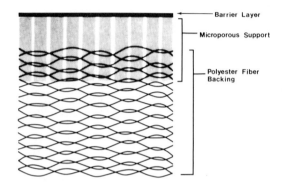

Figure 1.   Schematic of a thin-film-composite membrane

Table 1.   General Methods Used for Fabricating
            Composite Reverse Osmosis Membranes

A) Cast the ultrathin barrier membrane separately, then laminate
    to a porous support.

B) Dip-coat a polymer solution onto a support film, followed by
    drying.

C) Dip-coat a reactive monomer or prepolymer solution onto a
    support followed by heat or radiation curing.

D) Deposit a barrier film from a gaseous phase monomer plasma
    onto the support.

E) Interfacially polymerize a reactive set of monomers at the
    surface of the support.

film-composite membranes by Method B, using a cellulose nitrate-cellulose acetate porous support and a cellulose acetate barrier layer. A polyacrylic acid coating was first applied to the microporous support to prevent solvent intrusion into the micropores. The barrier layer was then applied by dip-coating techniques. Later under reverse osmosis conditions the polyacrylic acid interlayer was washed out through the support.

A notable example of Method C is the NS-200 membrane, which was first discovered at North Star in 1972 (10,11). The salt barrier in this case was a sulfonated polyfurane resin formed in place at 125 to 140°C. This membrane was preferentially formed by first impregnating a polysulfone support with an aqueous solution containing (in weight percentages) 20 isopropanol, 1 high molecular weight polyethylene glycol (Union Carbide Corporation, Carbowax 20M), 2 furfuryl alcohol, and 2 sulfuric acid. After excess solution was drained away, the coated film was placed directly in an oven, and formation of a black barrier resin occurred very rapidly. Typical oven cure time was 15 minutes or less. Laboratory-produced NS-200 membranes frequently exhibited seawater salt rejections as high as 99.9 percent at 20 gfd (tested at 1000 psi and 25°C). In spite of the excellent initial properties of the membrane, development efforts have not been successful because of a problem of long term instability of the membrane. Elemental analysis of the heat-cured membrane showed that a large proportion of the sulfuric acid catalyst was incorporated into the membrane, probably as sulfonic acid and sulfate ester groups. The high ionic charge on the membrane tended to produce excessive swelling in sodium chloride solution, but this could be counteracted with post-treatment of the membrane in 0.1 percent barium hydroxide. The actual cause of membrane instability, whether due to an unstable chemical bond or to a gradual, irreversible swelling of the structure, has not been determined.

Method D in Table 1 represents a case where dry support films were always used because of the need to employ a vacuum and because of the very nature of plasma deposition processes. Yasuda (12) showed that a wide variety of gas phase reactants could be used in this technique. Not only conventional vinyl monomers were used but also any organic compounds with adequate vapor pressure. Further, copolymers could be prepared by introduction of a second reactant such as nitrogen. Wydeven and coworkers (13,14) showed the utility of this method in preparing reverse osmosis membranes from an allylamine plasma.

Polysulfone supports are well suited for the fifth method listed in Table 1. In this approach, Method E, the support film is saturated with a water solution containing diamines, polyamines or diphenols, plus other additives such as acid acceptors and surfactants. The saturated film is contacted with a nonmiscible solvent containing di- or triacyl chloride reactants. A condensation polymer forms at the interface. The film is dried to bond the thin interfacial film to the support surface. In some

instances an additional heat-cure is required. The polysulfone
support tolerates the alkaline conditions of the reaction as well
as the drying and heat-cure steps in this process.

Two excellent examples of this membrane system have been
developed, NS-100 and PA-300 (5,15). The NS-100 membrane was made
by impregnating a polysulfone support with a 0.67 percent aqueous
solution of polyethylenimine, draining away excess reagent, then
contacting the film with a 0.1 percent solution of toluenediisocyanate in hexane. An ultrathin polyurea barrier layer formed at
the interface. This membrane was then heat-cured at 110°C. A
later version of this membrane was developed (designated NS-101),
which used isophthaloyl chloride in place of toluenediisocyanate,
producing a polyamide (16). With either type of membrane, salt
rejections in simulated seawater tests at 1000 psi exceeded 99
percent.

Two types of reactions took place in this process that were
believed to be important for controlling membrane properties.
The first reaction, which took place at the interface and which
involved the primary and secondary amine groups of polyethylenimine (PEI) with the difunctional reactant in hexane, proceeded
very rapidly at room temperature to produce, in the case of isophthaloyl chloride, a polyamide surface skin (see Reaction I).

The second reaction took place during drying of the membrane
at 110°C. The residual polyethylenimine under the polyamide surface skin was crosslinked by elimination of ammonia between
adjacent amine groups (see Reaction II).

The reactions produced a membrane having three distinct zones
of increasing porosity: 1) the microporous polysulfone support
film, 2) a thin, crosslinked polyethylenimine zone of intermediate
porosity and moderate salt rejection, and 3) the dense polyamide
(or polyurea) surface skin which acted as the high retention barrier.

The PA-300 membrane was commercially developed by Riley and
coworkers (15), and is similar to the NS-101 membrane in structure
and fabrication method. The principal difference is the substitution of a polyetheramine, the adduct of polyepichlorohydrin with
1,2-ethanediamine, in place of polyethylenimine. Use of the
polyetheramine was significant improvement in that considerably
higher membrane fluxes were possible at salt rejections equivalent
to the NS-100 membrane system. The actual barrier layer in the
PA-300 membrane is a polyamide formed by interfacial reaction of
isophthaloyl chloride with the polyetheramine.

Considerable activity has been generated on composite
reverse osmosis membranes by Japanese researchers. Patent applications were recently published, for example, covering research
at Teijin Ltd. on interfacially formed membranes prepared from
polydiallylamines (17) and from amine adducts of tris-(glycidyl)
isocyanurate (18). Both types of membranes were formed on microporous polysulfone supports. Kurihara and coworkers have developed
a composite membrane, designated PEC-1000, which is formed by an

acid-catalyzed polymerization process on the surface of a microporous polysulfone support (19). The chemical composition was
not specified, but the method of fabrication and the resulting
membrane properties are reminiscient of the NS-200 example.

Recent New Advances

In 1977 the North Star membrane research group was spun off
by Midwest Research Institute, forming FilmTec Corporation. Two
new thin-film-composite reverse osmosis membranes have been under
development at FilmTec Corporation since that time, the NS-300
and the FT-30 membranes.

NS-300 Membrane. The NS-300 membrane evolved from an effort
at North Star to form an interfacial poly(piperazine isophthalamide) membrane. Credali and coworkers had demonstrated chlorine-
resistant poly(piperazineamide) membranes in the asymmetric
form (20). The NS-100, NS-200, and PA-300 membranes were all
readily attacked by low levels of chlorine in reverse osmosis
feedwaters. In the pursuit of a chlorine-resistant, nonbiodegra-
dable thin-film-composite membrane, our efforts to develop
interfacially formed piperazine isophthalamide and terephthalamide
membranes were partially successful in that membranes were made
with salt rejections as high as 98 percent in seawater tests.
However, the variability of these membranes was extremely high in
regards to salt rejection, and the membranes generally exhibited
low flux.

A variant of this membrane was then made by replacing the
isophthaloyl chloride with its triacyl chloride analog, trimesoyl
chloride (benzene-1,3,5-tricarboxylic acid chloride)(21,22).
This membrane demonstrated a vastly improved flux compared with
the poly(piperazine isophthalamide) membrane, but its seawater
salt rejection was low -- in the range of 60 to 70 percent. A
reverse osmosis test with a magnesium sulfate feedwater showed
greater than 99 percent salt retention, however, dispelling
the possibility that low sodium chloride rejections were due to
defects in the polyamide barrier layer. The piperazine polyamide
was soon concluded to have the following structure (see Reaction III).

Two of the acyl chloride groups of trimesoyl chloride are
shown to be involved in the rapid interfacial polymerization with
piperazine to produce a polyamide which, most likely, is nearly
linear in configuration. The third acyl chloride group would then
hydrolyze in the aqueous environment to a carboxylate group,
although some of these latter groups probably also react with
piperazine to produce branching and crosslinking.

The trimesoyl chloride could be mixed with isophthaloyl
chloride to produce copolyamide barrier layers. Salt rejections
toward synthetic seawater improved as the isophthalamide content
of the barrier layer increased. Surprisingly, membrane flux
passed through a peak rather than simply declining as a function

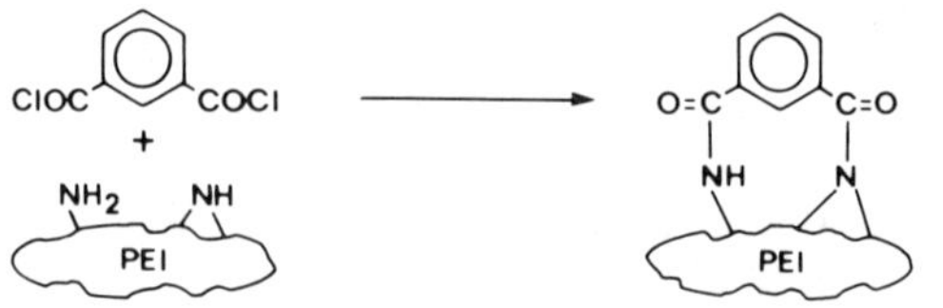

I

II

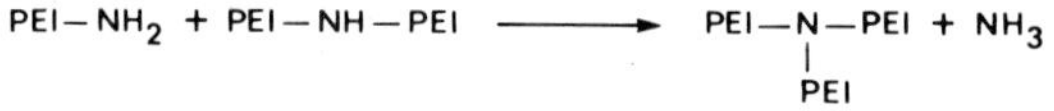

$$PEI-NH_2 + PEI-NH-PEI \longrightarrow PEI-N-PEI + NH_3$$
$$\qquad\qquad\qquad\qquad\qquad\qquad\qquad\quad | $$
$$\qquad\qquad\qquad\qquad\qquad\qquad\qquad PEI$$

III

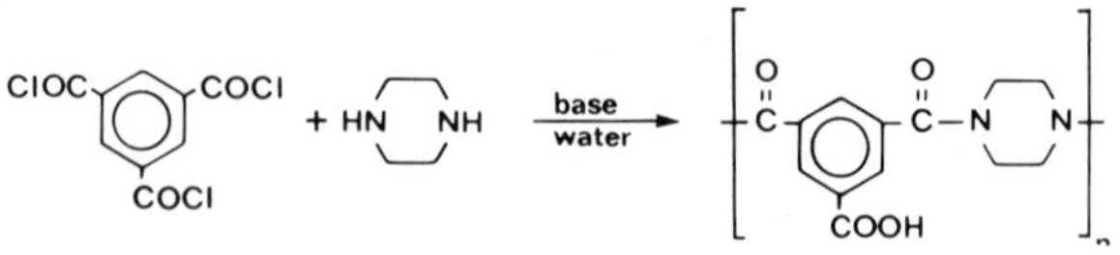

of increasing isophthalamide content. This is illustrated by the
data in Table 2. Maximum water permeability characteristics were
found at an approximate copolymer ratio of 67 percent isophthalic
and 33 percent trimesic groups.

The differences in the magnesium sulfate versus sodium
chloride rejection appear to be due to the charged nature of
the membrane barrier layer, since it is rich in carboxylate groups.
Table 3 illustrated this phenomenon, wherein a single test speci-
ment (made with the piperazine trimesamide homopolymer) was
sequentially exposed to feed solutions of sodium chloride, magnesium chloride, sodium sulfate, and magnesium sulfate. The chloride salts were both poorly retained while retention of the
sulfate salts was excellent. Thus, salt retention in the carboxy-
late-rich NS-300 membrane was controlled by the anion size and
charge. This membrane could not distinguish between the univalent
sodium ion and the divalent magnesium ion, which is quite the
opposite of the behavior observed for asymmetric cellulose acetate
membranes. Salt passage through the NS-300 membrane may be
described as anion-controlled.

The performance of this membrane system towards various
feedwaters in the laboratory trials is shown in Table 4, again
with a single set of test specimens exposed to the different
feedwaters. Initial salt rejections of the NS-300 membrane
specimens were poorer than average in this study, but the comparative results are nevertheless informative. The 90:10 isophthalic:
trimesic copolyamide membrane showed sufficient flux and salt
rejection to be useful in the reverse osmosis softening of a
"hard" well water. In this case, the well water contained about
500 ppm of calcium and magnesium bicarbonates. As might be
anticipated, the 67:33 copolyamide composite could not retain the
monovalent bicarbonate ion, such that hardness rejection was only
55 to 65 percent. Magnesium sulfate, sodium chloride, and
synthetic seawater rejections, while below average in this set of
membranes, followed the predicted pattern. It should be noted
that seawater rejections were always higher than dilute sodium
chloride solution rejections. The hydrophilic barrier layer
apparently tightens up in contact with concentrated salt solutions,
and barrier layer compaction at high pressures may be a contribu-
tive factor.

Tests were also run with simulated brackish agricultural
drainage water, as illustrated in Table 4. A feedwater composition
containing sodium, calcium, chloride, sulfate, and bicarbonate
ions was prepared in such a way as to duplicate the water in the
Mohawk-Wellton drainage canal at Yuma, Arizona. Salt rejections
were relatively poor toward this synthetic feedwater, but when
this water was line-softened and acidified to pH 5.5 with sulfuric
acid, salt rejection of the 90:10 copolyamide improved markedly.
However, the membrane's water flux declined by nearly 50 percent.
Salt rejection and flux were found in this and other examples to
be markedly dependent on pH. As the pH approached the pKa of

Table 2. Effect of the Isophthaloyl:Trimesoyl
          Chloride Ratio on the Performance of
          NS-300 Membranes in Reverse Osmosis Tests

| Acid Chloride Ratio[a] | | Reverse Osmosis Test Results | | | |
| | | 0.5% MgSO$_4$ 200 psig | | 3.5% Synthetic Seawater 1500 psig | |
Trimesoyl	Isophthaloyl	Flux (gfd)	Salt Rej. (percent)	Flux (gfd)	Salt Rej. (percent)
100	0	26	99.3	80	68
75	25	31	99.3	96	64
33	67	77	99.9	94	65
25	75	58	99.6	73	78
10	90	18	99.9	33	96
0	100	4	99.0	20	98

[a] Aqueous phase contained 1% piperazine, 1% Na$_3$PO$_4$, 0.5% dodecyl sodium
sulfate; hexane phase contained 1% (w/v) of acyl chlorides.

Table 3. Effect of Cation and Anion Valence on Salt
          Rejection Properties of NS-300 Membranes

Solute	Flux (gfd)[a]	Salt Rejection (percent)[a]
NaCl	42	50
MgCl$_2$	32	46
Na$_2$SO$_4$	41	97.8
MgSO$_4$	32	97.9

[a] Reverse osmosis test conditions: 0.5% salt
concentration, 200 psi, 25°C, poly(piperazine
trimesamide) membrane.

Table 4. Performance of NS-300 Membranes on Various
Feedwaters at Different Pressures

| Feedwater | Pressure (Psig) | Reverse Osmosis Test Results | | | |
| | | 90:10 IPC:TMC | | 67:33 IPC:TMC | |
		Flux (gfd)	Salt Rejection (percent)	Flux (gfd)	Salt Rejection (percent)
hard well water[a]	90	9.5	82	28.6	55
hard well water	200	18	91	58	65
0.5% $MgSO_4$	200	17	95	53	90
0.5% NaCl	200	15	78	56	56
3.5% synthetic seawater	1000	25	94.5	82	63
synthetic agricultural drainage water[b]	250	13	66	30	76
synthetic river water	600	44	85.5	47	76
synthetic lime-softened agricultured drainage water[c]	600	23	95.5	--	--

(a) ca. 500 ppm calcium and magnesium bicarbonates.
(b) 3390 ppm TDS
(c) 2880 ppm TDS

the membrane's carboxylate groups, the barrier layer tightened.
This same effect was since demonstrated in spiral-wound NS-300
membrane elements placed on test toward brackish water at
Roswell Test Facility operated by the Office of Water Research
and Technology, U.S. Department of the Interior.

Efforts to fabricate the NS-300 thin-film-composite membrane
by continuous machine casting at FilmTec Corporation have been
only partially successful. A severe problem of membrane variability was experienced, which was due in part ostensibly to minor
variations in machine-made polysulfone support films. This was
studied, and it was postulated that, since there was no intermediate porosity zone as the crosslinked polyethylenimine layer in the
NS-100 membrane, the poly(piperazineamide) membranes would be
more sensitive to the defects in the underlying polysulfone
support (22).

An approach to overcome this problem would be to form piper-
azine-terminated oligomers to replace piperazine in the interfacial reaction. These oligomers could possibly generate a lightly
crosslinked intermediate zone between the surface barrier layer
and the microporous polysulfone substrate. Oligomers were synthesized by reaction of acyl halides with an excess of piperazine in
1,2-dichloroethane. The amine-terminated polyamide oligomers had
poor solubility in this solvent system, and precipitated out
almost instantly upon formation. This served to limit the degree
of polymerization of the oligomers to less than ten monomer units.
Even so, portions of the products were insoluble in water and were
removed by filtration during the preparation of the aqueous oligomeric amine solutions.

Table 5 lists the best performance data obtained for piperazine oligomer membranes interfacially reacted with isophthaloyl
chloride. The objective of these tests was to achieve single-pass
seawater desalination membranes. As such, the presence of free
carboxylate groups was avoided; use was made of the trimesoyl
chloride or alternate triacyl halides in the oligomer formation
step. A few examples of seawater desalination membranes were
obtained. Best results were seen for piperazine-cyanurate pre-
polymers interfacially crosslinked by isophthaloyl chloride, but
fluxes were low in view of the operating test pressure of 1500
psi. Also, individual membrane results with piperazine oligomers
were equally as erratic as was experienced for piperazine directly.
The only notable advantage of the piperazine oligomer approach was
the ability to incorporate cyanurate rings into the membrane
structure. Cyanuric chloride was too prone to hydrolysis to
provide good interfacial membranes with piperazine, otherwise.

In summary, the NS-300 membrane system actually comprises a
family of membranes, with reverse osmosis properties determined
by the isophthalic:trimesic ratio. Exceptionally high fluxes are
possible at high retentivity levels for dissolved salts containing
polyvalent anions. This membrane type may find applications in
the desalination of brackish sulfate ground waters or industrial

Table 5. Membranes Formed Using Piperazine
Oligomers and Isophthaloyl Chloride

Composition of Oligomer	Acid Acceptor	Reverse Osmosis Test Data	
		Flux (gfd)	Salt Rejection (%)
trimesoyl chloride/ piperazine	NaOH	12.5	99.0
trimesoyl chloride/piperazine	triethylamine	58	93.8
cyanuric chloride/piperazine	NaOH	13.9	99.2
cyanuric chloride/piperazine	triethylamine	23.9	98.0
phosphorus oxychloride/ piperazine	N,N'-dimethyl-piperazine	45	93.9
1:1 trimesoyl:isophthaloyl chloride/piperazine	triethylamine	33.9	92.4
cyanuric chloride/6:1 piperazine:morpholine	NaOH	8.9	99.0

* Twenty to 24 hour tests, 1500 psi, 25°C, 2.5% synthetic seawater

process waters, and may have utility in food applications such as
sucrose and lactose concentration.

FT-30 Membrane. FT-30 is a new thin-film-composite membrane
discovered and developed by FilmTec. Initial data on FT-30
membranes were presented elsewhere (23). It was recently introduced in the form of spiral-wound elements 12 inches long and
2 to 4 inches in diameter (24). The barrier layer of FT-30 is of
proprietary composition and cannot be revealed at this time pending
resolution of patentability matters. The membrane shares some of
the properties of the previously described "NS" series of membranes, exhibiting high flux, excellent salt rejection, and nonbiodegradability. However, the response of the FT-30 membrane
differs significantly from other noncellulosic thin-film-composite
membranes in regard to various feedwater conditions such as pH,
temperature, and the effect of chlorine.

Table 6 lists several of the salient properties of this new
composite membrane. When salt rejection was evaluated at different
pressures in simulated seawater trials, potable water (containing
less than 500 ppm dissolved salts) was generated at as low as 600
psi, with very good flux (12 gfd) at that pressure. In spiral-
wound membrane element trials on actual 33,000 ppm seawater,
potable water was obtained even at 500 psi, albeit at low flux.
These results surpass by far the capabilities of any of the "NS"
series of membranes.

The FT-30 membrane was found to be resistant to swelling or
salt rejection losses at high feedwater temperatures. In
simulated seawater tests, the membrane had stabilized at about
99 percent salt rejection at temperatures of 40°C and higher.
The membrane has been successfully evaluated for sugar concentration at 95°C.

In trials at different feedwater concentrations, the FT-30
membrane showed single-pass seawater desalting capabilities at
up to 6.0 percent synthetic seawater. Basically, any combination
of pressure and brine concentration at room temperature that gave
a membrane flux of 15 gfd also resulted in a 99 percent level of
salt rejection.

Concerning the effect of pH, over a range of 5 to 11 the
FT-30 membrane exhibited 99 percent or greater salt rejection
towards synthetic seawater at 1000 psi. Below pH 5, salt rejections as measured by conductimetric techniques gave erratic
values. It is now believed that this reflected acidity transport
through the membrane rather than salt passage. At pH 12, salt
rejections fell below 98 percent due probably to membrane swelling.
Some membrane lots showed this lower salt rejection at pH 12;
others did not. The FT-30 membrane will withstand exposure to a
pH range of 1 to 12 for cleaning purposes. Both acidic and alkaline membrane cleaning reagents can be employed, including, for
example, 0.1 percent phosphoric acid or 0.5 percent trisodium
phosphate combined with an anionic surfactant. Nonionic surfac-

Table 6.   Flux and Salt Rejection of FT-30
Membranes as a Function of Temperature,
Pressure, and Brine Concentration.

Feedwater	Pressure (psi)	Temperature (°C)	Flux (gfd)	Salt Rej. (percent)
3.5% SSW[a]	400	25	4.3	95.5
	600		12	98.8
	800		20	99.3
	1000		30	99.4
3.5% SSW	1000	20	23	99.5
		30	35	99.2
		40	55	99.0
		50	65	98.9
		60	72	99.0
1.0% SSW	1000	25	54	99.5
2.0			43	99.4
4.0			25	99.4
6.0			16	99.0
8.0			7.5	97.8

[a]SSW = synthetic seawater.

tants have been found to interact negatively with the FT-30
membrane, reducing flux.

This thin-film-composite membrane has been found to have
appreciable resistance to degradation by chlorine in the feedwater. Figure 2 illustrates the effect of chlorine in tap water
at different pH values. Chlorine (100 ppm) was added to the
tap water in the form of sodium hypochlorite (two equivalents of
hypochlorite ion per stated equivalent of chlorine). Membrane
exposure to chlorine was by the so-called "static" method, in
which membrane specimens were immersed in the aqueous media
inside closed, dark glass jars for known periods. Specimens were
then removed and tested in a reverse osmosis loop under seawater
test conditions. At alkaline pH values, the FT-30 membrane showed
effects of chlorine attack within four to five days. In acidic
solutions (pH 1 and 5), chlorine attack was far slower. Only a
one to two percent decline in salt rejection was noted, for
example, after 20 days exposure to 100 ppm chlorine in water
at pH 5. The FT-30 tests at pH 1 were necessarily terminated
after the fourth day of exposure because the microporous polysulfone substrate had itself become totally embrittled by chlorine
attack.

In a related case, FT-30 membrane elements were placed on
chlorinated seawater feed at OWRT's Wrightsville Beach Test
Facility. Flux and salt rejection were stable for 2000 hours at
0.5 to 1.0 ppm chlorine exposure. Chlorine attack did become
noticeable after 2000 hours, and salt rejection had dropped to 97
percent at 2500 hours while flux increased significantly. Long
term laboratory trials at different chlorine levels led to the
conclusion that the membrane will withstand 0.2 ppm chlorine
in sodium chloride solutions at pH 7 for more than a year of
continuous exposure.

In summary, the FT-30 membrane is a significant improvement
in the art of thin-film-composite membranes, offering major improvements in flux, pH resistance, and chlorine resistance. Salt
rejections consistent with single-pass production of potable
water from seawater can be obtained and held under a wide variety
of operating conditions (ph, temperature, pressure, and brine
concentration). This membrane comes close to being the ideal
membrane for seawater desalination in terms of productivity,
chemical stability, and nonbiodegradability.

Scanning Electron Microscopy Studies

Various noncellulosic thin-film-composite membranes were
examined by scanning electron microscopy (SEM). Figure 3 illustrates the type of surface structure and cross-sections that exist
in these membranes. Figure 3a shows the surface microporosity of
polysulfone support films. Micropores in the film were measured
by both SEM and TEM; typically pore radii averaged 330 Å. Figure
3b is a photomicrograph of a cross-section of a NS-100 membrane.

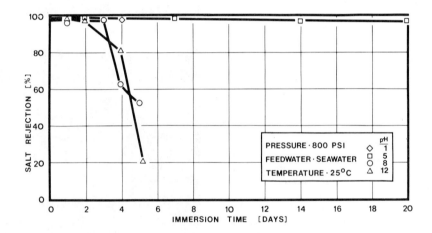

Figure 2.   Exposure of FT-30 membranes to 100 ppm chlorine in water at different pH levels.   Effect on salt rejection in simulated seawater reverse osmosis tests: (◇) pH 1; (□) pH 5; (○) pH 8; (△) pH 12.

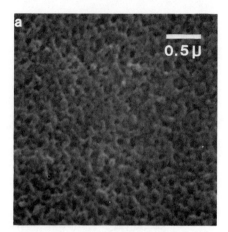

Figure 3a. SEM photomicrographs of composite membranes: surface structure of microporous polysulfone support material.

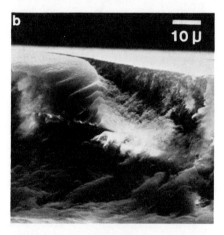

Figure 3b. SEM photomicrograph of composite membranes: cross-section of a NS-100 composite membrane showing the porous polysulfone substructure.

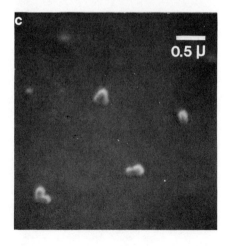

Figure 3c. SEM photomicrograph of composite membranes: surface view of the NS-100 membrane.

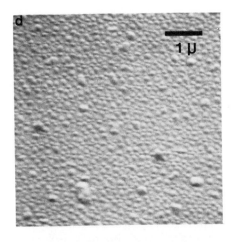

Figure 3d. SEM photomicrograph of composite membranes: surface view of the NS-200 membrane.

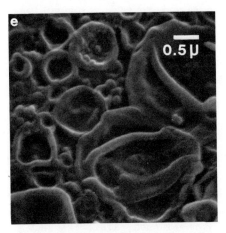

Figure 3e. SEM photomicrograph of composite membranes: surface view of the poly(piperazine trimesamide) version of the NS-300 membrane.

Figure 3f. SEM photomicrograph of composite membranes: surface view of the FT-30 membrane.

A smooth top surface corresponding to the dense barrier layer is
evident. The porous, spongy polysulfone matrix is evident below
this surface layer. Although not evident in this photomicrograph,
the thickness of the barrier layer and crosslinked polyethylenimine
intermediate layer, taken together, is approximately 2000 Å.
Figure 3c is a high magnification view of an NS-100 membrane surface, and shows a featureless plain punctuated by occasional
artifacts (loose polysulfone microbeads).

Figure 3d illustrates the surface of a NS-200 membrane. The
surface appears to contain nodules of the sulfonated polyfurane
resin, which apparently were present in the aqueous coating
before heat-curing, or formed during early stages of the heat-
curing operation. Figure 3e contains a photomicrograph of the
surface of a poly(piperazine trimesamide) barrier layer interfacially formed on a polysulfone support. Swelling of the
membrane apparently occurred concurrent with its formation to
produce the type of structure seen in Figure 3e. Reasons for
this surface structure are described elsewhere (22). Figure 3f
shows the surface of an FT-30 membrane. A fairly rough topography
is present.

It can be seen from these SEM photomicrographs that the
surface of thin-film-composite membranes can vary substantially
from one type to another. In fact, it is plausible that some of
these membranes can be identified by their characteristic surface
topography through examination by SEM.

Literature Cited

1. Reid, C.E.; Breton, E.J.; J. Appl. Polymer Sci., 1959, 1, 133.
2. Loeb, S.; Sourirajan, S.; Advan. Chem. Ser., 1962, 38, 117.
3. Francis, P.S.; "Fabrication and Evaluation of New Ultrathin
    Reverse Osmosis Membranes," National Technical Information
    Service, Springfield, VA, Report No. PB-177083, 1966.
4. Rozelle, L.T.; Cadotte, J.E.; Corneliussen, R.D.; Erickson,
    E.E.; "Development of New Reverse Osmosis Membranes for
    Desalination," ibid., Report No. PB-206329, 1967.
5. Rozelle, L.T.; Kopp, C.V.,Jr.; Cadotte, J.E.; Kobian, K.E.;
    "Nonpolysaccharide Membranes for Reverse Osmosis: NS-100
    Membranes," in "Reverse Osmosis and Synthetic Membranes,"
    Sourirajan, S., Ed., National Research Council Canada, Ottawa,
    1977, p.249.
6. Riley, R.L.; Lonsdale, H.K.; Lyons, C.R.; Merten, U.;
    J. Appl. Polymer Sci., 1967, 11, 2143.
7. Carnell, P.H.; Cassidy, H.G.; J. Polymer Sci., 1961, 55, 233.
8. Carnell, P.H.; J. Appl. Polymer Sci., 1965, 9, 1963.
9. Lonsdale, H.K.; Riley, R.L.; Lyons, C.R.; Carosella, D.P.,
    Jr.; "Transport in Composite Reverse Osmosis Membranes,"
    in "Membrane Processes in Industry and Biomedicine," Bier,
    M., Ed, Plenum Press, 1971, p.101.

10. Cadotte, J.E.; Kopp, C.V., Jr.; Cobian, K.E.; Rozelle, L.T.;
    "In Situ-Formed Condensation Polymers for Reverse Osmosis
    Membranes: Second Phase," National Technical Information
    Service, Springfield, VA, Report No. PB-234198, 1974, p.6.
11. Cadotte, J.E.; Cobian, K.E.; Forester, R.H.; Petersen, R.J.;
    "Continued Evaluation of In Situ-Formed Condensation Polymers
    for Reverse Osmosis Membranes," ibid., Report No. PB-253193,
    1976, p.32.
12. Yasuda, H.; "Composite Reverse Osmosis Membranes Prepared
    by Plasma Polymerization," in "Reverse Osmosis and Synthetic
    Membranes," Sourirajan, S., Ed., National Research Council,
    Canada, Ottawa, 1977, p.263.
13. Bell, A.T.; Wydeven, T.; Johnson, C.C.; J. Appl. Polymer
    Sci., 1975, 19, 1911.
14. Hollahan, J.R.; Wydeven, T.; J. Appl. Polymer Sci., 1977, 21,
    923.
15. Riley, R.L.; Fox, R.L.; Lyons, C.R.; Milstead, C.E.; Seroy,
    M.W.; Tagami, M.; Desalination, 1976, 19, 113.
16. Cadotte, J.E.; U.S. 4,039,440 (1977).
17. Sasaki, H.; Hayashi, Y.; Hara, S.; Kawaguchi, T.; Minematsu,
    H.; Brit. UK Pat. Appl. 2,027,614 (1980); Chem. Abstr., 1980,
    92, 77403r.
18. Kawaguchi, T.; Hayashi, Y.; Taketani, Y.; Mori, Y.; Ono, T.;
    Fr. Demande 78-15546 (1978); Chem. Abstr., 1980, 92, 59897a.
19. Kurihara, M.; Kanamaru, N.; Harumiya, N.; Yoshimura, K.;
    Hagiwara, S.; Desalination, 1980, 32, 13.
20. Credali, L.; Chiolle, A.; Parinni, P.; Desalination, 1974,
    14, 137.
21. Cadotte, J.E.; Steuck, M.J.; Petersen, R.J.; "Research on
    In Situ-Formed Condensation Polymer for Reverse Osmosis
    Membranes," National Technical Information Service, Spring-
    field, VA, Report No. PB-288387, 1978, p.10.
22. Cadotte, J.E.; King, R.S.; Majerle, R.J.; Petersen, R.J.;
    "Interfacial Synthesis in the Preparation of Reverse Osmosis
    Membranes," paper presented at 179th Ann. Amer. Chem. Soc.
    Meeting, Houston, TX, March 23-28, 1980; Marcel Dekker, in
    press.
23. Cadotte, J.E.; Petersen, R.J.; Larson, R.E.; Erickson, E.E.;
    Desalination, 1980, 32, 25.
24. Petersen, R.J.; Larson R.E.; Majerle, R.J.; "Development of
    the FT-30 Thin-Film Composite Membrane for Desalting Appli-
    cations," Technical Proceedings, 8th Ann. Conf. National
    Water Supply Improvement Assn., San Francisco, CA, July
    6-10, 1980.

Acknowledgements

The authors are indebted to the Office of Water Research and
Technology and the former Office of Saline Water, U.S. Department
of the Interior, for their support of this work over the past

several years. Portions of the research on NS-300 and FT-30 were supported by OWRT under Contracts 14-34-0001-6512, 14-34-0001-8512, and 14-34-0001-8547.

RECEIVED December 4, 1980.

Poly(aryl ether) Membranes for Reverse Osmosis

D. R. LLOYD[1], L. E. GERLOWSKI[2], and C. D. SUNDERLAND

Department of Chemical Engineering, Virginia Polytechnic Institute
and State University, Blacksburg, VA 24061

J. P. WIGHTMAN, J. E. McGRATH, M. IGBAL[3], and Y. KANG

Department of Chemistry, Virginia Polytechnic Institute and State University,
Blacksburg, VA 24061

The development of the asymmetric cellulose acetate membrane
by Loeb and Sourirajan was a significant event in the history of
membrane science (1). These membranes subsequently found use in
a large number of applications including desalination by reverse
osmosis, the purpose for which they were originally developed.
However, it soon became evident that cellulose acetate lacked
universal applicability as a membrane material. Among the
shortcomings of cellulose acetate membranes are the susceptability
to creep-induced compaction (2), biological attack (3), acid
hydrolysis (4), alkaline degradability (5), and thermal instability
(6). For these reasons, attention has turned to the investigation
of new polymeric membrane materials capable of overcoming these
limitations. While the literature abounds with accounts of the
development of new membrane materials, the reader is directed to
four particularly good references (7-10). The development of new
membrane materials requires not only an understanding of membrane
transport phenomena, but also a knowledge of polymer chemistry,
morphology, mechanical and thermal properties, and polymer
interaction in the solute-solvent-membrane system. The research
reported in this article represents the initial stages of a long-
term program designed to develop a systematic and thorough approach
to the development and understanding of new materials for
asymmetric membranes. To serve as a model material for this study,
the poly(aryl ether) family of polymers was selected.

Poly(Aryl Ethers)

A prominent class of poly(aryl ethers) is the sulfone-containing
poly(aryl ethers); that is, poly(arylene ether sulfones), or
polysulfones (PSF), and their sulfonated derivatives. The structure
of a typical sulfonated polysulfone (SPSF) repeat unit is

[1] Current address: Department of Chemical Engineering, University of Texas, Austin,
TX 78712.
[2] Current address: Department of Chemical Engineering, Carnegie–Mellon University,
Pittsburgh, PA 15213.
[3] Current address: 3M Company, St. Paul, Minnesota, 55101.

illustrated (11)

$$\left[0-\underset{}{\bigcirc}-\underset{CH_3}{\overset{CH_3}{\underset{|}{\overset{|}{C}}}}-\underset{}{\bigcirc}-0-\underset{}{\bigcirc}-SO_2-\underset{}{\bigcirc}\right]_n$$

where R may be a free acid ($-SO_3H$), a salt (e.g., $-SO_3^-M^+$), or an
ester ($-SO_3X$). The properties of PSF, in particular Bisphenol A
—polysulfone (Bis A-PSF), which is the antecedent of the polymer
illustrated above, have been studied (12). Bis A-PSF has been
used as an asymmetric ultrafiltration/microfiltration membrane and
as a rigid, porous support material in composite membranes (13,14).
The reasons for the usefulness of this polymer as a membrane
material are its superior strength, which gives resistance to
creep-induced compaction (see discussion below), resistance to
biological and chemical degradation, as well as wet-dry
reversibility and therefore ease of handling (13).
       In order to fully appreciate the potential presented by
these materials, it is necessary to look at the structure of the
polymer in relation to what is presently perceived as desirable
qualities for polymers which are to be employed as asymmetric
reverse osmosis membranes. The elevated hydrostatic pressures
which prevail during reverse osmosis impose the requirement of
polymer rigidity or resistance to creep deformation (compaction).
This property is found in macromolecules with a large degree of
stiffness (15), and is reflected by a high glass transition
temperature (Tg). Conversely, excessive chain stiffness can mean
a loss of tractability. Therefore, a balance must be struck
between these properties. Poly(arylene ether sulfones) possess
such a balance, as a result of containing flexible -O-, -S-, and
-C- linkages as well as chain stiffening structure due to aromatic
rings. The beneficial effects of chain inflexibility/stiffness
may not be entirely attributable to the improved compaction
resistance. Blais (16) points out that all polymers showing good
permselectivity are either inherently stiff macromolecules or
initially flexible or water plasticized macromolecules
which can be crosslinked to form relatively rigid three
dimensional structures. Unfortunately, the poly(aryl ethers) are
hydrophobic and thereby limited in their usefulness as reverse
osmosis membranes for aqueous systems.

Sulfonation of Poly(Aryl Ethers)

       In light of the discussion above, it is desirable to alter
the chemical nature of these polymers to induce a measure of
hydrophilicity while maintaining the excellent physical character.
Sulfonation has been known to dramatically alter a number of
characteristics of polymeric materials (for example, dyeability (17),
tensile strength (18), and, of particular interest to the present
studies, hydrophilicity (19)). In fact, sulfonation has been used
to improve the reverse osmosis performance of poly(phenylene oxide)

membranes (20) as well as membranes of Bis A-PSF (21-25). The property changes resulting from sulfonation of Bis A-PSF have been investigated by Noshay and Robeson (26). Some of their results are presented in Table I along with data relating to cellulose acetate (CA) for comparison. The mechanical superiority of the polysulfone and its sulfonated derivative are obvious.

Bisphenol A - Polysulfone Membranes

The only poly(arly ether) membrane material to have been investigated to any extent and reported in the literature is the Bis A-PSF and its sulfonated derivative (designated here as SPSF). Noshay and Robeson (26) included in their investigations limited flux and salt separation studies using dense membranes of Bis A-PSF which was sulfonated and neutralized with a sodium counter-ion (SPSF-Na). Even though their studies were restricted to dense membranes of the free acid and sodium salt sulfonated forms of the commercially available PSF (Union Carbide P-1700), their results were encouraging. The results indicated that, in order to optimize the strength/stability and flux/separation performance, the degree of sulfonation (D.S.) must be optimized at some moderate value (where D.S. represents the statistical fraction of repeat units which are sulfonated).

The same base material has been used by Rhone-Poulenc Industries to develop ion-exchange membranes for desalination (21-25). Their research has concentrated on polymers of moderate D.S. and low molecular weight (a restriction imposed by their technique of sulfonation which may cause polymer degradation). While their method of membrane preparation is not entirely clear, it is evident that the Rhone-Poulenc membranes possess the desired structural asymmetry. In this form the SPSF membranes have proven to be equal to, and in some ways superior to, CA membranes.

The Union Carbide P-1700 base material was also employed by Environgenics Systems Company to investigate SPSF membranes for desalination (28). Their results are comparable to those of Rhone-Poulenc and are equally encouraging.

Poly(Aryl Ether) Membranes

The above discussion indicates that only one poly(aryl ether) has been explored as a membrane material (the commercial, amorphous, homopolymer P-1700 produced by Union Carbide). The present program expands these studies to include other poly(aryl ethers).

Sulfonation has been shown to provide a convenient means of controlling the hydrophilic/hydrophobic character of a variety of polymers. Therefore, this study has employed sulfonation to accomplish this goal. The degree of sulfonation is known to effect the hydrophilic character of these polymers; therefore, the influence of D.S. on the membrane performance has been investigated.

TABLE I

Comparison of Mechanical Properties

	Tensile Modulus (kPa x 10^{-6})		Tensile Strength (kPa x 10^{-6})		Elongation (%)		Tg (°C)
	Ambient	Wet	Ambient	Wet	Ambient	Wet	Ambient
SPSF-Na*							
D.S. = 0.0	2.48	----	7.03	----	50	--	180
D.S. = 0.1	2.05	1.83	6.90	5.65	7	14	180
D.S. = 0.5	1.60	1.08	6.27	3.81	25	98	240
D.S. = 1.0	1.21	0.24	3.86	0.83	17	30	300
CA	0.48(a)	0.32 (a)	0.94(a)	0.49(a)	3.1(a)	18(a)	68.6(b)

*   SPSF-Na represents Bisphenol A-polysulfone which has been sulfonated and
        neutralized to the sodium salt form. D.S. represents "degree of sulfonation"
        (i.e., the statistical fraction of repeat units which have been sulfonated).
        CA represents cellulose acetate

Note: All data for SPSF-Na is taken from Reference 26. Film thickness = 0.254 mm

Note: Data for cellulose acetate (film thickness = 0.088 mm) is taken from (a)
        Reference 27; (b) Reference 8, p. 136.

It has been shown that the nature of the sulfonation group can influence polymer stability (26) as well as ion-exchange character (24). Therefore, the polymers are being investigated in the free acid form and in the salt form with a variety of counter-ions (e.g. Li^+, Na^+, K^+, Mg^{++}, Zn^{++}, etc.).

In light of the above discussion, it is of interest to investigate sulfonated Bis A-PSF more fully than has been previously reported. Bis A-PSF of different molecular weights and the entire range of D.S. (from 0.0 to 1.0) with a variety of counter-ions can be investigated. Through the use of castable, but partially crystalline poly(arylene sulfones) such as

$$\left[O\text{-}\bigcirc\text{-}O\text{-}\bigcirc\text{-}SO_2\text{-}\bigcirc\right]_n \quad \text{and} \quad \left[O\text{-}\bigcirc\text{-}\bigcirc\text{-}O\text{-}\bigcirc\text{-}SO_2\text{-}\bigcirc\right]_n$$

and their sulfonated derivatives, it is possible to determine the influence of degree of order upon membrane performance. Non-sulfone containing poly(aryl ethers) and their sulfonated derivatives can also be investigated. For example,

$$\left[\bigcirc\text{-}\overset{CH_3}{\underset{CH_3}{C}}\text{-}\bigcirc\text{-}O\text{-}\bigcirc\text{-}X\text{-}\bigcirc\text{-}O\right]_n$$
$$ A B n$$

where $X = O, \bigcirc, \overset{O}{\underset{\|}{C}}$, or a chemical bond. The possibility of sulfonation in two positions per repeat unit (that is, in locations A and B) presents an interesting feature in terms of membrane performance. Random copolymers also present an interesting alternative. For example, Bisphenol A and hydroquinone can be copolymerized with 4,4'-dichlorodiphenyl sulfone.

$$\left[O\text{-}\bigcirc\text{-}O\text{-}\bigcirc\text{-}SO_2\text{-}\bigcirc\text{-}O\text{-}\bigcirc\text{-}\overset{CH_3}{\underset{CH_3}{C}}\text{-}\bigcirc\text{-}O\text{-}\bigcirc\text{-}SO_2\text{-}\bigcirc\right]_n$$

As one increases the proportion of hydroquinone, the degree of crystalline order in the resulting copoly(aryl ether) will increase. Block copolymers of Bis A-PSF and Bis S-PSF can be synthesized. The Bis A-PSF can be sulfonated on the Bis A residue, but the Bis S-PSF will not sulfonate due to the deactivating effect of $-SO_2-$ on electrophilic aromatic substitution. Therefore, such a block copolymer would allow the study of sequence length effects on membrane performance.

$$\left[O\text{-}\bigcirc\text{-}\overset{CH_3}{\underset{CH_3}{C}}\text{-}\bigcirc\text{-}O\text{-}\bigcirc\text{-}SO_2\text{-}\bigcirc\right]_n \qquad \text{Bis A-PSF}$$

$$\left[O\text{-}\bigcirc\text{-}SO_2\text{-}\bigcirc\text{-}O\text{-}\bigcirc\text{-}SO_2\text{-}\bigcirc\right]_n \qquad \text{Bis S-PSF}$$

The preceding discussion demonstrates the vast array of
possibilities presented by the poly(aryl ether) family of
polymers. A number of these polymers are presently under
investigation in our laboratory while others are planned for
future studies. The work reported here represents our initial
studies dealing with these polymers. Bis A-PSF was selected
for these initial studies in order to permit performance
comparisons with a proven, successful reverse osmosis membrane
material. A great deal has been written about the mechanism of
formation of the asymmetric structure of cellulose acetate membranes
(29). However, little is known about the formation of other
asymmetric membranes. A systematic investigation of the preparation
of sulfonated Bis A-PSF asymmetric membranes is providing some
additional insight into the mechanism involved in forming
asymmetric membranes.

Membrane Property Analysis

The interfacial properties of membranes are thought to
influence the mechanism and therefore the extent of separation in
reverse osmosis (30). To date, this aspect of membrane science has
received little detailed analysis. A knowledge of such surface
properties is considered by the present authors to be of great
importance in membrane development and characterization. One
objective of this study is to demonstrate the usefulness of various
techniques of surface analysis in the characterization and therefore
development of new membrane materials. Contact angle and water
sorption measurements provide insight into the hydrophilic/hydrophobic
character of the polymer. It is important to recognize that the
surface composition of any given polymer film can be markedly
different from the bulk composition (31). Electron spectroscopy
for chemical analysis (ESCA) or X-ray photoelectron spectroscopy
(XPS) provides a detailed analysis of surface elemental composition
(32,33) allowing comparison to the bulk polymer composition.
Membrane morphology is studied with scanning electron microscopy
(SEM) thereby providing an insight into the relationship between
asymmetric membrane preparation, structure, and performance (29,34).
The extent of ion exchange of the salt form of the SPSF membranes
is studied with atomic absorption spectroscopy (AAS), neutron
activation analysis (NAA), and ESCA. AAS is used for solution
analysis, NAA for the bulk membrane analysis, and ESCA for the
surface analysis.

Experimental

Polymer Preparation and Characterization. Bisphenol A-
polysulfones of different molecular weight and sulfonated to
various degrees have been prepared. In addition, the commercial
Bis A-PSF has been sulfonated to various D.S. values and
neutralized with sodium or potassium counter-ions. The

method of polymer preparation is similar to that reported
elsewhere (26,35,36). The D.S. achieved was established primarily
by nuclear magnetic resonance (NMR) and infrared (IR) spectroscopy.
The glass transition temperatures (Tg) were determined by
differential scanning calorimetry carried out on powder samples in
a Perkin-Elmer DSC-2 thermal analyzer. The scanning speed was
typically 40°C/min over a range from 30°C to 400°C. Indium was
used as a calibration standard. Reduced viscosities for 0.2%
solutions of SPSF in DMSO and PSF in DMF were measured at 25°C
using a Ubbelohde viscometer. Details of these analyses are either
in the literature (37) or will be published shortly by the present
authors along with the details of the polymer preparation.

Dense Membrane Preparation. Dense membranes were prepared
from 10-15% solutions of polysulfone or sulfonated polysulfone in
DMSO or DMF. Polymer solutions were cast using a doctor's knife
on a glass plate which had been annealed at 600°C overnight before
each casting. The cast membranes were dried initially in a
circulating dry air oven at room temperature for 12 hours and then
for 5 hours at 80°C. The membranes were peeled from the glass
plate by moistening the edge with water and placed in a vacuum
oven at 100°C for 12 hours to further remove the solvent. Membranes
were removed from the oven and stored over Drierite.

Dense Membrane Characterization. Small pieces of membranes
(about 2 cm^2) were kept in desiccators at relative humidities of 0,
18.8, 47.2, 80.5 and 100.0%. The 0% relative humidity was
achieved with Drierite and the various relative humidities were
obtained by varying the composition of aqueous H_2SO_4 solutions.
The relative humidity was measured with a YSI 91 HC Dew Point
Hygrometer. Water sorption was measured gravimetrically. The
weight of the membranes under 0% relative humidity was taken as
the weight of the membrane alone with no sorbed water. Hence, the
difference (increase) in weight was considered as the weight of water
sorbed by the membrane. Contact angles of water on the membranes were
measured using a goniometer in an apparatus similar to that described
by Good (38). Both advancing and receding angles can be determined
for a drop of at least 8 mm diameter. Good et al. recently reported
on the dependence of the contact angle on the drop size (39),
particularly with smaller droplets.
   A duPont 650 ESCA electron spectrometer was employed with a
magnesium anode (1254 eV) as the X-ray source. Binding energies
were calibrated by taking the background carbon 1s photopeak as
284.6 eV. Quantitative data were obtained by correcting the peak
areas under the photo electron peak using the photo cross-section
(40). Sulfur 2s and oxygen 1s photo electron peaks were curve
fitted to obtain the binding energies of different types of sulfur
and oxygen found in sulfonated polysulfone.
   Photomicrographs were obtained using an AMR-900 scanning
electron microscope. The microscope operates at 20KV and has an

International Model 707 energy dispersive analysis of X-rays (EDAX) accessory.

Asymmetric Membrane Preparation. The preparation of the asymmetric membranes was done in a fashion similar to the "classical" technique referred to below, although the casting solutions often deviated from the "classical" formulations. In all cases, a solution of polymer plus at least two other components was cast on a glass plate with a doctor's knife set at a thickness of 15 mils (0.381 mm). After a brief evaporation period the membrane was gelled in a non-solvent bath. Finally, the membrane was thoroughly washed in distilled, deionized water.

Asymmetric Membrane Characterization. For separation and flux studies, circular sections were cut from the film and placed in the reverse osmosis cells, with a test area of $1.443 \times 10^{-3} m^2$ for each membrane (30). The membranes were prepressurized at 1200 psi (8160 kPa) until the pure water flux varied less than three percent per hour. After allowing the membrane to relax for a period of time, desalination studies were conducted with a 3.5 wt-% NaCl aqueous solution at a circulation rate of 400 ml/min., 1000 psi (6800 kPa) cell pressure, and 25°C. Feed, permeate, and retentate samples were analyzed either by differential refractive index (LDC Refracto Monitor) or conductivity (YSI 31 Conductivity Meter) to determine salt rejection. In addition, the characterization of the asymmetric membranes involved ESCA, SEM, and ion-exchange studies. For ESCA studies, the membranes were air dried. In order to preserve the pore structure upon dehydration, it was necessary to pretreat the asymmetric membranes before the SEM study (41). The pretreatment process involved placing the membrane for 24 hours in a solution containing water, glycerol, and Triton X-100 of 69.5, 30 and 0.5 weight percent, respectively. After the treatment, the membrane was removed from the solution, air dried, and freeze cleaved under liquid nitrogen to obtain a fresh membrane cross section. For the ion-exchange study, a piece of SPSF-K(0.48) was placed in 10 cm^3 of 0.1% NaCl solution and a piece of SPSF-Na(0.42) in 10 cm^3 of 0.1% KCl solution for 24 hours. After being removed from the salt solutions, the membranes were rinsed thoroughly with distilled, deionized water. The salt solutions were analyzed with a Varian 175 series atomic absorption spectrometer (AAS). Na and K concentrations were determined using the 590.8 nm and 768.5 nm absorption bands, respectively. Before and after the ion-exchange studies, the membranes were dried and analyzed with ESCA and NAA.

Results and Discussion

Polymer Preparation and Characterization. The results of the measurements to determine D.S. are shown in Table II. The data illustrate that the D.S. determined by the three methods are in reasonable agreement. For convenience, in the remainder of this paper the D.S. as determined by NMR will be used for reference purposes. Also listed in Table II are the Tg values for the Na and K polymers. The increase in Tg with D.S. is attributed to increased ionic aggregation due to electrostatic interaction in the polymeric solid (42). The relationship between D.S. and reduced viscosity (η_{red}) is also shown in Table II. The increase in reduced viscosity with D.S. is attributed to selective solvation of the metal counter ion. The influence of ionic aggregation and selective ion solvation on membrane preparation and performance will be investigated in future studies.

TABLE II

Characterization of Polymers

SPSF	Target	NMR	IR(a)	IR(b)	Tg(°C)	η_{red}
-Na	0.20	0.16	0.10	0.11	210	0.46
	0.40	0.34	0.33	0.40	227	0.94
	0.50	0.42	----	----	218	1.12
	0.60	0.53	0.52	0.63	224	1.36
	0.80	0.68	0.68	0.83	---	1.78
	1.00	1.00	1.00	1.00	316	2.30
-K	0.20	0.12	0.07	0.10	201	0.43
	0.40	0.33	0.37	0.40	225	0.87
	0.60	0.48	0.45	0.55	235	1.32
	0.80	0.72	0.70	0.85	277	1.66
	1.00	0.87	0.87	0.87	315	2.02
PSF	----	----	----	----	186	0.31

(a) Calculated from ratio: (absorbance at 1028 cm^{-1} due to SO_3)/ (absorbance at 1010 cm^{-1} due to -0-)

(b) Calculated from ratio: (absorbance at 1028 cm^{-1} due to SO_3)/ (absorbance at 1308 cm^{-1} due to CH_3)

Dense Membrane Studies. The weight of water sorbed by SPSF-Na membranes at 100% relative humidity is plotted as a function of time in Figure 1. Water uptake increased with increasing D.S.. The same trend was observed for the K salt membranes. The results are summarized in Table III. The point to be noted here is that the absolute amount of water sorbed by the SPSF-Na membranes is greater (by a factor of two) than that of the SPSF-K membranes. It is clear that hydrophilicity increases with increasing D.S. and is dependent on the nature of the counter ion.

Contact angles of water on the top (interfaced with air during film preparation) and the bottom (interfaced with the glass plate) surfaces of both the SPSF-Na and SPSF-K membranes are listed in Table IV along with the value for cellulose acetate (CA). The reported values are the average of ten separate measurements made immediately after introduction of the water droplet onto the membrane. Contact angles on the top side of the SPSF-Na series

TABLE III

Water Sorbed by Dense Membranes
at 100% Relative Humidity and 25°C

g H$_2$O/g membrane

PSF		0.006
SPSF-Na	(0.34)	0.075
	(0.53)	0.114
	(0.68)	0.190
	(1.00)	0.192
SPSF- K	(0.12)	0.017
	(0.33)	0.029
	(0.48)	0.053
	(0.72)	0.106
	(0.87)	0.122

decreased with increasing D.S.. This trend was also detected with
the SPSF-K series although the extent of decrease was smaller when
compared to the SPSF-Na series. The contact angle measurements
are supportive of the water sorption studies in showing that the
SPSF-Na series have greater hydrophilic nature than the SPSF-K series.
Notice that a D.S. value between 0.34 and 0.53 is required for the
SPSF-Na polymer to have a water contact angle similar to that for
CA. By comparison, even at a D.S. of 0.87 the SPSF-K polymer does
not achieve a water contact angle comparable to CA. No apparent
trend was observed for the bottom side of both series of membranes
since the bottom side is sensitive to the condition and impurities
present on the glass plate.

TABLE IV

Contact Angles of Water on Dense Membranes

	Top	Bottom
PSF	75.1	73.5
SPSF-Na(0.16)	64.4	34.8
-Na(0.34)	66.4	46.0
-Na(0.53)	39.3	55.3
-Na(0.68)	32.2	41.1
-Na(1.00)	25.5	56.4
SPSF- K(0.12)	71.9	42.0
- K(0.33)	67.8	42.0
- K(0.48)	63.7	29.5
- K(0.72)	69.1	68.1
- K(0.87)	60.3	38.3
CA	53.2	52.9

It has been demonstrated by Sourirajan (7) that the ability of
solution components to establish a sorbed layer on the membrane
surface plays a significant role in reverse osmosis separations.
The ability of a liquid to "wet" the membrane material is an
indication of that liquids ability to establish and maintain such
an interfacial layer. Liquids of surface tension values less than
the critical surface tension (γ_c) of the membrane material are
capable of completely "wetting" the polymer. It may be possible
therefore, to select membrane materials capable of accomplishing
specific separations by their ability to be wet by one solution
component but not by the other. For this reason γ_c of membrane
materials is important. By employing the standard techniques
of Zisman (43), the critical surface tension for PSF and CA were
determined to be 43.0 and 36.5 dynes/cm, respectively. This data
indicates that PSF is more readily wet by a larger number of
liquids than is CA. Similar measurements for the various sulfonated
polysulfones are underway.

ESCA analysis was performed on all membranes. Na and K were
detected in the corresponding Na and K SPSF membranes as expected.
Table V lists the typical binding energies of the S 2s, Na 1s, K 2p3
and O 1s photo peaks. The S 2s composite peak was curve fitted
into two peaks as shown in Figure 2. The determined binding energies
of sulfur in sulfonate and sulfone groups were 232.3 and 231.9 eV,
respectively.   The observed values are consistent with the reported
literature values (44). Sulfonates have a higher binding energy
compared to sulfones even though the oxidation states of the two
are both formally 6. This is due to the fact that sulfonates have
three electro-negative groups (oxygen) compared to two for sulfones.
Thus, the sulfur in sulfonate is slightly more positive in nature
and therefore has a higher binding energy. Also, it should be
mentioned that the ratio of the area under the two peaks is 2:1,
sulfone to sulfonate. This data is consistent with the
stoichiometric ratio of the two in SPSF-Na(0.42).

TABLE V

ESCA Analysis of Sulfonated Polysulfone

Element	B.E. (eV)
O 1s C-O-C	533.6
$-SO_3X$	532.0
$-SO_2-$	531.8
S 2s $-SO_3X$	232.3
$-SO_2-$	231.9
Na 1s	1071.9
K 2p3	292.9

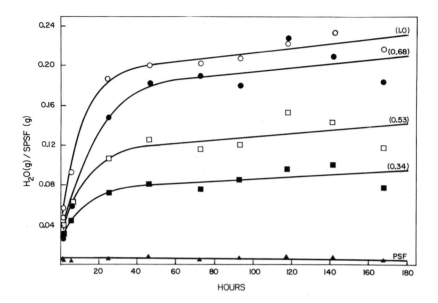

*Figure 1.   Water uptake by polysulfone and SPSF–Na membranes with respect to
time at 100% relative humidity*

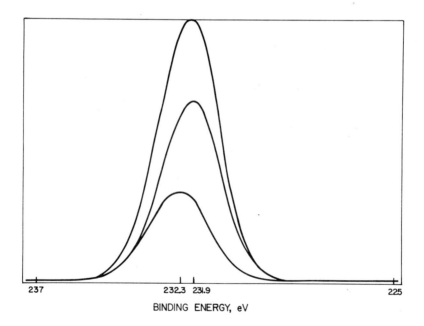

Figure 2.   Curve-fitted S 2s photoelectron peak for SPSF–Na (0.53)

The SEM photomicrographs of the dense membrane indicated extreme flatness and evenness. There was no observable differences between the top and bottom sides. EDAX showed an intense S peak but only a small Na peak.

Asymmetric Membrane Studies. In light of the results presented in the preceding two sections, plus those found in the literature (21-26,28), the decision was made to commence the asymmetric membrane studies with SPSF-Na(0.42). The selection of the sodium salt polymer was based on the desire to limit ion exchange in desalination. The selection of D.S. of 0.42 represents a compromise of hydrophilic/hydrophobic balance and structural stability. The exploration of asymmetric membranes cast from the polymers of other salts and various D.S. values is planned for the future.

A great deal has been written about the mechanism involved in the formation of asymmetric cellulose acetate membranes (29). Briefly, a solution of polymer, volatile solvent, and less volatile non-solvent or swelling agent is cast on a smooth support surface. After an evaporation period to remove some solvent, the film plus support are submerged in a non-solvent, which serves as a gelation medium. The resulting asymmetric membrane is separated from the support and may undergo a series of treatment steps prior to being employed as a separation device. In this paper, the casting solution and the sequence of events listed above shall be referred to as the "classical" casting solution and the "classical" technique for asymmetric membrane preparation - as opposed to the "novel" casting solutions discussed below. The "structure" of the polymer in the casting solution (that is, polymer conformation and aggregation) is considered to be important in determining the structure and performance of the membrane (45); therefore, the nature of the casting solution is important. In order to pursue the "classical" casting solution, solubility studies were conducted. The results for SPSF-Na(0.42) are given in Table VI. It is noted that only four liquids were capable of yielding solutions of sufficient homogeneity and viscosity required for casting. Each of these solvents has a solubility parameter (δ) in the range 12 ± 0.7 $(cal/cm^3)^{\frac{1}{2}}$ (indicating that the value of δ for the polymer is approximately 12), medium hydrogen bondability, and low volatility (indicated by a high boiling point). Dimethyl formamide (DMF) was selected for further study since it has the lowest boiling point of the solvents and a δ in the middle of the desired range. Assmmetric membranes cast from DMF require long evaporation periods at elevated temperatures to drive off the solvent. In addition, the casting solution must contain a less volatile non-solvent or swelling agent. While a variety of liquids meet this description, diethylene glycol monoethyl ether (DEGME) was selected because of its high boiling point and its similarity to DMF in terms of hydrogen bondability. (Note: DEGME is most likely a swelling agent for the polymer rather than a non-solvent). Membranes cast

TABLE VI

Solubility Evaluations

| | | Solubility Parameter(46) | | |
Solvent	Max wt-% SPSF–Na(0.42)	δ $(\frac{cal}{cm^3})^{\frac{1}{2}}$	Hydrogen Bondability	$T_B(°C)$ @1 atm
1-Methyl-2-Pyrrolidinone	15.3	11.2	Medium	202
Dimethyl Formamide	15.1	12.1	Medium	153
Dimethyl Sulfoxide	14.9	12.0	Medium	189
γ-Butyrolactone	10.7	12.6	Medium	205
2-Pyrrolidone	7.3	14.7	Strong	250
Diethylene Glycol	2.3	12.1	Strong	245
2-Methoxy Ethanol	2.3	----	------	125
Diethylene Glycol Monoethyl Ether	2.3	10.2	Medium	195
Carbon Disulfide	2.1	10.0	Poor	46

from solutions of these liquids were tested and the results are given in Table VII. It can be seen that it was not possible to achieve membranes of acceptable quality (high flux and high separation). The reason for the failure of this method of preparation is postulated to be the failure to form an adequate skin layer. Rather than pursue further this avenue, the studies were directed towards additional solubility studies and a systematic investigation of casting solution formulation and membrane preparation.

TABLE VII

Performance of Membranes Prepared from Classical Casting Solutions

SPSF –Na(0.42) (wt-%)	DMF (wt-%)	DEGME (wt-%)	Oven Temp (°C)	Oven Time (min)	Flux (kg/m^2·s) x10^2	Salt Rejection (percent)
16.4	80.5	3.1	65	45	0.0037	85
17.5	79.5	3.0	70	45	0.0014	<2
17.5	79.5	3.0	70	30	0.0021	50
17.5	79.5	3.0	70	45	0.0014	<2
17.5	80.9	1.6	70	30	0.0014	<2
17.5	80.9	1.6	70	45	0.0014	<2
17.5	81.0	1.5	72	20	31.22	2
17.5	81.0	1.5	72	20	22.02	2
17.5	79.5	3.0	72	20	0.0083	<2
17.5	79.5	3.0	72	20	3.39	2

While the solubility parameter can be used to conduct solubility studies, it is more informative, in dealing with charged polymers such as SPSF, to employ the three dimensional solubility parameter (47,48). The solubility parameter of a liquid is related to the total cohesive energy (E) by the equation $\delta = (E/V)^{\frac{1}{2}}$, where V is the molar volume. The total cohesive energy can be broken down into three additive components: $E = E_d + E_p + E_H$, where the three components represent the contributions to E due to dispersion or London forces, permanent dipole-dipole or polar forces, and hydrogen bonding forces, respectively. This relationship is used in conjunction with the definition above to obtain $\delta^2 = \delta_d^2 + \delta_p^2 + \delta_H^2$. For plotting data on a triangular diagram it is convenient to use $f_i = \delta_i/(\delta_d + \delta_p + \delta_H)$ where i = d, p, or H. By employing literature values for these components (49), every liquid has a specific location on the triangular diagram. Experimentation to determine which liquids serve as solvents at a given concentration and temperature establishes a solubility envelope within which the liquids serve as solvents at the given conditions. Once the envelope has been established it is possible to predict that any liquid which falls within the envelope will serve as a solvent. The results of such experiments are shown for SPSF-Na(0.42) in Figure 3, and for the other SPSF-Na polymers in Figure 4. In Figure 4 it is noted that increased sulfonation increases the polar character of the polymer as indicated by the fact that liquids of a more polar character are required to achieve the desired solutions.

The experiments for establishing the envelopes in Figures 3 and 4 indicated that it is possible to mix two liquids, which individually are not solvents, in the appropriate volumetric proportions such that together they form a "cosolvent system." For example, in Figure 3 it is demonstrated that tetrahydrofuran (THF) and formamide can be mixed 40:60 to establish a cosolvent as designated. Recognition of this fact makes it possible to explore a number of casting solutions which, because they contain a volatile component, do not require the difficult evaporation procedures discussed above. In addition, it is possible to explore a number of non-classical or novel casting solutions as will be demonstrated below.

The first novel casting solution to be investigated consisted of THF and formamide, a pair of non-solvents combined to serve as a cosolvent system. This system was selected because by simply varying the proportions of the two liquids it has the ability to dissolve SPSF-Na of all degrees of sulfonation under the desired conditions (15 wt-% polymer, 25°C). In a similar manner, dioxane-formamide mixtures may be employed.

Membranes cast from THF-formamide, dried for 200 seconds in room temperature air, and gelled for one hour, were tested for desalination performance. The results are listed in Table VIII. The best results were obtained with membranes cast from 40:60 and 70:30 THF-formamide and gelled in isopropyl alcohol (IPA)-see discussion below concerning gelation media. Of these two systems the 40:60 is superior. This

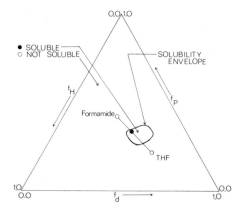

Figure 3.   Solubility diagram for SPSF–
Na (0.42)

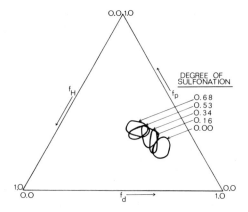

Figure 4.   Solubility diagram for PSF, SPSF–Na (0.16), SPSF–Na (0.34), SPSF–
Na (0.53), and SPSF–Na (0.68)

result is in agreement with the findings of Klein and Smith (50).
Based on cellulose acetate studies, they predicted that superior
performance is achieved with casting solutions which meet the
following requirements:
(1) the initial composition is located near the edge of the
solubility envelope.
(2) the initial composition is such that the loss of the volatile
component moves the mixture out of the envelope rather than through
it.
The present results confirm these hypotheses for SPSF-Na systems.
Further work is required to test the validity of these hypotheses
for other polymers.

TABLE VIII

Effect of Cosolvent Composition and
Gelation Medium on Reverse Osmosis Performance

THF (Vol-%)	Formamide (Vol-%)	Gelation Medium	Flux (kg/m^2·s) x10^2	Salt Rejection (%)
70	30	H_2O	1.34	<2
70	30	.75H_2O-.25IPA	1.43	3
70	30	.50H_2O-.50IPA	1.48	7
70	30	.25H_2O-.75IPA	1.72	11
70	30	IPA	0.25	50
70	30	methyl alcohol	----	<2
60	40	n butyl alcohol	9.26	1
60	40	t butyl alcohol	2.31	7
60	40	H_2O	----	<2
40	60	n butyl alcohol	8.16	0
40	60	IPA	0.61	45
40	60	IPA	0.63	44
40	60	H_2O	*	*

*membrane swelled in gelation bath

The results in Table VIII indicate that the nature of the
gelation medium plays a significant role in determining the
performance of the membrane. Consider the gelation process.
Cosolvent remaining in the membrane must be leached out during
gelation. For this to be accomplished, the gelation medium must
enter the micropores of the membrane support layer at the same rate
that the cosolvent components leave the pores. If the gelation
medium diffuses into the micropores faster than the cosolvent
diffuses out, the polymer swells due to the expansion of the
micropores. On the other hand, if the opposite occurs and the
cosolvent diffuses out too quickly, the membrane collapses due to
micropore collapse. This exchange can be related to a number of

factors including the solubility parameter, the diffusion
coefficient, and the activity of the gelation medium (50-52). The
cosolvent must be similar to the gelation medium with regard to
the later two parameters in order for proper membrane formation to
occur. From the experimental results listed in Table VIII it
appears that IPA has the best combination of these parameters to
match the properties of the THF-formamide cosolvent system. It is
likely that the solubility parameter, diffusion coefficient, etc.
of the THF-formamide system will be affected by changes in the
cosolvent composition. Therefore, the optimal gelation medium will
be different for each casting solution. Further experimentation is
required to clarify this point.

ESCA was employed to analyze membranes before and after use
in the desalination cell. Wide scan ESCA spectra were obtained on
the last two membranes listed in Table VII. Table IX lists the
binding energies (B.E.) and the atomic fractions (A.F.) for the
membranes studied. In addition to the expected carbon, oxygen,
sodium, and sulfur peaks, two small peaks were attributed to
nitrogen and silicon, which may be due to the contamination in
the air (silicon grease). A smaller photo peak was observed at
51.3 eV and remains unassigned. Overall, there is no significant
surface contamination of the membranes.

TABLE IX

Wide Scan ESCA Results on RO Membranes

| | | | Low Flux Membrane | | High Flux Membrane | |
			Top Side	Bottom Side	Top Side	Bottom Side
C	1s	A.F.	0.721	0.787	0.798	0.751
O	1s	B.E.	532.1	532.2	532.2	532.2
		A.F.	0.196	0.150	0.129	0.181
N	1s	B.E.	399.7	399.7	399.7	399.7
		A.F.	0.040	0.020	0.023	0.019
Na	2s	B.E.	63.4	63.4	264.0*	63.3
		A.F.	0.018	0.016	0.008	0.019
S	2s	B.E.	231.8	231.9	231.7	232.0
		A.F.	0.015	0.012	0.005	0.017
Si	2p3	B.E.	102.3	102.7	102.2	102.5
		A.F.	0.010	0.013	0.036	0.014

*Na Auger line (KLL)

Numerous asymmetric membranes were prepared under various conditions and their cross-section was examined by SEM. Typical of the results are those shown in Figure 5 for the membrane cast from 70:30 THF-formamide and gelled in IPA. Close inspection of Figure 5 reveals a thin, relatively dense skin supported by a microporous layer. The support layer contains macrovoids, the cause of which is presently under investigation.

The extent of ion exchange of the salt form of the SPSF membranes was studied with atomic absorption spectroscopy (AAS), neutron activation analysis (NAA), and ESCA. Initially, a 0.1% KCl solution showed an absence of Na. However, after being equilibrated with SPSF-Na, a significant level of Na was detected in the solution using AAS. Similar results were found using SPSF-K polymer in a 0.1% NaCl solution. The extent of ion exchange was calculated based on the weight of salt per gram of each polymer membrane. The average calculated values of the percentage of ion exchange were 77% and 76% for the SPSF-Na(0.42) and SPSF-K(0.48) membranes, respectively. After the ion-exchange studies, the membranes were analyzed by NAA and the calculated percents of ion exchange were 92% for the SPSF-Na(0.42) and 63% for the SPSF-K(0.48) membranes. Taking the standard error in NAA to be ± 10%, the ion exchange observed was consistent with the ion-exchange studies discussed above. ESCA analysis provides additional support for the ion-exchange process. Figure 6 shows the ESCA spectra of the Na and K photo electron peaks of SPSF-Na(0.42) before and after the ion-exchange study. Since the polymer is SPSF-Na(0.42), there was initially no K present. The small shoulder observed was the $\pi^* \leftarrow \pi$ carbon shake-up peak. However, after the ion exchange, the Na photo electron peak decreased significantly and the K photo electron peak was detected. Combining the results of ESCA and NAA, the ion-exchange process does not just occur at the membrane surface but is a relatively extensive bulk phenomenon.

Summary

This paper has provided the reader with an introduction to a class of polymers that show great potential as reverse osmosis membrane materials -- poly(aryl ethers). Resistance to degradation and hydrolysis as well as resistance to stress induced creep make membranes of these polymers particularly attractive. It has been demonstrated that through sulfonation the hydrophilic/hydrophobic, flux/separation, and structural stability characteristics of these membranes can be altered to suit the specific application. It has been illustrated that the nature of the counter-ion of the sulfonation plays a role in determining performance characteristics. In the preliminary studies reported here, one particular poly(aryl ether) has been studied -- the sulfonated derivative of Bisphenol A - polysulfone. This polymer was selected to serve as a model for the development of experimental techniques as well as to permit the investigation of variables

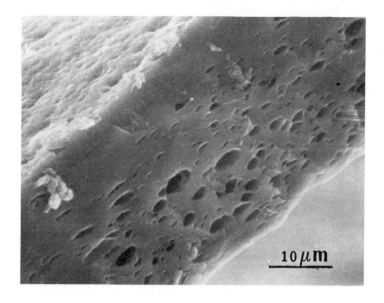

*Figure 5.   SEM of the cross-section of a SPSF–Na (0.42) membrane cast from
70:30 THF–formamide solution, dried for 200 s, and gelled in IPA*

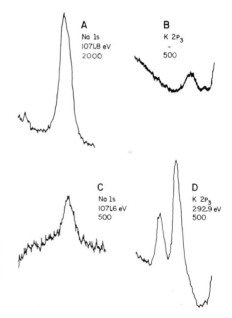

*Figure 6.   Photoelectron peaks of Na
1s and K 2p₃ in a SPSF–Na (0.42) membrane before (A, B) and after (C, D) ion
exchange. Binding energies (in electron
volts) and peak intensities (counts/second) are indicated.*

such as degree of sulfonation, nature of counter-ion, polymer molecular weight, and casting procedure. The casting procedure reported here represents a departure from the classical casting methods in that the casting solution consisted of the polymer dissolved in a pair of non-solvents which served as a cosolvent system. It has been demonstrated that the selection of casting solution components influences membrane structure and performance and can be based, in part, on the solubility parameter and thus visualized through ternary diagrams. Similarly, the nature of the gelation medium can influence the structure and performance of poly(aryl ether) membranes. This paper also included an introduction to a variety of surface analysis techniques which provide insight into the factors influencing the performance of reverse osmosis membranes.

The continuing goals of this project are:
(1) To demonstrate the usefulness of a wide spectrum of poly(aryl ethers) as reverse osmosis membrane materials.
(2) To investigate the relationship between polymer structure and membrane performance.
(3) To demonstrate the usefulness of surface analysis techniques in providing insight into point (2) above as well as the relationship between membrane structure and performance.
(4) To demonstrate the variety of procedures available for the preparation of sulfonated poly(aryl ether) membranes (for example, (i) classical casting techniques (ii) casting from two non-solvents (iii) neutralization of membranes cast from free acid sulfonated polysulfone (iv) sulfonation of cast polysulfone membranes).
(5) To investigate the mechanism of membrane formation as a function of the casting techniques listed in point (4) above.

Acknowledgments

Work supported under Office of Water Research and Technology Grant #14-34-0001-9404.

Literature Cited

1. Loeb, S.; Sourirajan, S. UCLA, Dept. of Eng., Report No. 60-60, 1961.

2. Lonsdale, H. K. in "Desalination by Reverse Osmosis"; Merten, U., Ed.; M.I.T. Press: Cambridge, Mass., 1966.

3. Reese, E. T.; Mandels, M. in "Cellulose and Cellulose Derivatives"; Bikales, N. M.; Segal, L., Ed.; Wiley Interscience: New York, 1971; Part V, p. 1079.

4. Hassid, W. Z.; Ballou, C. E. in "The Carbohydrates: Chemistry, Biochemistry, Physiology"; Pigman, W., Ed.; Academic Press: New York, 1957; p. 489.

5. Meller, A. Hozforschung 1960, 14, 78.

6. Vos, K. D.; Barris, F. O.; Riley R. L. J. Appl. Polym. Sci. 1966, 10, 825.

7. Sourirajan, S. "Reverse Osmosis"; Logos Press: London, 1970.

8. Kesting, R. E. "Synthetic Polymeric Membranes"; McGraw-Hill: New York, 1971.

9. Lonsdale, H. K.; Podall, H. E., Ed. "Reverse Osmosis Membrane Research"; Plenum Press: New York, 1972.

10. Sourirajan, S., Ed. "Reverse Osmosis and Synthetic Membranes"; National Research Council of Canada Publications: Ottawa, Canada, 1977.

11. Turbak, A. F.; Noshay, A. U.S. Patent 3 206 492, 1965.

12. Johnson, R. N.; Farnham, A. G.; Clendinning, R. A.; Hale, W. F.; Merriam, C. N. J. Polym. Sci. A-1 1967, 5, 2399.

13. Rozelle, L. T.; Cadotte, J. E.; Senechal, A. J.; King, W. L.; Nelson, B. R. in Reference 9; p. 419.

14. Yasuda, H. in Reference 10; Chapter 13.

15. Flory, P. J. "Principles of Polymer Chemistry"; Cornell University Press: Ithica, N. Y., 1953.

16. Blais, P. in Reference 10; Chapter 9.

17. Turbak, A. F.; Noshay, A.; Karoly, G. U.S. Patent 3 205 285, 1965.

18. O'Farrell, C. P.; Surniuk, G. E. U.S. Patent 3 836 511, 1974.

19. Goethals, E. J. in "Encyclopedia of Polymer Science and Technology"; Wiley: New York, 1970; Vol. 13, p. 465.

20. LaConti, A. B.; Chludzinski, P. J.; Fickett, A. P. in Reference 9; p. 263.

21. Quentin, J. P. U.S. Patent 3 709 841, 1973.

22. Bourganel, J. U.S. Patent 3 855 122, 1974.

23. Bourganel, J. U.S. Patent 4 026 977, 1977.

24. Quentin, J. P.; Milas, M.; Rinaudo, M., 5th Intern. Symp. on Fresh Water from the Sea. 1976, 4, 157.

25. Brousse, C.; Chapurlat, R., Quentin, J. P. Desalination 1976, 18, 137.

26. Noshay, A.; Robeson, L. M. J. Appl. Polym. Sci. 1976, 20, 1885.

27. Merten, U.; Lonsdale, H. K.; Riley, R. L.; Vos, K. D. U. S. Dept. Interior, OSW, Res. and Dev. Prog. Rpt. No. 265; Washington, D. C., 1967.

28. Graef, A. F.; Schell, W. J.; Saltonstall, C. W.; Stannett, V. T.; Hopfenberg, H. B. U.S. Dept. Interior, OSW, Res. and Dev. Prog. Rpt. No. 932; Washington, D. C. 1974.

29. Kesting, R. E. in Reference 10; Chapter 5.

30. Sourirajan, S.; Matsuura, T. in Reference 10; Chapter 2.

31. Dwight, D. W.; McGrath, J. E.; Wightman, J. P. J. Appl. Polym. Sci.: Appl. Polym. Symp. 1978, 34, 35.

32. Clark, D. T. in "Progress in Theoretical Organic Chemistry"; Crizmadia, I. G., Ed.; Elsevier: Amsterdam, 1976; Vol. 2.

33. Thomas, H. R.; O'Malley, J. J. Macromolecules 1979, 12, 323.

34. Kesting, R. E.; Engdahl, M.; Stone, W., Jr. J. Macromol. Sci.-Chem. 1969, A3(1), 157.

35. Robeson, L. M.; Farnham, A. G.; McGrath, J. E. J. Appl. Polym. Sci: Appl. Polym. Symp. 1975, 26, 373.

36. Robeson, L. M.; Farnham, A. G.; McGrath, J. E. in "Molecular Basis for Transitions and Relaxations"; Meier, D. J., Ed., Midland Macromol. Inst. Monograph, Vol. 4, Gordon and Breach: New York, 1978; p. 405.

37. Tran, C. M. S. Thesis, Virginia Polytechnic Inst. and State U., Blacksburg, VA 1980.

38. Good, R. J.; Neumann, A. W. in "Colloid Surface Science"; Good, R. J.; Stromberg, R., Ed.; Wiley: New York, 1979; Vol.11, 31.

39. Good, R. J; Koo, M. N. J. Colloid Inter. Sci. 1979, 71, 283.

40. Scofield, J. H. J. Elect. Spect. and Rel. Phen. 1976, 8, 129.

41. Kesting, R. E.; Menefee, A. Kolloid Z. Z. Polymere 1969, 230(1), 341.

42. Eisenberg, A. Macromolecules 1970, 3, 147.

43. Zisman, W. A.; Fox, H. W. J. Coll. Sci. 1950, 5, 514.

44. Muilenberg, G. E. "Handbook of X-ray Photoelectron Spectroscopy"; Perkin Elmer Corp.: Eden Prairie, 1978.

45. Kunst, B.; Sourirajan, S. J. Appl. Polym. Sci. 1970, 14, 2559.

46. Brandrup, J.; Immergut, E. H., Ed. "Polymer Handbook", 2nd Ed.; Wiley-Interscience: New York, 1974; p. IV-339.

47. Hildebrand, J.; Scott, R. "Solubility of Non-Electrolytes", 3rd Ed.; Reinhold: New York, 1949.

48. Hansen, C. M. I & EC Prod. Res. Devel. 1969, 8, 1.

49. Hansen, C. M.; Beerbower, A. in "Encycl. Chem. Technol.", 2nd Ed., Suppl. Vol.; Standen, A., Ed.; Interscience: New York, 1971; p. 889.

50. Klein, E.; Smith, J. K. in Reference 9; p. 61.

51. Frommer, M. A.; Lancet, D. in Reference 9; p. 85.

52. Strathmann, H.; Kock, K. Desalination 1977, 21, 241.

RECEIVED December 4, 1980.

Transport of Ions and Water in Sulfonated Polysulfone Membranes

N. VINNIKOVA and G. B. TANNY

The Weizmann Institute of Science, Department of Plastics Research, Rehovot, Israel

Ion-exchange type, charged membranes were amongst the first materials recognized to be suitable for desalting water by reverse osmosis (R.O.) (1). However, subsequent to the development of neutral, asymmetric cellulose acetate membranes (2), they were paid relatively little attention. The first step toward the attainment of a charged equivalent of a conventional asymmetric R.O. membrane was the development of thin-film composites of sulphonated poly-(phenylene-oxide) (3,4). These membranes showed some promise, but did not give sufficiently high rejection of concentrated salt solutions to be considered practical for seawater desalting.

Sulphonated polysulphone (SPS) membranes, on the other hand, have been shown to have excellent salt rejections and water fluxes (5-7) which are maintained even for feeds of very high salt concentration. In fact, both the magnitude of the salt rejections cited and their independence of feed concentration are remarkably non-characteristic of the behaviour of any charged membrane heretofore examined. Utilizing a previously derived relation between salt rejection and transport number (8) in porous charged membranes it was found that the high salt selectivity of a dense SPS film appeared to be incompatible with a Donnan exclusion mechanism (9). In the present contribution, a more comprehensive study of the transport coefficients has been carried out on dense sulphonated polysulphone membranes. To achieve some physical understanding of these measurements, morphological investigations relating to the distribution of ions in the matrix have also been carried out utilizing the techniques of X-ray scattering and electron microscopy.

0097–6156/81/0153–0351$05.00/0

Experimental

A. Materials. Polysulphone resin P-1700 and P-3500 were obtained from Union Carbide. Their weight average molecular weight, $\bar{M}w$, was determined by ultracentrifuge:
    $\bar{M}w$ = 35400 for P-1700   and
    $\bar{M}w$ = 38600 for P-3500.
The sodium salt of sulphonated polysulphone Na-SPS was obtained by reaction of polysulphone resin (P-1700 or P-3500) with chlorosulphonic acid in 1,2-dichloroethane (5). This was followed by dissolution in dimethyl formamide, precipitation in 10% NaCl, and rinsing with large volumes of water until the washings were free of NaCl.
    The ion-exchange capacity (IEC) of the samples was determined by potentiometric titration of the SPS-H$^+$ form solution (90% dimethylformamide, 10% water) with sodium hydroxide.
    The polymer film was cast on glass plates from a 20% (by weight) solution of polymer in dimethylformamide. After the film was dried at 50°C for 40 min it was removed from the glass plate by immersion in water. No difference was found in the properties of sulphonated products based on the P-1700 resin or P-3500 resin.

B. Methods.
1. WAXS: Wide angle X-ray scattering was done on a PW 1830 horizontal goniometer with Cu Kα (1.54Å) radiation (32 kV, 20 mA). Slits of 1° were employed.
2. SAXS: Small angle diffraction patterns were obtained at room temperature using a "Searle" X-ray camera with Cu Kα (1.54Å) radiation (35 kV, 25 mA). The exposure times were about 65 hours. The photographs were microdensitometered using a Joyce-Loebl double beam microdensitometer.
3. Transmission electron microscopy: Prior to embedding, the 20 μm thick polymer film was converted to its Cs$^+$ or Fe^{+3} form. A mixture of vinylcyclohexene dioxide (10 g), diglycidyl ether of polypropyleneglycol (6 g) nonenyl succinic anhydride (26 g) and dimethylaminoethanol (0.4$_o$g) was used as an embedding material. Ultra-thin sections (∿800A) were cut with an Ultra-microtome MT-2, using a diamond knife. Micrographs were obtained using a Phillips EM 300 electron microscope at an accelerating voltage of 80 kV.
4. Filtration coefficient: The filtration coefficient, Lp, was measured under osmotic pressure utilizing thermostated glass cells (±0.05°C) equipped with graduated cappillaries (±0.001 cc). The cells had an effective membrane area of 1.77 cm^2 and each compartment contained ∿25 cc of solution. One compartment was filled with deionized water and the second with a 1 or 2 molal solution of sucrose (depending upon IEC).
    To obtain the water flow J_V, we followed the rates of the meniscus movements in the capillary. The mean value of several measurements was used to calculate Lp according to the equation(1):

$$J_v = - \sigma \, Lp \, \Delta\pi \qquad (1)$$

where σ is reflection coefficient, and $\Delta\pi$ is the osmotic pressure difference across the membrane.

To calculate the osmotic pressure we used values of osmotic coefficients from ref. (10). Total organic carbon analysis (Beckman 914A) of samples from the water filled compartment verified that the membranes are impermeable to sucrose, so that the reflection coefficient σ is equal to unity.

The obtained values of the membrane constant $Lp\Delta x$ are considered to contain an uncertainty of $\pm 20\%$, mostly due to the uncertainty of $\pm 15\%$ in the measurement of Δx by a dial micrometer.

5. The self-diffusion measurement: The membrane was clamped between two identical plexiglass half cells (volume of each, $V_1 \approx 75$ ml). The compartments were filled with deionized water. After temperature equilibration, 0.1 ml of tritiated water HTO activity 5 mCi/ml was introduced, in one of the compartments ("hot" side (')). Simultaneously, stirring was started and samples were taken from the "hot" side. At the chosen time intervals, samples from the "cold" (") side were taken. The total number of samples taken during the experiment was about 14 - two duplicates at every time interval. Each sample volume was 50 µl so the volume changes during experiment can be effectively neglected. Each sample was put into a vial containing 4 ml scintillation mixture (Triton-X solution) and 0.5 ml of water. For counting we used a Packard TRI-CARB Liquid Scintillation spectrometer.

Plotting then c''_{HTO} (number of counts at time t, in the "cold" solution) as a function of time t, resulted in a straight line, the slope of which yielded the corresponding constant tritiated water flux J_d

$$J_d = (V/A) \, \frac{dc''_{HTO}}{dt} \qquad (2)$$

where A is a membrane area, varied from 9.6 cm^2 for lower values of IEC to 2.5 cm^2 for the higher. Applying Fick's Law,

$$J_d = P_T \, \frac{\Delta c_{HTO}}{\Delta x} \qquad (3)$$

where Δx is a membrane thickness, P_T is a diffusion permeability and Δc_{HTO} is a difference in tritiated water concentration across the membrane. The experiment was ended when an amount of tracer, not larger than 5% of the original, had crossed the membrane, therefore Δc_{HTO} can be taken equal to c'_{HTO} - a number of counts in the "hot" side at the beginning of the experiment. Thus, the expression shown in equation (4) was used to calculate P_T:

$$P_T = \left(\frac{dc''_{HTO}}{dt}\right) \left(\frac{V}{A}\right) \frac{\Delta x}{c'_{HTO}} \qquad (4)$$

All the diffusion measurements were carried out at $25° \pm 0.05°C$. Membrane thickness was measured by a micrometer. The values used for calculations were the average of several measurements and the accuracy of the membrane thickness measurements was ±15%.

6. <u>Electrical conductance</u>: The conductance measurements were made in a glass cell consisting ot two equivalent electrode sections. Circular platinized platinum electrodes parallel to the plane of the membrane were embedded in each section. The membrane area was 0.98 cm^2. Resistance measurements were made with and without the membrane in 0.1N NaCl solution.

The conductance measurements were made with an Automatic Capacitance Bridge Assembly (General Radio Company 1680) at a frequency of 1 kHZ.

7. <u>Salt Rejection</u>: The salt rejection of the membrane was calculated from the chloride contents of the feed, and product as measured by chloride titration(Aminco Cotlove, Silver Springs). The apparent salt rejection R_{obs} is defined as:

$$R_{obs} = 1 - \frac{C_p}{C_f} \qquad (5)$$

where C_f is the salt concentration of the feed, and C_p is the product concentration. Measuring R_{obs} and volume flow (J_v) as a function of the pressure difference, ΔP, the limiting salt rejection, R_∞, was obtained from $1/R_{obs}$ vs. $1/J_v$ plot by linear regression analysis according to formula (6) (<u>11</u>).

$$\frac{1}{R_{obs}} = \frac{1}{R_\infty} + \frac{(L\pi/Lp - R_\infty^2)Lp\pi}{R_\infty} \frac{1}{J_v} \qquad (6)$$

where Lp is the hydrodynamic permeability (cm/sec), Lπ is the osmotic permeability (cm/sec) and π is the osmotic pressure of the feed solution (atm).

Two typical examples of data for R_∞ obtained via equation (6) for various external salt concentrations and membrane IEC are presented in Table I.

TABLE I

Calculation of the Limiting Salt Rejection, R_∞ for Na-SPS Membranes

IEC (meq/g)	Molality of NaCl	Slope x 10^5	Intercept	R_∞	Correlation Coefficient to Equation(6)
0.78	0.855	0.1047	1.0204	0.976	0.9837
1.30	0.1	1.077	1.013	0.987	0.9698

8. <u>Annealing procedure</u>: A piece of SPS in the Na$^+$ form, dried at 60°C in vacuum over P_2O_5 overnight, was placed in an aluminum foil envelope and heated at 280°C during 30 min, after which it was immersed in water.

Results and Discussion

A.   Morphological Study

1.   Small Angle X-ray Scattering (SAXS). A small angle peak $2° < 2\theta < 3°$ was observed for the Cs^+, Ca^{2+} and Fe^{3+} forms of SPS for high and moderate IEC's. This peak is absent in the H^+ form of the polymer (Fig. 1). The presence of a scattering peak shows that heterogeneities on the colloidal level exist in the electron density distribution, and the appearance of scattering for Cs^+, Ca^{2+}, and Fe^{3+} forms of SPS, but not for the H^+ form, confirms the assumption that these scattering centers are ion containing regions.

The average distance between scattering centers, which is connected to the period derived from the angular position of the peak, cannot be calculated directly from the classical Bragg equation which is meant for point scattering centers of negligible volume. However, it was proposed (12) that the Bragg equation can be used in the following form:

$$d = K\, d_{Bragg} = \frac{K\lambda}{2\,Sin\theta} \tag{7}$$

where K is a dimensionless constant, usually between 0.8-1.22 (12).

Fig. 2 shows that the angular position of the "ionic" peak is a function of the IEC. The average distance between scattering centers, calculated according to equation (7) with K=1, decreases as the IEC increases, until the IEC approaches a value ca. 1 meq/g. At IEC's above the latter value, the position of the scattering angle remains constant. We also observed that the SAXS peak is not influenced by the water content of the sample. This is in contrast to other ionomer systems in which the "ionic" peak disappears upon water saturation (12).

2. Transmission Electron Microscopy (TEM). Pictures obtained by TEM show that the electron density of the membrane in its Cs^+ form is higher than that of the embedding material. However, the membrane is dark in a very homogeneous fashion and no regions of elevated electron density could be observed down to a resolution of $\sim 50 Å$. These observations are in fact in agreement with the recent work by C. Heitner et al. (13). A low temperature study of hyperfine splitting in a Mossbauer study of SPS (IEC=1.21 meq/g) in the Fe^{+3} form revealed the presence of three types of iron species: (a) small units or monomers whose diameter is below 30A (28%); (b) ferric dimers (36%) and (c) clusters whose average diameter is about 34Å (35%). Keeping this distribution of the charge groups in mind, we can hypothesize that the dimers and monomers decrease the electron density difference between the clusters and the rest of the matrix and consequently, the TEM sensitivity decreases. In addition, one has to take into account that the sample is much thicker than the cluster diameter (800Å vs. 34Å) which also decreases the sensitivity.

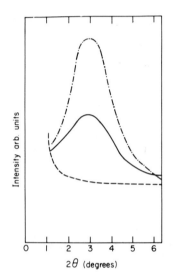

Figure 1. Comparison of the intensities of the SAXS peak for the acid and its salts of SPS IEC = 1.2 mequiv/g: (– – –) H⁺ form; (– · – ·) Cs⁺ form; (———) Fe⁺³ form.

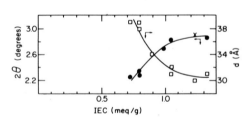

Figure 2. Position of the SAXS peak (●) SPS obtained by sulfonation of P-3500 resin; (×) SPS obtained by sulfonation of P-1700 resin) and distance between scattering centers (□) calculated according to the Bragg's equation 7 vs. IEC.

3. Wide Angle X-ray Diffraction Study. The broad peak shown in Figure 3 was observed for both SPS and PS itself. This type of scattering at wide angle has been seen in several non-crystalline polymers and its' appearance is connected with some type of short range order, which may be related to an interchain distance (14). Rigorous determination of the actual interchain distance must be carried out by Fourier transformation of X-ray intensities, and is usually found to be about 20% greater than that calculated from Bragg's equation (14).

Thus, the application of the Bragg's equation to the scattering peak at $2\theta = 18°$ and applying a correction of 20% yields an interchain distance ca 6Å. As a function of the degree of sulphonation and relative humidity, this distance appears to be constant.

B.   Transport Study

1. Water Transport. The dependence of the diffusive permeability of tritiated water P_T, (HTO) and hydraulic permeability $Lp\Delta X$ on the IEC are presented in Figures 4 and 5. Both P_T and $Lp\Delta X$ can be seen to increase exponentially as a function of IEC. Since the volume fraction of water, ϕ, is also a linear function of the IEC, a similar exponential relation is obtained for these parameters vs. ϕ. In terms of the pore model, the increase in either diffusion permeability or the hydraulic permeability may be caused by one or both of the following possibilities: (a) an increase in the number of passageways, or (b) by increase in the radius of the pores. This question may be resolved by examining the g factor, defined as a ratio of two permeabilities (15):

$$g = \frac{Lp\Delta xRT}{P_T\bar{V}_W} \tag{8}$$

where $\bar{V}_W$ is the molar volume of water and RT has its usual meaning.

Fig. 6 shows that near an IEC = 0.9 meq/g the g factor, which was nearly constant at lower IEC's, begins to increase. This finding indicates that below an IEC of ca. 0.9 meq/g, the mechanism of water transport through the membrane was primarily diffusive in nature and the increase in the overall water permeability is due to an increase in the number of passageways rather than an increase in their dimension.

We may also use g to calculate an equivalent pore radius, r, according to equation (9) derived by Kedem and Katchalsky (15):

$$r = \{\frac{8 \, \eta_W \, D_W \, \bar{V}_W}{RT}(g-1)\}^{\frac{1}{2}} \tag{9}$$

where η_W and D_W are the viscosity and self diffusion coefficient of bulk water. While the assumptions underlying the pore model (bulk water properties, Poiseuille flow, etc.) are clearly suspect, such an approach does provide a useful experimental test.

Fig. 7 shows that equivalent pore radius remains quite constant below an IEC of ∿0.9 meq/g, while above this IEC an increase in ion concentration is associated with an increase in pore size.

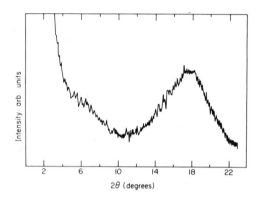

Figure 3.   Wide-angle X-ray scattering, SPS Na⁺ form, IEC = 1 mequiv/g

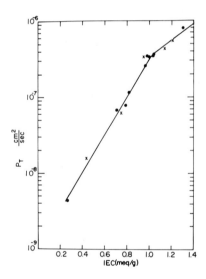

Figure 4.   Diffusive permeability, P_T vs. IEC: (●) SPS obtained by sulfonation of P-3500 resin; (×) SPS obtained by sulfonation of P-1700 resin

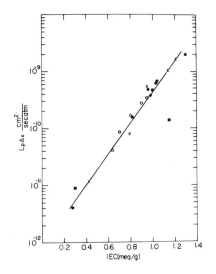

Figure 5. Intrinsic membrane hydraulic permeability vs. IEC: (●) SPS obtained by sulfonation of P-3500 resin; (×) SPS obtained by sulfonation at P-1700 resin); (○) SPS, Ref. 5; (■) SPS, Ref. 6.

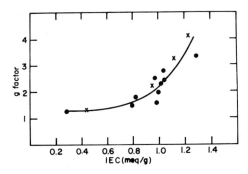

Figure 6. The g factor vs. IEC: (●) SPS obtained by sulfonation of P-3500 resin; (×) SPS obtained by sulfonation of P-1700 resin.

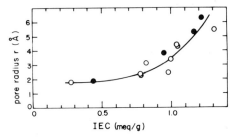

Figure 7. An equivalent pore radius, r, vs. IEC: (○) SPS obtained by sulfonation of P-3500 resin; (●) SPS obtained by sulfonation of P-1700 resin.

Returning to the SAXS results, it may be recalled that at this IEC
the distance between scattering centers begins to approach a constant value despite an increase in the concentration of charged
groups, i.e. additional scattering centers are not created. One
can therefore conclude that at this point a change occurs in the
nature of the distribution of ion-exchange sites between clusters,
dimers, and monomers. Above an IEC $\sim$0.9 meq/g additional charged
groups form fewer ionic aggregates and are present predominantly
as dimers and monomers. One can picture the ionic aggregates as
islands of high concentration of charge while monomers and dimers
are distributed in the inter-connecting regions between them.
Apparently, an increase in the concentration of monomers and dimers in the pore causes an increase in the equivalent pore size.

   2. Ionic Transport. a. Conductivity: The specific conductance of the SPS (Na$^+$ form) membranes is shown in Fig. 8, whose
data are summarized in Table II, including values of an apparent
energy of activation. An exponential increase in ionic conductance
together with a decrease in an apparent energy of activation may be
related to a decrease in a "jump" distance between ion-exchange
sites as a function of IEC.

TABLE II

Specific Conductance and an Apparent Energy of Activation
for Various SPS Membranes (Na$^+$ Form)

IEC (meq/g)	$\kappa \cdot 10^4$ ohm^{-1}cm^{-1}	Ea (Kcal/mol)
0.3	0.006	17.9
0.75	0.78	10.1
0.78	1.4	8.85
0.82	1.85	-
0.98	5.2	-
1.03	7.81	-
1.30	33.3	-

   In Table III the specific conductance and electro-osmotic coefficient (β) for the SPS membrane are shown together with the data
for a conventional ion-exchange membrane, AMF C103 ([16],[17]) (poly-
ethylene-styrene graft copolymer containing sulphonic acid groups).
It appears that there is a close similarity in properties of both
membranes.

   The β value for Na$^+$ - SPS is slightly low (nearly equal to
the water of hydration of sodium ion), however, it is in a range
common to   other ion-exchange membranes (0.1-0.2 1/F) ([1],[18]).

TABLE III

Comparison of the Transport Properties of SPS Membrane
with a Conventional Ion-Exchange Membrane

Membrane (Na$^+$ form)	IEC (meq/g)	Water cont. (%)	$\kappa \cdot 10^3$ (ohm^{-1}cm^{-1})	β (mol/F)
SPS	1.30	23	3.3	5.0
AMF-103	1.33	18.2 (Ref.16)	4.0 (Ref.16)	7.0 (Ref.17)

b. Salt rejection: Through measurements of salt rejection at different operating pressures, the limiting salt rejection, R_∞, was obtained by extrapolation of equation (6) for a number of membranes of different IEC and at two external salt concentrations (cf. Experimental). The concentration of 0.8M NaCl was chosen to allow a comparison of the data on Na-SPS to that of Sarbolouki and Miller (19), for cellulose acetate membranes. In Figure 9, R_∞ for various membranes (of differing IEC) has been plotted versus the equivalent pore radius, r. It is interesting that the data for Na-SPS and that of cellulose acetate fall on the same curve for 0.8M concentration. It also quite surprising, for the following reasons: (i) the mechanism of salt exclusion for cellulose acetate membranes has been shown to be primarily via the low dielectric constant of the pore wall (20) whereas that of Na-SPS has been claimed to be via Donnan exclusion (7) [Heyde et al. (21) did see some contribution of the few charges present in CA by the additional exclusion observed at low external salt concentrations]. (ii) since the IEC of the Na-SPS membranes is not the same for each pore radius, the charge density in the pore is not necessarily identical and thus the contribution of the charge density to the ion exclusion should be different at each pore radius. For both the above reasons one would not expect the intrinsic rejection data in Fig. 9 to coincide as well as they do. However, there is one feature which is very similar for both membranes and that is the state of water, contained within the pores. Indeed, neither the high salt rejecting homogeneous CA membranes, nor the SPS-Na membranes show a freezing transition in the DSC down to temperatures of -60°C (22,23). Furthermore, simultaneous transport measurements of HTO and H$_2$O^{18} show similar ratios of T/O^{18} (24,25).

Schultz and Asunmaa (26) proposed that the structured water found within the pores of CA membranes was responsible for a significant portion of the membrane's salt rejecting properties. In light of the data in figure 9, this hypothesis appears to be very plausible, since it is one feature which is common to both membranes and which provides an explanation for the remarkable coincidence of the data in the figure. However, this statement should not be taken to imply that the presence of the ionic charges is of no consequence. Also shown in figure 9 is data at a feed

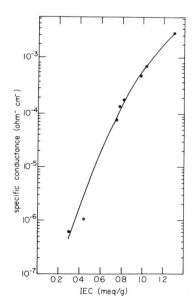

Figure 8.   Specific conductance vs. IEC

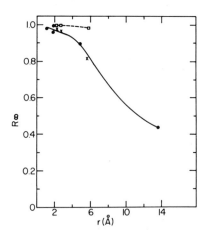

Figure 9.   Limiting salt rejection, R_z, vs. equivalent pore radius; r: (□) SPS, 0.1M NaCl; (×) SPS, 0.855M NaCl; (●) CA, 0.855M NaCl (19).

concentration of 0.1M NaCl. For a given pore radius, R_∞ is clearly higher at 0.1M than that at 0.8M, probably due to ionic contributions which are diminished at high external ionic strength.

c. Effects of Chain Reorganization: Previous discussions involved the influence of membrane structure on different transport processes, in which the changes in this structure were considered only as a function of IEC. It therefore seemed to be a critical point to effect a change in the distribution of ion-exchange sites between monomers, dimers, and clusters, while keeping their total amount constant. This goal was attempted by annealing the sample at a temperature above its Tg.

Data for the electrical conductance of annealed samples shows that ionic transport is more restricted in comparison with those which are nonannealed (Table IV). Since the total number of ion-exchange sites is unaffected by the annealing process (cf. experimental) we may assume that the site to site distance has increased.

TABLE IV

Influence of Annealing on the Properties of Na^+ SPS Membranes

SPS IEC = 0.82 meq/g.

	Before annealing	After annealing
Water up-take (%)	14	11
$\rho \cdot 10^{-4*}$ (Ohm cm)	0.542	1.265
$\frac{P_T \Delta x \bar{V}_W}{RT} \cdot 10^{10}$ (cm^2/sec atm)	0.82	0.50
$Lp\Delta x \cdot 10^{10}$ (cm^2/sec atm)	1.41	0.62
g	1.7	1.24
Pore diameter d, Å	6.0	3.5

*Specific resistance of annealed sample reprepared from DMF solution:$0.529x10^4$ ohm cm.

Effects of annealing are also observed on the water transport properties. Both the diffusional permeability and the permeability under osmotic pressure decrease in comparison with the sample before annealing (Table IV). Moreover, the g ratio also decreases, which, in terms of the equivalent pore radius, means that the membrane becomes tighter upon annealing.

To examine the possibility that the changes in membrane properties were caused by permanent chemical changes in the Na^+SPS, a portion of the annealed sample was redissolved in DMF, recast as a film and its conductance measured. As Table IV indicates, the recast film returned to its original conductance, which clearly proves that the annealing process only effected the physical properties of the Na-SPS ionomer film. This point is reinforced by our discovery that an annealed sample which was stored in water over a period of a week slowly changed back to its original conductance value.

At present we do not yet have sufficient information to determine whether the annealing process exerts an effect primarily through changes in chain conformation or the distribution of ionic aggregates, or both. Measurements of Tg showed no change for annealed vs. unannealed samples, while SAXS measurements were inconclusive and require repetition. Further Mossbauer measurements would also be required before definitive conclusions of this nature could be drawn.

Literature Cited

1. McKelvey, J.G.; Spiegler, K.S.; Wyllie, M.R.J. Chem. Eng. Progr. Symp. Ser., 1959, 55, 199.
2. Loeb, S.; Sourirajan, S. ACS Advan. Chem. Ser., 1962, 38, 117.
3. Chludzinski, P.J.; Fickett, A.P.; LaConti, A.G. Amer. Chem. Soc., Div. Polym. Prepr., 1971, 12, 276.
4. Kimura, S.G. Ind. Eng. Chem., Prod. Res. Develop., 1971, 10, 335.
5. Brousse, C.L.; Chapurlat, R.; Quentin, J.P. Desalination, 1976, 18, 137.
6. Noshay, A.; Robenson, L.M. J. Appl. Polym. Sci., 1976, 20, 1885.
7. Quentin, J.P.; Milas, M.; Rinando, M. 5th Int. Symposium on Fresh Water from the Sea, 1976, 4, 157.
8. Kedem, O. Israel J. of Chem., 1973, 11, 313.
9. Kedem, O.; Tanny, G. Pure & Appl. Chem., 1976, 46, 187.
10. Robinson, R.A.; Stokes, R.M. "Electrolyte Solutions", Butterworths, London, 1959.
11. Push, W. Ber. Bunsenges, Phys. Chem., 1977, 81, 854.
12. Marx, C.L.; Caulfield, D.F.; Cooper, S.L. Macromolecules, 1973, 6, 344.
13. Heitner-Wirguin, C.; Bauminger, E.R.; Levy, A.; Labensky de Kanter, F.; Ofer, S. Polymer, in press.
14. Kavesh, S.; Shultz, J.M. J. Polymer Sci., A-2, 1971, 9, 85.
15. Kedem, O.; Katchalsky, A. J. Gen. Physiol., 1961, 45, 143.
16. Kawabe, H.; Jacobson, H.; Miller, J.F.; Gregor, H.P. J. Colloid. Interface Sci., 1966, 21, 791.
17. Lakshminarayanaiah, N. "Transport Phenomena in Membranes", Academic Press, New York, 1969, p. 256.
18. Lakshminarayanaiah, N.; Subrahmanyan, V. J. Phys. Chem., 1968, 72. 1253.
19. Sarbolouki, M.N.; Miller, I.F. Desalination, 1973, 12, 343.
20. Sourirajan, S. Ind. Eng. Chem. Fundamen., 1963, 2, 51.
21. Heyde, M.E.; Peters, C.R.; Anderson, J.E. J. Colloid. Interface Sci., 1975, 50, 467.
22. Sivashinsky, N.; Tanny, G. J. Appl. Polym. Sci., in press.
23. Frommer, M.A.; Shporer, M. J. Appl. Polym. Sci., 1973, 17, 2263.
24. This laboratory, unpublished results.
25. Thau, G.; Bloch, R.; Kedem, O. Desalination, 1966, 1, 129.

26. Shultz, R.D.; Asunmaa, S.K. "Recent Progress in Surface Science", Dannielli, J.F.; Riddiford, C.A.; Rosenberg, M.D. eds., Academic Press, New York, 1970, 3, p. 291.

RECEIVED December 4, 1980.

Hollow-Fiber Reverse-Osmosis Composite Membranes: Process and Properties

R. B. DAVIS, D. K. SCHIFFER, and C. E. KRAMER

Albany International Research Co., Route 128 at U.S. 1, Dedham, MA 02026

Albany International Research Co. has developed an advanced hollow fiber composite reverse osmosis membrane and module under the name of Quantro II^{TM}. This composite membrane is comprised of a porous hollow fiber substrate on which has been deposited a rejection barrier capable of fluxes of commercial importance at high rejection of dissolved salts at elevated temperatures. Resistance to active chlorine has been demonstrated. Proprietary processes have been developed for spinning of the fiber, establishment of the rejection barrier and processing of the fiber to prepare modules of commercial size. Prototype modules are currently in field trials against brackish and seawater feed solutions. Applications under consideration for this membrane include brackish and seawater desalination as well as selected industrial concentration processes.

Earlier publication[1] concerning work of Albany International Research Co. described elements of processes involved in the preparation of the Quantro II. That publication identified an earlier candidate rejection barrier as a sulfonated, furan-based polymeric material. The instability of the furan membrane in field evaluations and its sensitivity to oxidizing agents including chlorine recommended a substitution of alternative rejection barrier chemistry. Recent work resulted in the rejection barrier of Quantro II which is an alternative highly sulfonated polymeric composition. Specific chemistry involved in the preparation of the rejection barrier will be published after patent coverage. The following presents details of unit processes in the preparation of this membrane and results of laboratory and field evaluation. The final portion of this paper will discuss certain elements of the potting procedure and testing necessary to the identification of successful potting materials.

Membrane Unit Processes

Dope Preparation. A porous wall substrate fiber is prepared by the extrusion of a quasi-solution, the principal component of

which is a polysulfone. Several polysulfone materials have been
surveyed. At least two are acceptable for this process. These
are Udel® (Union Carbide Corp.) and Victrex® (ICI Americas).

A fiber spinning dope is prepared by mixing the polysulfone,
solvent and a nonionic surfactant. A preferred solvent is dimethylformamide (DMF); a preferred surfactant is an alkylaryl
polyether alcohol. The dope is prepared such that its bulk viscosity is typically between 9000 and 12000 poises. Successful
dopes demand control of the mode of addition, degree of polymer
comminution, the temperature protocol and agitation rate. The
dope is typically filtered through a 10 micron filter under pressure prior to spinning.

Dry-jet Wet Spinning. Substrate fiber is prepared in a
proprietary process by an apparatus developed and built at Albany
International Research Co. Filtered dope is expressed from a
multihole hollow fiber spinneret. Each orifice of the spinneret
contains a centered needle for the delivery of an inert fluid,
typically dry nitrogen. The dope passes through an air gap of
approximately one centimeter and into an aqueous coagulation
bath. A critical element of this process is that the coagulation
bath is so arranged as to permit the passage of the coagulating
stream through several meters of coagulation bath before it is
touched by any solid. This permits the establishment of a surface of uniform physical and chemical characteristics. After
extensive washing in the coagulation bath, fiber is wound into
packages by equipment common in the handling of textile fibers
but modified to accomodate the sensitive nature of a 50% dense
polymeric structure. Fiber is maintained wet until subsequent
use. The coagulation bath is comprised of an aqueous solution of
DMF and surfactant. Temperature control is maintained with variation less than 1°C. Deionized water is used in the preparation
of the bath. Fiber thus prepared contains less than 2% DMF.
Virtually all of the surfactant in the dope is retained in the
fiber.

Extraction of Surfactant. The influence of surfactant on
the physical properties of the fiber require its removal prior to
the establishment of the reverse osmosis rejection membrane.
Surfactant is removed in a pressure extraction apparatus by the
recirculation of hot aqueous alcohol. Surfactant is removed to
concentrations less than 2% on the weight of dry fiber.

Preparation of Rejection Barrier. Subsequent to the field
trials of the furan membrane, many alternative sulfonated materials were surveyed. The present and preferred rejection barrier
of Quantro II is prepared by the deposition in and on the surface
of the substrate fiber a complex solution of a sulfonated polymeric material prepared in our laboratory. This sulfonated polymeric material is codissolved in aqueous alcohol with ingredients

found necessary to the development of high flux and rejection. Extracted fiber as a multifilament strand is conducted from an aqueous storage bath, around a driven roll and into such a solution. It then passes into a two-stage forced hot air tower. In order to develop both high flux and rejection two stages of heating are employed. Solvent is removed at temperatures less than 100°C. The final curing air temperature is typically up to 150°C. After exiting the tower, yarn is passed around a second driven roll and wound up as a package. The larger linear velocity of the second roll relative to the first imparts an overall stretch of a few percent to the yarn during membrane formation.

Bundle Preparation. Packages of multifilament yarns are backwound to prepare bundles necessary for the manufacture of a reverse osmosis module. A proprietary winder for this operation has been designed and constructed at Albany International Research Co. This device is capable of helically winding multifilament yarns into bundles around a mandrel. This is done in a manner such that the resulting bundle has uniform cylindrical dimensions and uniform fiber density. This minimizes channeling and optimizes exposure of membrane surface area.

A critical element of the winding equipment is that it successfully delivers fiber whose membrane properties cannot tolerate more than a few percent extension. Ceramic or metal guides, typical of textile winding equipment, cause such friction that this extension is exceeded with variable adverse effects on membrane properties. Another critical element in winding is that a uniform loop length of yarn is maintained during the development of the bundle. The reverse osmosis characteristics of a hollow fiber membrane of permeability typical of Quantro II are seriously affected by the pressure drop of permeate down the lumen of the fiber[2]. Therefore it is desirable that the loop length remain constant and relatively short throughout the advancing radial growth of the bundle. To accomplish this, the bundle winding apparatus changes the helix angle in a constant manner in order to deliver a uniform loop length of yarn.

Potting. Several resin formulations have been surveyed as candidates for the potting of Quantro II fiber bundles. This topic is treated in detail below. Critical elements in the choice of formulation include its viscosity, absence of volatiles, pot life, maximum exotherm limit and its adhesion to the fiber[3].

The objective of the proprietary potting procedure is to seal all fibers in a mass of cured epoxy such that the transmembrane pressure may be brought to ground through the pot without failure due to creep or shear along the fiber surface. In this procedure one face of the pot is maintained flat against a base plate of the module. Resin is delivered to the bundle mass through a centrifugal system which forces the viscous formulation through the fiber mass. Speed of delivery is so regulated that air is not entrapped by occlusion. The exotherm develops sufficient reaction to result in a mechanically tractable "green state".

Fiber ends are exposed by excision of a portion of the pot and fiber bundle at several points in the circumference of the pot. A sufficiently high and deep slice at frequent enough intervals will guarantee the exposure of each fiber loop at least once. Due to the physical texture of polysulfone fiber it was found necessary to slice the fiber in tension in order to avoid smearing of the polymer with lumen closure. This may be accomplished through the expedient of advancing the cure of the epoxy resin to a green state at which it is mechanically stable enough to be removed from the mold and sliced. Apparatus for slicing resin and fiber has been designed and constructed. The sliced bundle is reinserted in a mold and the epoxy cure is completed by advancing the temperature.

Module Assembly. After the final cure of epoxy the potted bundle is assembled into a module in which the feed solution and permeate are separated by O-ring seals in a pressure shell. Design of the module is proprietary. Patent applications have been filed. Prototype modules capable of delivering several hundred gallons a day of permeate are in test in various facilities against brackish and sea water.

Membrane Properties

Many Quantro II membranes varying incrementally in composition have been under test for 18 months at Albany International Research Co. Tests are performed on experimental samples of fiber. Approximately 16 inches of multifilament yarn are typically subjected to various feeds and conditions. Such a yarn sample is embedded in epoxy which is sealed into a pressure system. Several test facilities are in operation to provide various feeds and conditions.

A typical test loop includes a pump capable of pressure development to 1000 psig and sufficient valving and piping to permit multistation installation of fiber samples. Feed solutions are delivered from reservoirs which are thermostated and isolated in order to maintain constancy of temperature and composition. The facility is so established that both permeate and concentrate are returned continuously to the reservoir.

Test feeds include synthetic brackish water typical of southwest United States at approximately 3500 ppm, and a typical synthetic seawater at approximately 35,000 ppm. Test conditions include brackish water at 400 psig, 25°C and 760 psig, 25°C. Seawater testing is done at 1000 psig at 25°C and at 50°C. Chlorine sensitivity is evaluated through the use of a feed of brackish water, doped to include a nominal 100 ppm hypochlorite ion at pH 7.5 to 8.5. Chlorine concentration is monitored daily and adjusted to the nominal.

The membrane composition of Quantro II has been under continuous research for 19 months. Early samples were put on test
in order to establish a long-term data base for this chemistry.
While that early composition has been modified to achieve higher
flux and rejection, its durability can be judged from Table I.
Table I plots data obtained daily over the time period indicated.
Curves on all tables have been smoothed to avoid daily fluctuations. It should be understood that fluctuations of as much as
0.2% rejection and 0.2 gfd in flux are routinely experienced and
are not shown.

Table I displays the results over several thousand hours of
exemplary samples tested at zero length, zero recovery. Brackish
water rejection under conditions specified are in excess of 99%
at high pressure and greater than 98.5% at lower pressure such as
400 psi. Flux values displayed are those typical of early samples in the development of Quantro II. At low pressure against
brackish water such values were 1-2 gfd. Recent values of samples tested under identical conditions have exhibited rejections
of 94+% at a flux of 5-7 gfd at 400 psi.

Table II displays several thousand hours' data on various
samples of Quantro II tested against synthetic seawater at 15-
20°C. Routine samples exhibit a flux in excess of 1 gfd at rejection of 98-99%. It is possible with composite membrane preparation to trade rejection for flux within certain limits. The
objective of present work is to maintain a rejection of 99+
against seawater while modifying formulation in order to achieve
a higher flux.

As a result of prior field experience with the furan system,
a qualifying test has been employed at Albany International Research Co. to measure the durability. Table III displays data of
typical samples tested against synthetic seawater at 1000 psig
maintained at a temperature of 50°C. Samples of cellulosic seawater membrane and polyamide membrane were found to fail in several hours of challenge by these conditions.

Quantro II has exhibited a decline in rejection of a few
percent over 8000 hours. Flux has declined implying a change in
the physical chemistry of the rejection barrier. Polysulfone
composite membranes in our experience have not exhibited long-
term compaction. The decline in flux in Table III indicates,
however, that the higher temperature and pressure in the presence
of seawater may be compacting Quantro II. The results, however,
are equivocal. More testing will help to identify the magnitude
of this change.

A continuing major objective in the search for alternative
commercial membranes is stability against active chlorine. Control of biological growth upstream of the membrane appears desirable in most practical water systems. Removal of chlorine
prior to membrane treatment is expensive and potentially hazard-
ous should the removal system fail. The polymer chosen for the

Table I

Feed: 3500 ppm Brackish, 760 psi → 400 psi, 25°C

——————— Rejection   ---------- Flux

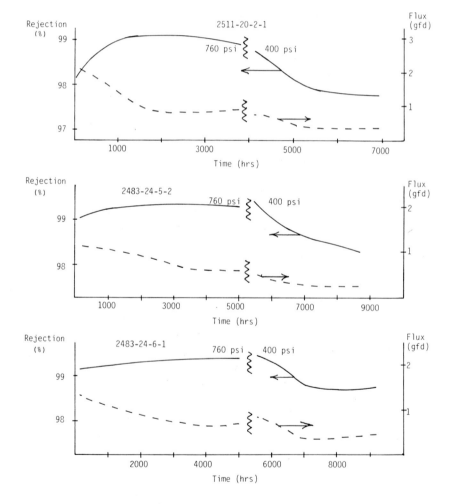

Table II

Feed: 1000 psi Sea Water at 15°-20°C

_____ Rejection ---------- Flux

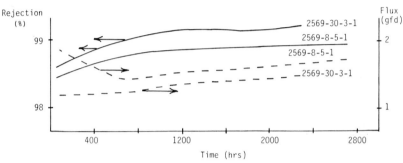

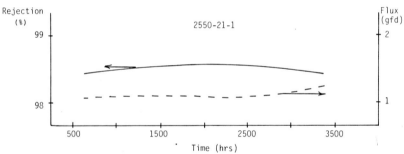

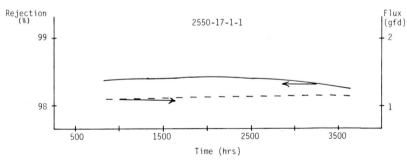

Table III

Feed: 1000 psi, Sea Water, 50°C

———— Rejection   ------ Flux

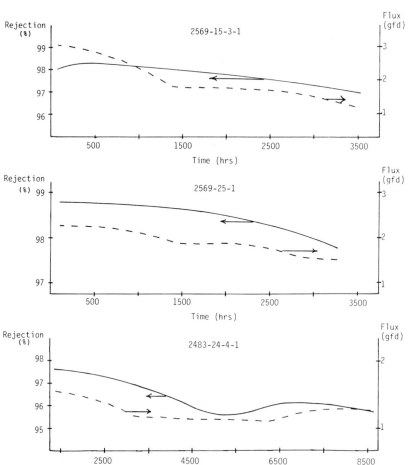

Quantro II rejection barrier was selected with chlorine stability
as an objective. Sulfonation is an oxidation reaction. High
levels of sulfonation imply the potential for stability against
chlorine and other oxidizing agents.

Table IV exhibits data recorded for several typical examples
tested under conditions described. A nominal 100 ppm active
chlorine was selected as an accelerated test of chlorine sensitivity. Over 2000 hours there is a slight measurable decline in
rejection with no significant change in flux. The pH of the test
solution is typically 7.5-8.5 in order to maintain a reasonably
stable concentration of hypochlorite ion. Tests are in progress
at an acid pH of 5-6 in a test loop in which the reservoir is not
sealed under pressure. Therefore a stable concentration of
chlorine is difficult to maintain due to the evolution of chlorine gas. It is possible for a change in the rate of degradation
to occur due to a change in chemical mechanism of attack. This
will be evaluated in the near term.

Table V displays data recorded at the test facility in
Roswell, New Mexico, maintained by the Office of Water Research
and Technology, U. S. Department of Interior. This facility
delivers a feed of brackish water pretreated to control bacterial
growth and to deliver a feed free of chlorine. Modules 148 and
152 were nominally identical samples. They are constructed of
fiber bundles approximately 2 inches in diameter, 10 inches in
length and containing approximately 25 square feet of membrane
surface area. The increase in productivity over time can be explained by an increase in feed temperature over the course of the
test. The decline in rejection of module 148 is not fully understood. However, it is probable that the decline is similarly the
responsibility of a temperature increase. Recent data indicates
a stabilization at a rejection level of 94%.

Module 152 has been challenged by the injection of nominal
one ppm hypochlorite ion under pressure immediately upstream of
the module. The pH of the feed is maintained at approximately 5.
The decline in rejection is possibly an indication of chemical
degradation at the lower pH. However, it has been determined
that this test feed has also included a substantial loading of
soluble iron due to the fact that the injection pump was suf-
fering substantial corrosion during the course of this trial. At
approximately 1000 hours the module was found to be heavily involved with an iron oxide precipitate. This was subsequently
treated with aqueous citric acid for cleaning. The decline in
rejection stabilized at 92%. It is possible that the combination
of chlorine and soluble iron initiated a chemical influence resulting in data unlike that generated at higher pH in our laboratory. Tests will continue to quantify the impact of iron and
chlorine on Quantro II.

Table IV

Feed: 760 psi, 3500 ppm Brackish Water, 25°C

~ 100 ppm Active Chlorine as OCl⁻

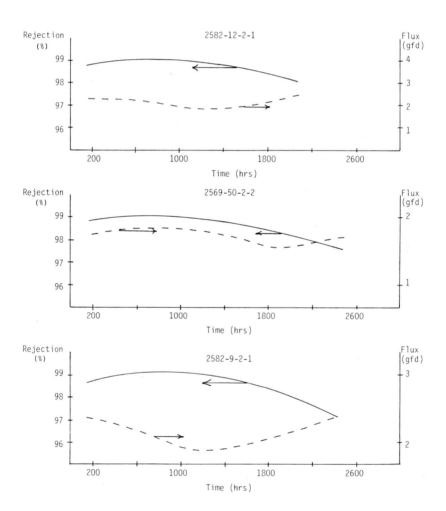

Table V

On Test at Roswell

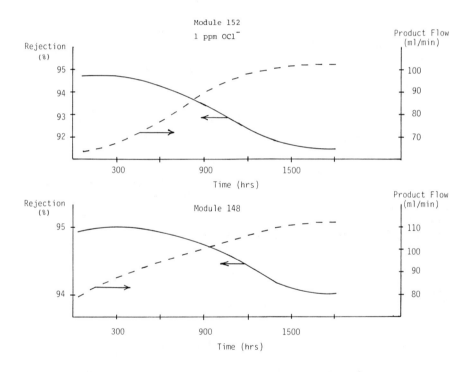

Epoxy Resin Selection

Quantro II assembled in a bundle must be sealed at least at
one end prior to assembly in a module.   In order to make use of
the membrane, fiber must be cut to permit collection of permeate.
The membrane differential pressure must be brought to ground
through the seal.   The pot seal must be resistant over time to
creep, adhesive interface loss and chemical degradation.   The
proprietary development by Albany International Research Co. of
the potting process and fiber end exposure[3] describes a design
in which pressure is brought to ground through the pot at the
module seal plate.   Permeate exiting from exposed fiber ends
passes into a gallery and is removed at atmospheric pressure.
The total force of upstream pressure is distributed over the
uncut face of the pot in contact with the module face plate.   The
epoxy pot must have such dimensional stability that the circumference of the pot makes excellent contact with the O-ring seal
of the pressure shell.   These multiple demands imply numerous
interactive and restrictive parameters in the choice of the epoxy
system chosen for pot manufacture.

Formulation Requirements.   In order to penetrate the mass of
fiber at one end of the bundle, the formulation must have sufficiently low viscosity to move easily through the bundle completely wetting all fiber surface area.   Typically, formulations
of viscosity less than 8000 poises have been successful.   Too low
viscosity or too rapid delivery of the formulation can result in
the occlusion of air and the ultimate development of voids with
loss of mechanical integrity.   Our process demands that formulation be delivered and partially cured to an intermediate plateau
termed green state.   This requires a minimum pot life of 30 minutes after blending of resin and curative.   The physical chemistry of the composite membrane requires that the initial exotherm not exceed approximately $150^{\circ}C$.
After subsidence of temperature following initial exotherm,
the fiber bundle with the partially cured pot is removed from the
mold for fiber end exposure.   The mechanical integrity of the
potted end in this green state must be sufficiently great to permit careful handling and insertion in the machine necessary for
fiber-epoxy excision.
The proprietary device employed for exposure of fiber ends
slices the pot on a diagonal and at an angle through the lower
end of the mass.   Several slices are taken until the necessary
depth is achieved in order to assure exposure of all fiber ends.
The texture of the pot of the epoxy is such as to permit smooth
scission while permitting the fiber to be cut in tension.   This
avoids smearing fiber ends closed.   The sliced pot is reinserted
in a heated mold and at temperatures necessary for the development
of ultimate physical properties a final cure is achieved.

Cured Epoxy Requirements. In order to comply with multiple needs identified above, the epoxy pot should have a compressive yield strength of greater than 9000 psi. In addition, for brackish and seawater applications an arbitrary specification of zero creep at $50^{\circ}C$ at 1000 psi under seawater for 3000 hours has been established. Applications at higher temperatures would obviously demand a higher zero creep temperature.

A minimum shrinkage of 5% or less, more typically 1% or less, has been specified in order to maintain excellent seal transference in the cured mass. This requirement has been met through much experimentation involving various levels of filler. Fillers typically result in lower shrinkage with lower bulk viscosity. Fillers also present difficulty in this application due to the inherent problem presented by a fibrous mass with its high surface area. The present formulation has avoided the use of fillers.

To be successful the fiber-pot interface must survive indefinitely at temperature and pressure against the feed liquor. The qualifying test for a given formulation at Albany International Research Co. has been survival for greater than 3000 hours of multiple samples tested at $50^{\circ}C$ at 1000 psig against synthetic seawater. Samples are tested by potting small numbers of fibers in a plug of epoxy sealed with a Swagelok® fitting into a pressure shell. This is a test of creep, shear failure, adhesion and chemical durability.

Finally, most formulations successful in meeting other criteria have been tested for heat distortion temperature as a final criterion for judgment. A commercial device (Tinius-Olsen) has been employed for these tests.

Analysis. It has been our objective to determine criteria for resin, curative or formulation which would permit prediction of sucess prior to potting tests. Many tests, both chemical and physical in nature, have been executed on commercial resin systems. These have included high pressure liquid chromatography (HPLC), Fourier Transform infrared spectrometry (FTIR), gel permeation chromatography, compressive tensile tests by Instron on resin plaques in air and under various aqueous solutions and heat distortion temperature.

Over 30 commercial formulations have been surveyed in depth. Compressive strength measurements permit the exclusion of materials obviously prone to fail under pressure. FTIR (MX-1, Nicolet Instrument Corp.) analysis has identified formulations with volatile diluents capable of chemically modifying the composite membrane. Through the use of FTIR it was possible with an otherwise successful formulation to identify the presence of butyl glycidyl ether (BGE) as a diluent. Subsequently experimentation showed that vapor of BGE is capable of plasticizing porous polysulfone with a drop in both flux and rejection of the membrane. Collaboration with the supplier resulted in substitution of a nonvolatile glycidyl ether diluent to avoid the problem.

FTIR has shown the close similarity of most resins based on Bis-Phenol A and has helped narrow the focus of development on the curative as the principal contributor to successful formulation. For present applications oligomeric polyamide amines appear successful in meeting present criteria. However, the only objective analysis of cured resin to date exhibiting a correlation of measured value with success in creep resistance as well as adhesion is heat distortion temperature. The following presents a correlation of heat distortion temperatures and adhesion for several formulations tested. In most cases, pass/fail criteria was based on the majority of six samples tested.

Heat Distortion Temperature vs. Adhesion

Formulation	HDT (°C)	Adhesion (50°C, 1000 psi Sea Water)
A	77	+
B	92	−
C	76	+
D	72	+
F	114	−
G	67	+
H	159	−
I	157	−
J	146	−

After approximately one man-year of effort at analysis of the potting problem, the best advice is still to test the pot with membrane in an application. An objective measurement predicting success of resin, diluent and formulation before and after cure is still not secure.

Summary

Research effort at Albany International Research Co. has developed unit processes necessary for pilot scale production of several species of reverse osmosis hollow fiber composite membranes. These processes include spin-dope preparation, a proprietary apparatus for dry-jet wet-spinning of microporous polysulfone hollow fibers, coating of these fibers with a variety of permselective materials, bundle winding using multifilament yarns and module assembly. Modules of the membrane identified as Quantro II[TM] are in field trial against brackish and seawater feeds. Brackish water rejections of 94+% at a flux of 5-7 gfd at 400 psi have been measured. Seawater rejections of 99+% at 1-2 gfd at 1000 psi have been measured. Membrane use requires sealing of some portion of the fiber bundle for installation in a pressure shell. Much effort has been devoted to identification of potting materials which exhibit satisfactory adhesion to the fiber while

permitting staged curing necessary to our proprietary fiber end
exposure. Exposing fiber ends requires the curing of epoxy potting compound to a gel which permits excision of a portion of the
pot and bundle. Changes in surface chemistry from membrane to
membrane have required requalification of potting compounds.
Analysis has focused on unsuccessful and successful formulations
to identify critical elements.

Acknowledgements

The authors wish to acknowledge the leadership and assistance of M. J. Coplan, Corporate Senior Scientist and Director.
They wish to further acknowledge the support and technical
competence of the following co-workers: R. D. Burchesky,
C. H. Park, G. Götz, J. K. Nelson, A. M. Fejes, F. Bilewski,
S. C. Williams and R. C. Woglom. Finally, the authors wish to
acknowledge the financial support of Albany International Corp.
and, since 1976, partial support of the Office of Water Research
and Technology, U. S. Department of the Interior.

(1) R. B. Davis, R. D. Burchesky, M. J. Coplan, Desalination,
     22(1977) 221-227.
(2) J. H. Beale, M. J. Coplan, D. B. Eagles, S. Middleman,
     "Advanced Quantro™ Hollow Fiber Membranes," Membrane Sym-
     posium, Clemson University, Clemson, S.C., 15 August 1977.
(3) M. J. Coplan, J. H. Beale, R. B. Davis, U.S.Patent 4,220,489,
     "Method of Fabricating a Hollow Filament Separator Module,"
     September 2, 1980.

RECEIVED December 4, 1980.

Poly(vinyl alcohol) Membranes for Reverse Osmosis

MOSHE G. KATZ[1] and THEODORE WYDEVEN, JR.

NASA—Ames Research Center, Moffett Field, CA 94035

Polyvinyl alcohol(PVA) has been shown at very early stages to have very poor salt selectivity (1). Without treatment it has salt rejections in the range between 20-50%. Being a material with very good film forming properties and high water permeability, it always seemed an attractive material for high water flux,reverse osmosis(RO) membranes. Chemical crosslinking is known to improve considerably the selective permeability to water and salts of the PVA. Thus PVA membranes crosslinked with formaldehyde were shown (2) to have salt rejections in the range of $4-8\times10^{-8} cm^2/s$. Even better results were obtained by crosslinking the PVA membranes using tolylene diisocyanate (3). By this method PVA membranes with salt rejections of up to 99.2% and water permeability coefficients in the range of $2-5\times10^{-7} cm^2/s$ were reported.

Another attractive quality of the PVA is its outstanding chemical stability. Peter and Stefan (4) investigated the chemical stability of PVA vis a vis a series of solvents and reagents and some of their results are summarized in Table I. This table presents a comparison between the chemical resistances of PVA, polyvinyl butyral(PVB), polyvinyl acetate(PVAc), and cellulose acetate(CA). It is evident from this table that the PVA is considerably more stable than the rest of the tested materials.

In this article, results of studies of the water and salt transport properties of PVA membranes and a method for preparing thin skinned, high flux PVA membranes are reported.

Transport Properties of PVA Membranes

The transport properties studies were made in the framework of the evaluation of the effect of radiation crosslinking and heat treatment on the PVA, and the possibility to improve the RO performance of these membranes using these methods. The water

[1] Current address: Pure and Applied Radiation Chemistry Department, Soreq Nuclear Research Center, Yavne, Israel.

0097–6156/81/0153–0383$05.00/0

Table I
Chemical stability of PVA at $20^{\circ}C$
(from Peter et al. (4))

Reagent	Concentration (weight %)	pH	Membrane material			
			PVA	PVB	PVAc	CA
HNO_3	12	0	3	0	0	0
H_2SO_4	48	0	3	0	0	0
HCl	7	0	3	0	0	0
NH_4OH	25	13	3	0	0	0
NaOH	10	14	3	0	0	0
Phenol	0.1	3	3	0	0	0
Phenol	1.0	3	3	0	0	0
Phenol	2.0	3	3	0	0	0
Ethanol	100	7	3	0	0	0
DMF	100	7	3	0	0	0
DMSO	100	7	3	0	0	0
Formamide	100	7	3	0	0	0

Stability degrees:
0=Destruction of membrane
1=Strong swelling, decrease of membrane properties
2=Little swelling, membrane still usable
3=Stable, no alteration of membrane properties

and salt permeabilities through radiation crosslinked and heat
treated PVA were measured at various applied pressures, temperatures, and salt concentrations. For the analysis of the experimental results, the Lonsdale solution diffusion model was employed,where the water flux(F_w), salt flux(F_s), and salt rejection(R_s)
are given by the following equations:

$$(1) \qquad F_w = - \frac{D_{wm} \, c_{wm} \, V_w}{RT} \, \frac{\Delta P - \Delta \pi}{\lambda}$$

$$(2) \qquad F_s = - D_{sm} K \, \frac{\Delta c_s}{\lambda}$$

$$(3) \qquad R_s = (1 + \frac{D_{sm} K \, RT \, c_w''}{D_{wm} c_{wm} V_w (\Delta P - \Delta \pi)})^{-1} = \frac{c_s' - c_s''}{c_s'}$$

where D_{wm} and c_{wm} are the diffusion coefficient of water and the
water concentration in the membrane, respectively; V_w is the partial molar volume of water in the membrane; ΔP and $\Delta \pi$ are the
differences in applied pressure and osmotic pressure across the
membrane; R and T are the gas constant and the absolute temperature respectively; λ is the effective membrane thickness; D_{sm} and
K are the diffusion coefficient of salt and the salt distribution coefficient, respectively; and $\Delta c_s = c_s' - c_s''$ is the difference
between the salt concentration on the high pressure side and the
salt concentration on the low pressure side of the membrane.

Radiation Crosslinked PVA Membranes. The water and salt
permeability coefficients of the radiation crosslinked PVA membranes, obtained by using equations 1 and 2 were found to decrease with increasing the applied pressure. A linear correlation was found between the reciprocal of the water permeability
coefficient and the pressure, as shown in Figures 1 and 2, at
various temperatures. This linear correlation can be expressed
by the following equation:

$$(4) \qquad \frac{1}{D_{wm} c_{wm}} = a + b\Delta P$$

Substituting equation 4 into the water flux equation(equation 1)
yields a correlation between the water flux(F_w) and pressure,
which is identical with the empirical relationship suggested earlier by Paul (5), for solvent permeation through swollen hydro-
gels:

$$(5) \qquad \frac{1}{\lambda F_w} = \frac{a \, RT}{V_w} \frac{1}{\Delta P} + \frac{b \, RT}{V_w} \qquad\qquad \text{or}$$

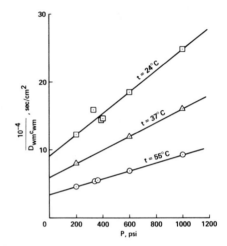

Figure 1.   Dependence of the water permeability coefficient on pressure (radiation cross-linked, 86,000 mol wt, 100% hydrolyzed PVA)

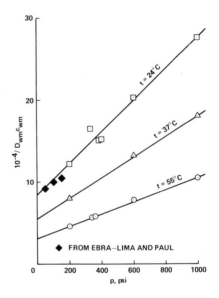

Figure 2.   Dependence of the water permeability coefficient on pressure (radiation cross-linked, 115,000 mol wt, 100% hydrolyzed PVA): (♦) derived from data reported by Ebra–Lima and Paul (6).

$$(6) \qquad F_w = \frac{V_w}{\lambda RT} \frac{\Delta P}{a + b\Delta P}$$

Ebra–Lima and Paul also studied the water transport through terephtalaldehyde crosslinked PVA membranes (6). From the dependence of the water flux on pressure, reported by them, and shown in Figure 3, we were able to evaluate the corresponding permeability coefficients at the various pressures.   These data are also plotted along with our data in Figure 2, showing   good agreement. This agreement between the two sets of data can also be visualized by a plot of the reciprocal of the water flux(F_w) vs. the reciprocal of the pressure drop(ΔP), as shown in Figure 4, where the fluxes were normalized for the membrane thickness λ.

The temperature dependence of the water permeability of radiation crosslinked PVA membranes is shown in Figure 5.   From this dependence an activation energy of 6.0 ± 0.2 kcal/mole can be derived, in good agreement with data reported earlier by Peter and Mittelstadt (7) and by Paul(6).

The salt rejection of the radiation crosslinked PVA membranes was very low, around 20-50%, i.e. in the same range as found earlier for untreated PVA. No systematic change of the salt rejection with temperature was observed in the temperature range between 24-65°C, suggesting that the activation energy of the salt permeability was identical with that of the water, and therefore, the salt flux was increasing proportionally with the water flux at higher temperatures. However, the rejection was found to be strongly concentration dependent, as shown in Figure 6.

The very low salt rejections, i.e. the high salt fluxes and the identical temperature dependence of the water and salt permeabilities may be considered as suggesting a coupled water and salt transport. However, it is evident from the salt rejection data in Figure 6 that the salt rejection is increasing with pressure, as expected from the solution-diffusion model.   The plots of the reciprocal of the salt rejection(R_s) vs. the reciprocal of the pressure drop(ΔP),shown in Figure 7, are linear and intercepting at 1.0 or very close to it. This is in agreement with the Lonsdale equation for salt rejection (equation 3) by solution-diffusion membranes, and   suggests   uncoupled salt and water flows.

Diffusive Salt Permeability Through PVA Membranes. In order to verify the interdependence between the water and salt transport through PVA, the diffusive permeability of salt through an unpressurized PVA membrane was measured. The diffusion system employed in this experiment is described schematically in Figure 8. The diffusion cell consists of an upper cell and a lower cell, separated by the tested membrane, a 150 micron thick, untreated PVA membrane. Initially, the lower cell contains distilled water, which is circulated through a conductivity cell, and the

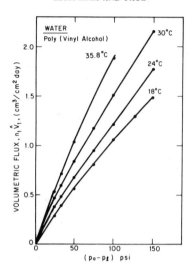

Figure 3.   Hydraulic permeation data for
PVA–water system (6)

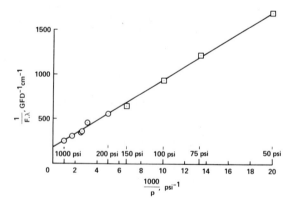

Figure 4.   Pressure dependence of water fluxes through PVA membranes as deter-
mined by Ebra–Lima and Paul (6) and in this work: (□) Ebra–Lima and Paul's
data at 24°C (λ = 35μm); (○) data for radiation cross-linked, 115,000 mol wt,
100% hydrolyzed PVA (λ = 4.0 μm).

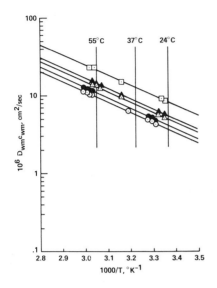

Figure 5. Temperature dependence of the water permeability of radiation cross-linked PVA membranes under various pressure differentials: (□) ΔP = 200 psi; (△) ΔP = 600 psi; (○) ΔP = 1000 psi. Open symbols refer to 100% hydrolyzed, 115,000 mol wt PVA; solid symbols refer to 100% hydrolyzed, 86,000 mol wt PVA. The lines are the best fit to the data points evaluated by linear regression analysis.

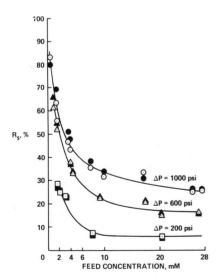

Figure 6. Feed concentration dependence of the salt rejection of radiation cross-linked PVA membranes under various pressure differentials: (□) ΔP = 200 psi; (△) ΔP = 600 psi; (○) ΔP = 1000 psi. Open symbols refer to 100% hydrolyzed, 115,000 mol wt PVA; solid symbols refer to 100% hydrolyzed, 86,000 mol wt PVA.

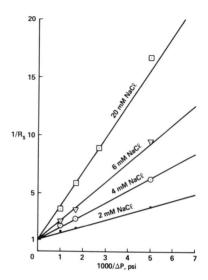

Figure 7. Pressure dependence of the rejection at various feed concentrations

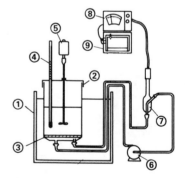

Figure 8. Diffusive permeability measurement system: (1) thermostated bath; (2) diffusion cell; (3) membrane; (4) thermometer; (5) stirrer; (6) circulation pump; (7) conductivity cell; (8) conductivity meter; (9) recorder.

conductivity is recorded continuously. The upper cell is filled
with a salt solution of known concentration and the rate of change
of the salt concentration in the lower cell is determined.

Some of the results obtained by these measurements are presented in Table II. These data are comparable with corresponding

Table II
Diffusive salt permeability through untreated PVA membranes
measured at atmospheric pressure ($cm^2/s \times 10^6$)

Salt concentration in upper cell (weight%) Temperature (^{o}C)	20	0.1	0.025
25	1.16	1.31	1.82
37	1.54	1.87	2.41
50	2.21	2.70	3.52
Activation energy (kcal/mole)	5.0±0.4	5.5±0.5	5.1±0.5

Table III
Salt permeability of radiation crosslinked PVA determined
by reverse osmosis experiments ($cm^2/s \times 10^6$)

Salt concentration of feed solution (weight%) Temperature (^{o}C)	0.125	0.025
24	1.69	0.62
37	2.52	0.92
55	4.08	1.49
Activation energy (kcal/mole)	6.0±0.2	6.0±0.2

results derived from RO experiments with radiation crosslinked
membranes, listed in Table III, above.

Heat Treated PVA Membranes. The concept of independent water
and salt transport through PVA is further supported by the permeability properties of heat treated PVA membranes. It was found
that by subjecting the PVA membranes to heat treatment, a sharp
decrease of the water and salt permeabilities is caused. The

effect of the heat treatment duration at 175°C on the water and
salt permeabilities through PVA is presented in Figure 9. It is
evident in this figure that the decrease in salt permeability is
much steeper than the decrease in water permeability as a result
of the heat treatment.

Study of the temperature dependence of the salt and water
permeabilities through heat treated PVA membranes indicates that
the heat treatment effect is expressed mainly in changes in permeability activation energies. The activation parameters for water and salt permeability of PVA membranes following various
treatments are presented in Table IV. It is evident that the salt
permeability activation energy is increasing about 2-3 times as

Table IV
Temperature dependence of water and salt
permeabilities of heat treated PVA membranes

$$P = P_\infty e^{-E_a/RT}$$

Heat treatment		Water permeability		Salt permeability		Feed concentration
Temp. (°C)	Duration (min)	E_a ($\frac{kcal}{mole}$)	P_∞ (cm^2/s)	E_a ($\frac{kcal}{mole}$)	P_∞ (cm^2/s)	(mM)
Untreated		6.39±0.16	0.18±0.04	6.63±0.21	19±6	15.8
120	80	6.12±0.23	0.14±0.04	6.00±0.61	13±9	16.6
160	70	7.54±0.26	0.27±0.10	6.79±0.39	3±3	25.0
175	35	7.86±0.27	0.24±0.08	8.87±0.28	11±4	1.10
175	70	7.53±0.14	0.13±0.03	9.52±0.20	9±4	1.70
Radiation crosslinked		6.03±0.07	0.10±0.01	6.03±0.07	3±2	2.00

fast as the activation energy for water permeation as a result of
the changes induced by the heat treatment in the PVA membranes.
The different activation energies of salt and water transport
through the heat treated membranes also suggest uncoupled transport of salt and water.

We may conclude that our findings support independent water
and salt permeation processes, and suggest that the salt permeation is governed by a solution-diffusion transport mechanism.

Preparation of Thin Skinned, Asymmetric PVA Membranes

In order to obtain thin skinned, high flux membranes from
PVA, several approaches were tried. The method presented in this
article is reminiscent of the classical phase inversion method,
which is widely applied in casting of asymmetric RO membranes.
However, instead of using a gelling bath composed of a nonsolvent

for the membrane material and miscible with the solvent from which
the membrane is cast, a "complexing" bath was used, which was a
solution of a complexing agent in water, i.e. water was the only
liquid involved in the casting procedure.

The casting procedure consisted of drawing an aqueous solution of PVA to a thin layer, and after an evaporation period, im-
mersing in the complexing bath. The complexing bath used in our
study was basically a saturated $CuSO_4$ solution, with or without
a series of possible additives. After a period of equilibration
of over 24 hours, the membranes were dried and subjected to dry
heat treatment,in order to stabilize the asymmetric structure obtained. The preparation conditions of several membranes prepared
by this method are shown in Table V.

Table V
Preparation conditions of asymmetric
polyvinyl alcohol membranes*

Membrane	Drying time (sec)	Time in saturated $CuSO_4$ (hr)	Heat treatment	
			Temperature (^{o}C)	Time (min)
AS 3	90	24	175	10
AS 4	90	185	175	10
AS 5	30	160	175	13
AS 23	480	119	175	10

*The membranes were cast from a 9% aqueous solution
of 100% hydrolyzed, 115,000 MW polyvinyl alcohol.

The salt and water permeabilities of these membranes were
compared with those of homogeneous PVA membranes heat treated
under similar conditions. The salt rejections of several homogeneous and asymmetric membranes are presented in Figure 10.
The solid lines in this figure are based on results obtained from
homogeneous membranes, while the data points refer to the asymmetric membranes. It is evident from this figure that the salt
rejections of the homogeneous and asymmetric membranes are in the
same range. Comparison of the the water fluxes through these
membranes, given in Table VI, reveals however, that while through
6 micron thick homogeneous membranes only fluxes below 1 GFD were
obtained, the fluxes through the asymmetric membranes were higher
by more than an order of magnitude. Also a clear correlation between the water flux and the drying period before "quenching" in
the complexing solution is evident from the data listed in this
table. Thus for 30 seconds drying period, membranes with fluxes
of 38 to 50 GFD were obtained, while longer drying periods are
followed by a gradual decrease in the water flux.

These findings were interpreted as indicating that a thin
skinned, asymmetric structure was obtained. In order to verify

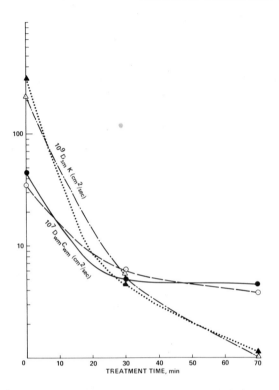

Figure 9.   Effect of the duration of heat treatment at 175°C on salt and water permeabilities of PVA at 30°C: (△) salt permeability coefficients; (○) water permeability coefficients. Open symbols refer to 100% hydrolyzed, 86,000 mol wt PVA; solid symbols refer to 100% hydrolyzed, 115,000 mol wt PVA.

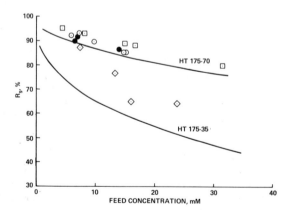

Figure 10.   Salt rejection of heat-treated asymmetric and homogeneous PVA membranes as a function of feed concentration at $\Delta P = 1000$ psi and $t = 30°C$: (◇) AS5; (□) AS23; (○) AS4; (●) AS3. The solid lines represent the data obtained for the heat-treated homogeneous PVA membranes.

Table VI

Comparison of water fluxes through heat treated
asymmetric and homogeneous polyvinyl alcohol
membranes*

Membrane	Thickness (microns)	Drying time (sec)	Water flux (GFD)
HT175-70	6.0		0.6-0.7
HT175-35	6.0		0.8-1.1
AS 5		30	38-50
AS 3		90	19-25
AS 4		90	24-30
AS 23		480	14-16

*Measured at $\Delta P=1000$ psi, 30-40°C

this, the dense and the porous sides of these membranes were
inspected by a scanning electron microscop(SEM). As expected,
the backside of the membranes were found to have a characteristic
porous structure with pore sizes in the range of 2 to 3 microne.
Figure 11(a)and(b)presents the SEM pictures of the dense and porous sides of the inspected membrane at a magnification of x3000.
Other SEM pictures were also obtained at magnifications of up to
x5000. At these magnifications there is no evidence of porosity
on the skin side. In order to ascertain that the picture is focused at the membrane surface, a segment covered with fine particles, which are visible in the micrographs,was selected.

So far, the selectivity of these membranes was tested only
with regard to solutions of salt in water. There are indications
however, from various sources, like the work of Peter and Stefan
(4), that these membranes may be valuable for other separations.
In principle, it is also possible to improve and modify the selectivity properties of these membranes by using other methods
for crosslinking them, such as formalization or reaction with
tolylene diisocyanate, mentioned earlier, or by selecting other
complexing agents for the casting procedure.

Abstract

The results of a reverse osmosis study of radiation crosslinked and heat treated polyvinyl alcohol(PVA) membranes are reported.
In the framework of this study the permeability of water and salt
through these membranes was investigated. In parallel, the diffusive transport of salt through PVA was also studied. The results
suggest that the transport of salt and water through PVA is uncoupled. The salt transport data can be rationalized in terms of a
modified solution-diffusion model.
A new procedure for casting thin skinned asymmetric PVA mem-

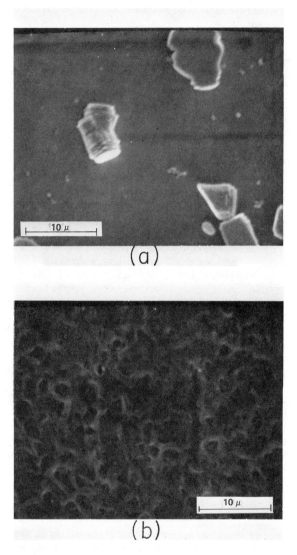

Figure 11.   SEMs of asymmetric PVA membranes at ×3000 magnification: (a) the
dense side (skin) of the membrane; (b) the porous side of the membrane.

branes was developed. The characteristics of these membranes
were found to be closely controlled by the casting conditions and
by the posttreatments. Data on the reverse osmosis performance
and structure of some of these membranes are reported.

List of Symbols

a	intercept in equation 4
b	slope in equation 4
CA	cellulose acetate
c'_s	salt concentration in the solution on the high pressure side of the membrane
c''_s	salt concentration in the solution on the low pressure side of the membrane
c'_w	water concentration in the solution on the high pressure side of the membrane
c''_w	water concentration in the solution on the low pressure side of the membrane
c_{wm}	water concentration in the membrane under the conditions of the RO test.
Δc_s	$= c'_s - c''_s$
DMF	dimethyl formamide
DMSO	dimethyl sulfoxide
D_{sm}	diffusion coefficient of salt in the membrane under the conditions of the RO test
D_{wm}	diffusion coefficient of water in the membrane under the conditions of the RO test
E_a	activation energy
F_s	salt flux
F_w	water flux
GFD	gallons/square foot, day
K	salt distribution coefficient
MW	molecular weight
P	permeability coefficient (the product of diffusion coefficient and the concentration of the permeating species in the membrane)
P_∞	preexponential factor in the Arrhenius representation of the permeability coefficient
psi	pounds/square inch
PVA	polyvinyl alcohol
PVAc	polyvinyl acetate
PVB	polyvinyl butyral
ΔP	hydrostatic pressure differential across the membrane
R	gas constant
R_s	salt rejection
RO	reverse osmosis
SEM	scanning electron microscope(microscopy)
T	absolute temperature

V_w partial molar volume of water in the membrane

λ membrane thickness

$\Delta\pi$ osmotic pressure differential across the membrane

Acknowledgement. This study was done in the framework of a National Research Council, Postdoctoral Resident Associateship awarded to M.G.K.

Literature Cited

1. Michelsen, D.L.; Harriott P., Appl.Polym.Symp., 1970, 13, 27.
2. Chen, C.T.; Chang, Y.T.; Chen, M.C.; Tobolsky, A.V.; J.Appl. Polym.Sci., 1973, 17, 789.
3. Dick, R.; Nicolas, L.; Desalination, 1975, 17, 239.
4. Peter, S; Hese, N.; Stefan, R.; Desalination, 1976, 19, 161.
5. Paul, D.R.; Ebra-Lima, O.M.; J.Appl.Polym.Sci., 1970, 14, 2201
6. Ebra-Lima,O.M.; Paul, D.R.; J.Appl.Polym.Sci., 1975, 19, 1381
7. Peter, S.; Mittelstadt, D.; Kolloid-Z. u Z. Polymere, 1973, 251, 225.

RECEIVED January 2, 1981.

Successful Operation of a Permasep Permeator Reverse-Osmosis System on Biologically Active Feed Water

H. W. POHLAND and G. E. BETTINGER

Plastic Products Division, E. I. du Pont de Nemours and Company, Inc., Wilmington, DE 19898

A "Permasep" permeator reverse osmosis (RO) installation, capable of producing 1500 cubic meters of product water per day, was successfully operated for six months with RO feed water drawn from an estuary and having 1200 to 1400 mg/ℓ total dissolved solids (TDS).

The plant shown in Figure 1 consists of a water pretreatment plant and four separate blocks of "Permasep" units. All blocks are fed by the same high pressure pump, and each block consists of 4-inch modules, reject-staged in a 2 to 1 ratio. The total conversion is about 70 percent -- this means that about 70 percent of the feed water is converted to product, with 30 percent discarded as a brine stream.

Reject staging was used to achieve flow rates necessary to counteract the effects of concentration polarization. During this initial period local water authorities completed a dam, cutting the sea connection to the estuary and causing a gradual drop in the RO feed water to 250 mg/ℓ TDS. With this drop in TDS was a marked decrease in overall plant performance, as evidenced by a drop in productivity (Figure 2a) (flux) and an increase in the salt passage (Figure 2b). Normal cleaning measures temporarily restored the flux and halted the rise in salt passage. However, as shown in these figures, the plant soon began to deteriorate and periodic cleanings were used to attempt to maintain productivity.

After 24 months of operation a thorough analysis of the plant performance was made. No changes in the water pretreatment were observed; the Langelier Saturation Index (Ref. 1) had been kept negative with the changing water analysis; and the silt density index (SDI), a measure of suspended solids, was consistently below 2.5, well within the "Permasep" Guideline of SDI max. = 3.0. These findings ruled out scaling, iron, or colloidal fouling as the source of difficulty.

Red slime deposits, which appeared to be biological in origin, were observed in one disassembled permeator. A microscopic examination of the slime revealed a heavy growth of a

0097–6156/81/0153–0399$05.00/0

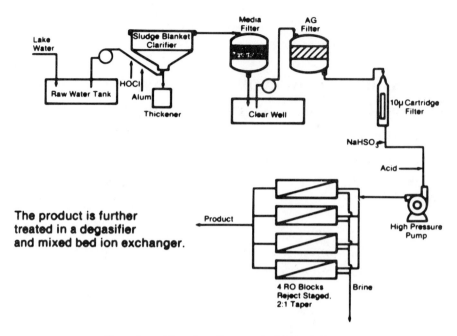

The product is further
treated in a degasifier
and mixed bed ion exchanger.

Figure 1a.   Plant flow diagram of a 1500 m³/D RO plant

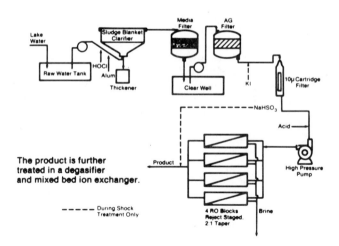

Figure 1b.   Plant flow diagram of a 1500 m³/D RO plant

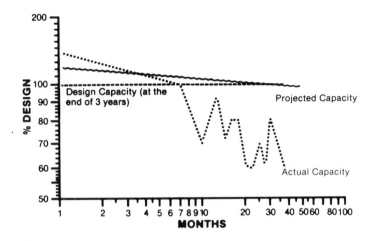

Figure 2a.   Plant performance history—productivity

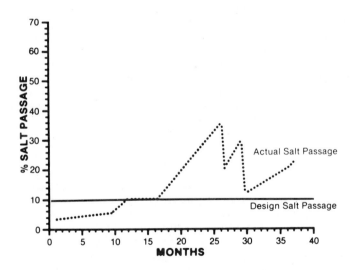

Figure 2b.   Plant performance history—salt passage

sheathed bacterium surrounded by a mass of precipitated iron, as
determined by the Prussian blue reaction (Ref. 2). This bacterium was isolated and later identified as Sphaerotilus natans.
S. natans is a common inhabitant of flowing water, and well
known for its ability to evolve large masses of cells capable of
clogging water distribution and discharge systems. It has the
ability to attach itself to surfaces, thereby avoiding being
swept away (Ref. 3, 4).

      S. natans is a heterotroph and requires an environment
having dissolved organic matter, but of a generally low salinity,
in the range from 300 to 2000 mg/ℓ (4). This organism is
apparently not common to highly brackish waters. Based on
these data, we diagnosed the problem being experienced at the
"Permasep" installation as biological fouling, and undertook
laboratory field tests to evaluate effective, economical, and
environmentally compatible measures for controlling it in the
"Permasep" modules.

      The results of these predictive tests indicated that
intermittent iodine treatment would be useful in restricting the
growth of S. natans, and this method was chosen for a full plant
evaluation. During normal operation the raw water is chlorinated
(upon entering the pretreatment plant) such that the treated
water has five ppm of residual chlorine. Immediately prior to
the high pressure portion of the system the RO feed water is de-
chlorinated by the addition of sodium-metabisulfite. The
"Permasep" aramid membrane is adversely affected by the action of
strong oxidants such as hypochlorous acid, and the dechlorination
step is necessary to preserve membrane integrity (Ref. 5). It
was decided to effect generation of the iodine by injecting an
excess of a 10 percent solution of potassium iodide into the
chlorinated feed water, while at the same time halting the flow
of sodium-metabisulfite. This method gave a single step biocide
generation/dechlorination procedure, according to the following
equation:

$$2 \text{ KI} + \text{HOCl} + \text{HCl} \rightarrow \text{I}_2 + 2 \text{ KCl} + \text{H}_2\text{O}$$

      The handling of the biocide supply as the potassium salt
rather than in the elemental form circumvented the toxicological
and corrosive problems associated with iodine. In addition, the
sodium metabisulfite stream is available to reduce the iodine
in the product stream prior to demineralization in the mixed bed
ion exchanger.

      Biological fouling was monitored using the customary indica-
tors of RO performance, including flux (productivity), salt
passage, and bundle pressure drops (ΔP). In addition, the total
bacteria count (TBC) of the RO feed water and the reject brine
stream were also obtained using the membrane filtration method
(Ref. 6). The increase in TBC between the feed and reject portions of the system had been found in the preliminary stages of

testing to provide a reasonable and sensitive measure of plant performance. Initially the iodine addition was for one hour every day, but was gradually reduced, towards the completion of the test to one-half hour every second day. Similarly, chlorine was provided to a residual of 5 ppm, but then dropped to 2.5 ppm towards the end. The drop in chlorine residual from 5.0 to 2.5 ppm reduced the iodine level from approximately 18 ppm to 10 ppm. Preliminary testing using this method of iodine generation showed that 4 ± 1 ppm of chlorine gave 14 ± 1 ppm of iodine. The generation of iodine by this method is nearly 100 percent of theoretical.

The plant demonstration was scheduled to operate for a three month period, using one-half of the total capacity. One block (36 permeators) consisted of entirely new four-inch units ("Permasep" Model 0440-042), while a second block still had the permeators that had been installed two years earlier and which were operated during the period of performance decline. A single four-inch permeator was operated on a separate small stand without biocide treatment. This permeator served as a positive control for the biofouling capability of the RO feed water.

The results of this plant demonstration in Figures 3a through 3d show the successful operation of the "Permasep" unit using water that has a high capability for causing biological fouling. The data in Figure 3b show that the salt passage of both blocks of permeators remained remarkably constant at 5 percent for the new permeators and 20 percent for the existing ones. The control permeator experienced a sudden and significant increase of from 5 to nearly 50 percent, beginning on the fiftieth day.

A second parameter of RO performance observed to have been seriously impaired during previous operation of the plant is flux, or productivity (Figure 2a). The flux of the block having the new permeators exhibited the expected initial flux decline seen when new units are first operated (Figure 3a), but this decline was well within projected figures (1). The flux of the old permeators remained constant during the same period, whereas that of the control permeator decreased more than projected. The pressure drop of these blocks and the test permeator are shown in Figure 3c. This parameter was essentially stable and constant for the permeators receiving iodine, whereas the pressure drop of the control permeator had increased nearly fourfold at the end of the test.

The TBC measurements in Figure 3d are reported as $\log_{10}$ values. The $\log_{10}$ TBC of the RO feed water was 0.81 ± 0.98 during the test, while the TBC observed in the reject stream of the new permeators was 2.45 ± 0.74 and for the older permeators was 3.68 ± 0.73. The control permeator had a mean TBC level of 4.94 ± 0.75. These differences in the TBC between the RO feed water and reject streams effectively measured the biocide treatment, and reflected overall RO performance.

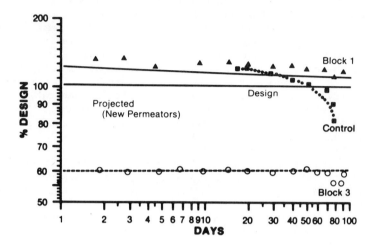

Figure 3a.   Plant test—productivity

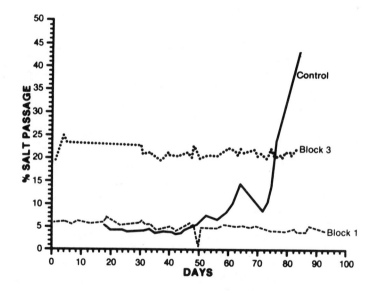

Figure 3b.   Plant test—salt passage

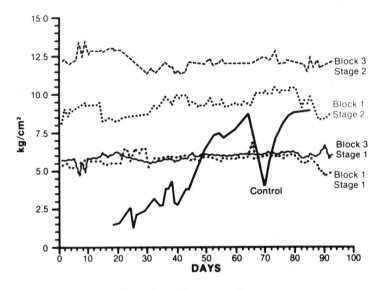

Figure 3c.   Plant test—ΔP

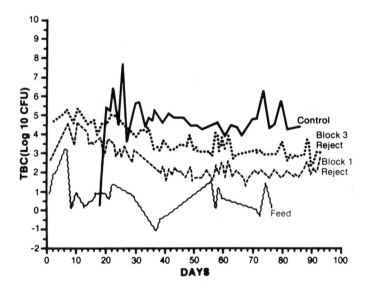

Figure 3d.   Plant test—TBC

The effect of the iodine biocide on the aramid fibers was determined by using fibers taken from a permeator previously exposed to this agent during tests. It was found that these fibers retained most of their physical strength, and the resulting damage should not significantly alter the life of the membrane. The much slower reaction of the aramid fiber with iodine than with chlorine has been shown before (7) and most likely derives from the different dissociation constants, K_d. For hypoiodous acid at the conditions used in the RO plant $K_d = 4.5 \times 10^{-13}$ compared with $K_d = 2.9 \times 10^{-8}$ for hypochlorous acid.

In summary, we have demonstrated the successful operation of a "Permasep" RO plant on biologically active feed waters by using the intermittent injection of iodine as a bacterial control measure. The use of this shock procedure allowed for steady, continuous performance of the plant and is expected to have significant impact on future applications of PA membranes to biological action as well as waste waters.

Literature Cited

1. Langelier, W. F., "The Analytical Control of Anti-Corrosion Water Treatment", J. Am. Water Works Assoc. 28, 1936, 1500-1521.
2. Standard Methods for the Examination of Water and Waste Water XIV Edition - APHA, AWWA, WPCF, Part 918A, 997.
3. Donders, N.C., Adv. Appl. Microbiol. 3, 1961, 77
4. Van Veen, W. L., Mulder, E. G., Deinema, M. H., Microbiol. Rev. 42, 1978, Chapter 16, 343-369.
5. Caracciolo, V. P., Rosenblatt, N. W., Tomsic, V. J., S. Sourirajan Reverse Osmosis and Synthetic Membranes N.R.C.C. 1977, Chapter 16, 343-369.
6. Standard Methods fot the Exahmiation of Water and Waste Water XIV Edition - APHA, AWWA, WPCF, Part 909, 928 and following.
7. Glater, J., Effect of Halogens on Performance and Durability of RO Membranes, presented at 2nd Chemical Congress of the North American Continent, Las Vegas, 1980.

RECEIVED December 4, 1980.

The Effect of Fluid Management on Membrane Filtration

M. C. PORTER

Nuclepore Corporation, 7035 Commerce Circle, Pleasanton, CA 94566

The advent of the Loeb-Sourirajan asymmetric membrane some twenty years ago gave birth to an industry now exceeding 200 million dollars in annual sales. Reverse osmosis (RO) and ultra-filtration (UF) were previously only laboratory curiosities. To-day, there are many large membrane plants (up to 16 million gal-lons per day) in service for applications as diverse as desalinat-ing seawater; concentrating serum proteins, or the recovery of paint and other by-products from waste streams.

The break-through made by Loeb and Sourirajan was the for-mation of a relatively thin skin (0.1 to 2 μm) on the surface of a more open sponge-like structure (Figure 1) which offers reduced resistance to flow while still maintaining the retention required. However, the structure of these membranes precludes use in a con-ventional "flow-through" filtration mode due to the accumulation of retained species on the surface, rather than throughout the matrix of the filter (Figure 2). In the "flow-through" mode, the membrane will "plug" or "foul" much more rapidly than a conven-tional depth filter because the particle/solute loading capacity is less.

However, if the particulates or solutes accumulated on the surface can be dispersed back into the bulk fluid, these mem-branes can be used to great advantage since there is relatively little if any "internal-fouling" of the membrane structure. There is a high probability that a molecule or particle which penetrates the skin will not be trapped within the filter structure but will pass through into the filtrate. Schematically, the pores may be represented by ever-widening cones with no internal constrictions to restrain molecules or particles.

Since the successful exploitation of these membranes has been largely dependent on effective fluid-management techniques, it seemed appropriate for this symposium to review developments in this field over the last twenty years.

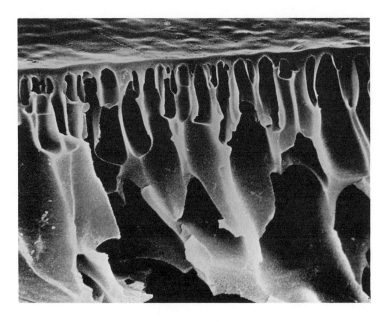

Figure 1.   Cross-section of Type A asymmetric UF membrane from a Nuclepore

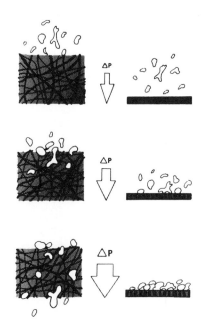

Figure 2.   Accumulation of particulates through the matrix of a depth filter and on the surface of an asymmetric membrane

Control of Concentration Polarization With Stirring and Cross-Flow
Techniques

    The simplest laboratory apparatus for reducing the accumula-
tion of retained species on the membrane (sometimes referred to
as concentration polarization) is still the stirred cell (Figure
3). Stable flux values may be obtained by a magnetically driven
stirring bar suspended above the membrane; otherwise, the flux
declines rapidly. It is interesting to note that one of the
first industrial UF units offered by ABCOR was a one foot diameter drum with a high-speed reciprocating stirrer located between
two one-foot diameter membranes to minimize concentration
polarization (Figure 4) (1).

    Currently, the most common fluid management technique used
in industry is "cross-flow" through tubes or channels with the
fluid velocity tangential to the membrane surface (Figure 5).
The hydrodynamic shear forces at the membrane surface tend to reduce the boundary layer and keep the membrane clean.

    In reverse osmosis, where the solutes retained are relative-
ly low in molecular weight and have a significant osmotic pressure, concentration polarization can result in osmotic pressures
considerably higher than those represented by the bulk stream
concentration. Higher pressures are required to overcome the osmotic pressure   (Figure 6).

$$J_w = \frac{\Delta P - \Delta \Pi}{R_m} \tag{1}$$

where J_w is the water flux through the membrane, ΔP is the transmembrane pressure drop, $\Delta \Pi$ is the osmotic pressure difference
across the membrane, and R_m is the membrane resistance to permeation. Thus, higher cross-flow velocities adjacent to the membrane will tend to decrease the boundary layer and the polarization modulus $\frac{C_s}{C_b}$ where C_s is the concentration of retained species
at the surface of the membrane and C_b = bulk stream concentration
of the retained species. The net result is to increase the flux
and reduce the salt passage through the membrane-which is more
dependent on C_s than on C_b.

    For ultrafiltration, the macromolecular solutes and colloid-
al species usually have insignificant osmotic pressures. In
this case, the concentration at the membrane surface (C_s) can
rise to the point of incipient gel precipitation, forming a dynamic secondary membrane on top of the primary structure (Figure 7).
This secondary membrane can offer the major resistance to flow.

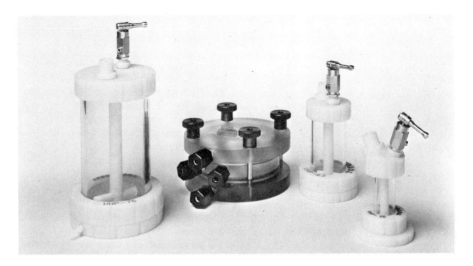

Figure 3.   Conventional stirred-cells

*Figure 4.   ABCOR drum ultrafilter with
high-speed reciprocating stirrer (1)*

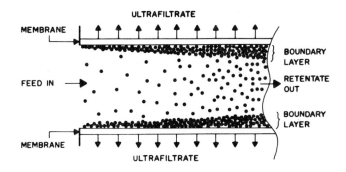

Figure 5. Crossflow fluid management in tubular membrane configuration

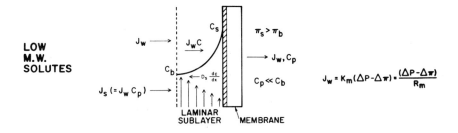

Figure 6. Concentration polarization with RO membranes

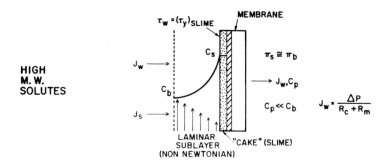

Figure 7. Concentration polarization with UF membranes

In the steady-state condition, this "gel-layer", as it is
sometimes called, will grow in thickness until the pressure-act-
ivated convective transport of solute with solvent toward the
membrane surface ($J_w C$) just equals the concentration gradient-
activated diffusive transport away from the surface $D_s \frac{dc}{dx}$ (Figure 8).

In cases where the limiting resistance to flow is the "gel-
layer" and the concentration at the membrane surface (C_s) is
fixed at a constant gel concentration (C_g), this simple differential equation:

$$J_w C = D_s \frac{dc}{dx} \tag{2}$$

may be solved to yield the result

$$J_w = \frac{D_s}{\delta} \ln \frac{C_g}{C_b} = k \ln \frac{C_g}{C_b} \tag{3}$$

where δ is the boundary layer thickness, and k is the mass-transfer coefficient. Thus, under gel-polarized conditions, the water
flux (J_w) is invariant with transmembrane pressure drop or permeability and is dependent only on the boundary layer thickness
(δ) and solute properties such as diffusivity (D_s) and gel concentration (C_g).

The invariance with pressure is demonstrated in Figure 9.
Above some threshold pressure, flux becomes independent of pressure. Any increase in pressure will cause a transient increase
in flux which results in more solute transport to the membrane.
Since the gel-concentration (C_g) cannot increase and the back-
diffusive transport away from the membrane is unchanged, an accumulation of solute at the membrane will thicken the gel-layer
and increase resistance to flow until the flux is reduced to its
former value. It is also obvious from Figure 9 that the back-
diffusive transport controls the flux through the membrane. Increasing the stirrer speed improves the mass transport away from
the membrane by reducing the boundary layer thickness (δ). Lower
bulk stream concentrations (C_b) improve the mass transport by increasing the concentration gradient. Lower concentrations become
gel-polarized at higher threshold pressures.

Equation 3 indicates that a semilog plot of flux against
concentration should be a straight-line intercepting the horizontal axis at the gel concentration (C_g). When the bulk-stream
concentration (C_b) equals the gel concentration (C_g) there is no
driving force for removal of solute from the membrane. The gel
layer increases in thickness until the flux is zero. Figure 10
provides experimental confirmation for a number of protein solutions and colloidal suspensions (2). The intercepts with the
horizontal axis are reasonable values for the gel concentration.

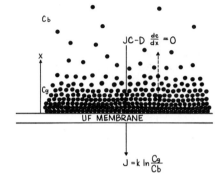

Figure 8.   *Steady-state gel polarization model*

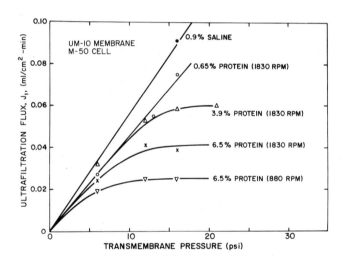

Figure 9.   *Flux–pressure data for BSA*

Proteins often form gels at concentrations between 20 and 30 percent. Likewise the "gel concentration" for colloidal particles should be equivalent to a value for close-packed spheres between 60 and 75 percent.

Higher tangential veloceties (or recirculation rates) should decrease the boundary layer thickness (δ) and increase the mass transfer coefficient (k) in Equation 3 resulting in higher slopes of the flux vs concentration curve (Figure 11) without changing the gel-concentration.

Even with effective cross-flow fluid-management techniques, membrane flux will usually decay with time due to tenacious deposits on the membrane surface. It has been observed that the rate of decay is minimized with high tangential velocities. Further, detergent cleaning of membrane surfaces is accelerated by higher tangential velocities (Figure 12) (3).

It should be obvious from the above that fluid-management techniques which improve the mass-transfer coefficient (k) with minimum power consumption are most desirable. However, in some cases, low-cost membrane configurations with inefficient fluid management may be more cost effective. In any case, it is important to understand quantitatively how tangential velocity and membrane/hardware geometry affects the mass-transfer coefficient.

The mass and heat transfer analogies make possible an evaluation of the mass-transfer coefficient (k) and provide insight into how membrane geometry and fluid-flow conditions can be specified to optimize flux (4). For laminar flow:

$$k = 1.62 \frac{U^{0.33} D^{0.67}}{d_h^{0.33} L^{0.33}} \tag{4}$$

where U = tangential fluid velocity
d_h = equivalent hydraulic diameter of the tube or channel
L = channel or tube length

For turbulent flow:

$$k = 0.02 \frac{U^{0.08} D^{0.67}}{d_h^{0.2} \nu^{0.47}} \tag{5}$$

where ν is the kinematic viscosity

Equations 4 and 5 have been used to predict flux values for a variety of macromolecular solutions and channel geometries (4). The theoretical values were in good agreement with the experimental values. Figure 13 illustrates the 0.33 power dependence on wall shear rate per unit channel length ($U/d_h L$).

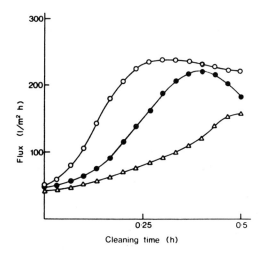

Figure 12.   The effect of detergent circulation rate (○, 1.51L/s, ●, 1.14L/s, △, 0.57L/s) and time on Flux (3)

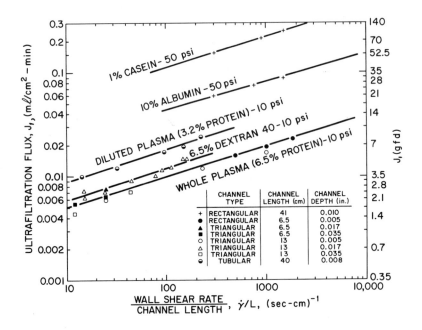

Figure 13.   Flux dependence on wall shear rate in laminar flow

Membrane-Hardware Geometry

The considerations above have been utilized by various manu-facturers in designing efficient ultrafiltration and reverse os-mosis equipment.

The most straight forward and trouble-free geometry is a simple tubular configuration (see Figure 14) with diameters large enough to pass all extraneous matter. As a practical matter, one-inch tubes may be easily cleaned by sponge-rubber balls which are forced through the tubes with hydraulic pressure. The disadvan-tages are cost and volume per unit area.

Plate and frame systems offer a great deal of flexibility in obtaining smaller channel dimensions. Equations 4 and 5 show that the increased hydrodynamic shear associated with relatively thin channels improves the mass-transfer coefficient. Membrane replace-ment costs are low but the labor involved is high. For the most-part, plate and frame systems have been troublesome in high-pres-sure reverse osmosis applications due to the propensity to leak. The most successful plate and frame unit from a commercial stand-point is that manufactured by The Danish Sugar Corporation Ltd. (DDS) (Figure 15).

The labor intensive replacement of membranes in plate and frame systems has been facilitated in the "leaf-module" design of Dorr Oliver   (Figure 16). Here a number of plates are as-sembled in a disposable cartridge where the process stream flows over the plates and the permeate is ducted to a common header.

Tubular systems can also be converted to thin-channel devices with the use of "volume displacement rods". In one such design (7), manufactured by Amicon and Romicon, a splined core has the membrane wrapped around it, sealed, and braided to form thin-channels between the core and the membrane (Figure 17). These braided tubes are then potted in a shell and tube module where the permeate is collected on the shell side (Figure 18).

As with any restricted channel system, strainers or pre-filters must be provided to remove debris which would otherwise clog the channels. Thin-channel tubular modules such as that pictured in Figure 18 provide extremely high flux-values at high tangential velocities. However, to achieve maximum performance, the power requirements for pumping are high; this is partially due to large "parasite drag" associated with the splined core.

The advent of hollow fiber membranes provided a low-cost membrane element with negligible parasite drag. In the case of ultrafiltration, optimum fluid management dictated flowing the process stream down through the lumen of the hollow-fiber (Figure 19); the skin is on the inside wall. This is not possible for reverse osmosis due to the high pressure of the process stream; in this case, the feed stream is on the outside of the hollow fiber and the permeate flows through the fiber lumen   (Figure 20).

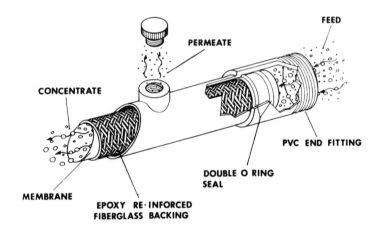

Figure 14.   ABCOR 1-in. tube (1)

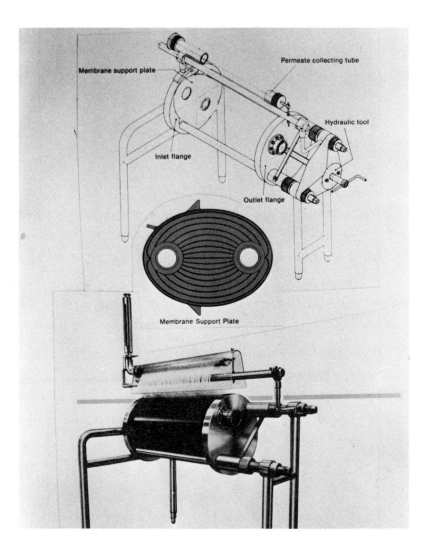

Figure 15.   DDS plate and frame UF module (5)

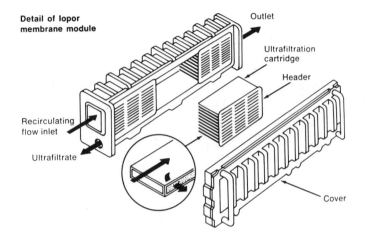

Figure 16.   Dorr Oliver leaf-module design (6)

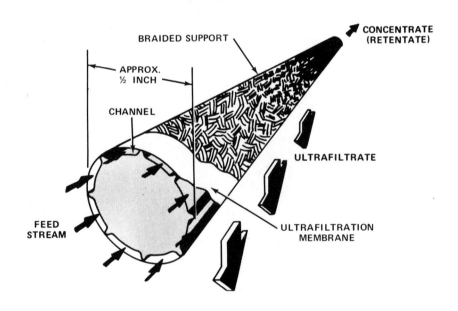

American Institute of Chemical Engineers Symposium Series

Figure 17.   Thin-channel tube with splined core (7)

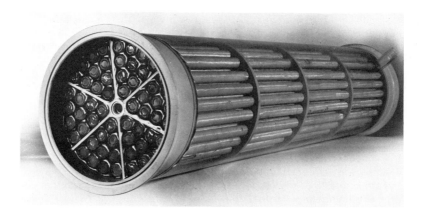

American Institute of Chemical Engineers Symposium Series

Figure 18. Thin-channel tubular module (7)

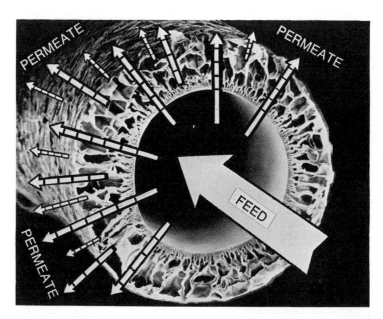

Figure 19. Nuclepore Type A UF hollow-fiber showing the direction of flow

Ultrafiltration hollow-fiber modules are usually made with a shell and tube configuration. The fibers are potted at both ends of the module with the fiber lumen open for recirculation of the process stream (Figure 21). Naturally, strainers or prefilters must be utilized to eliminate plugging of the fibers. At Nucle- pore, it has been shown that larger diameter hollow fibers, 1.5 to 3mm in i.d., are much less prone to fouling. Fortunately, all UF hollow fiber systems can be back-washed and are amenable to a number of cleaning techniques.

The basic membrane/hardware geometries-tubes, plate and frame, and hollow fibers can of course all be operated with fluid management techniques which are relatively efficient or non-effi- cient. The remainder of this paper will adress itself to novel fluid-management techniques which utilize the basic membrane/hard- ware geometries but which seek to augment the mass-transfer coef- ficient even further.

Pulsed-Flow Fluid Management

Kennedy et al (8) have achieved permeation increases of more than 70 percent while concentrating sucrose solutions with reverse osmosis by superimposing a harmonic pulse generator (Figure 22) on the normal flow down a 1.31 cm i.d. tubular membrane. Typical re- sults are shown in Figure 23. This study suggests that pulsed re- verse osmosis may offer a more economical means for reducing mem- brane area. Kennedy calculated that to duplicate the 80 percent permeation increase of Figure 23 by the conventional means would require a six-fold increase in velocity.

At Nuclepore, we have found that a hollow-fiber module (Fig- ure 24) can be operated in a dead-ended, through-flow mode on tap water with a 30 minute cleaning pulse every 24 hours to restore flux (Figure 25). The exit valve at the end of the unit pic- tured in Figure 24 is simply opened up to flush out the inside of the hollow fibers. With DI water, the cleaning pulse was not re- quired until after one-week of operation. This fluid management technique eliminates the need for pumps or power; the result is a small compact unit useful in removing bacteria or pyrogens.

Turbulence Promoters

Considerable interest has been generated in turbulence pro- moters for both RO and UF. Equations 4 and 5 show considerable improvements in the mass-transfer coefficient when operating UF in turbulent flow. Of course the penalty in pressure drop incur- red in a turbulent flow system is much higher than in laminar flow. Another way to increase the mass-transfer is by introducing tur- bulence promoters in laminar flow. This procedure is practiced extensively in enhanced heat-exchanger design and is now exploited in membrane hardware design.

HOLLOW FIBER PRINCIPLE

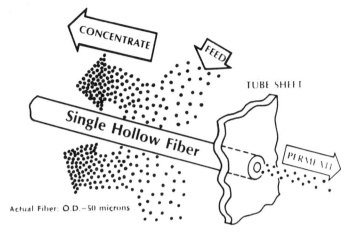

Figure 20.   RO hollow-fiber showing direction of flow

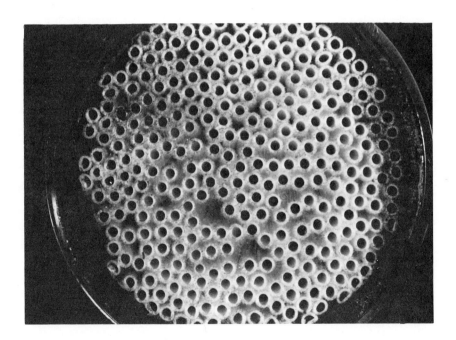

Figure 21.   Nuclepore hollow-fiber module end potting

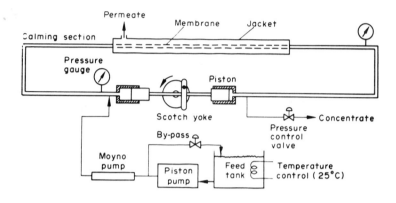

Chemical Engineering Science

Figure 22.   Schematic of pulsed-flow RO equipment (8)

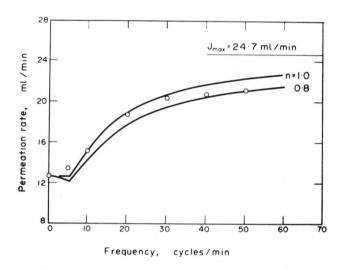

Chemical Engineering Science

Figure 23.   RO permeation rate as a function of pulsing frequency (8)

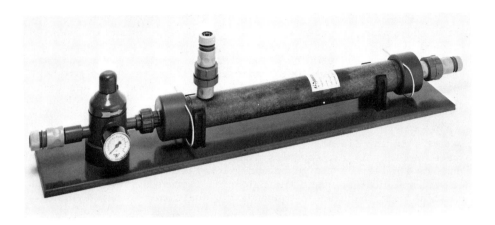

Figure 24. Nuclepore BST-1 hollow-fiber module

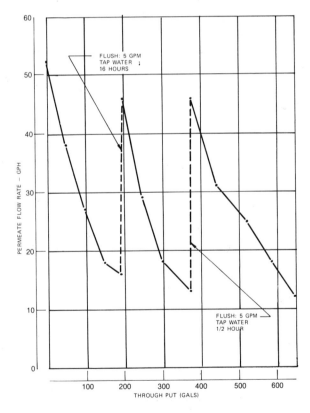

Figure 25. Tap water flux decay and regeneration with flush on BST-1

Thomas and Watson (9) of the Oak Ridge National Laboratory have shown that detached spiral wire turbulence promoters, positioned away from an RO membrane surface by small wire runners, markedly increased the rejection of salts and the permeation rate through the membrane. "Detached promoters" of this type may be designed to minimize stagnant regions; in addition, they are relatively easy to install.

Figure 26 presents their results for the rejection of 0.01 M $MgCl_2$ at 400 psi on a dynamic membrane as a function of $\frac{v}{U}(N_{Re}^{0.25})$ where U is the linear velocity down the tube, v is the permeation rate, and N_{Re} is the Reynolds number. It will be noted that the greatest effect of the turbulence promoter was observed at the lowest velocities, where the rejection increased from 25 to 72 percent. At the highest tangential velocities, the improvement was much less, from 90 to 93 percent. In addition, Thomas and Watson observed an increase in permeation rate varying from 10 to 50 percent. Thus, with turbulence promoters, the same rejection and flux, as in an unpromoted system, may be obtained at a considerable reduction.

Probstein et al (10) investigated the use of detached strip type turbulence promoters in the ultrafiltration of bovine serum albumin in laminar flow. His apparatus is shown in Figure 27; the detached strip type promoters tested were circular cylinders with a diameter (D) approximately one-half (0.46) of the channel height and were across the center of the channel cross-section, transverse to the flow.

Typical flux data with two interpromoter spacings (ΔL) are shown in Figure 28 as a function of the cross-flow rate. The flux increased by a factor of 3 for the best case. Though Probstein did not plot his data in this way, it is interesting to note that the empty channel flux has a predictable 0.33 power dependence on tangential velocity. With the turbulence promoters, the slope shifts closer to the 0.7-0.8 power dependence normally observed in turbulent flow. Unfortunately, data are not available in Probstein's paper on the increased pressure drop associated with the turbulence promoters, but it would appear that the flux to power ratio is greatly improved with turbulence promoters.

In current practice, turbulence promoters most often take the form of a net or screen material which also serves as a feed channel spacer between two membranes. For example, the familiar spiral wound modules (Figures 29) used extensively in reverse osmosis and to a lesser extent in ultrafiltration use a plastic screen material as the feed channel spacer. This is also used in some plate and frame systems (Figure 30).

Spherical turbulence promoters have also been used in tubular systems (Figure 31). In the author's experience, these spherical promoters are not as effective as detached spiral wire promoters (9). Particles collect in the dead stagnant areas between the spheres and foul the system. The spheres serve more effectively as volume displacement spheres than as turbulence promoters.

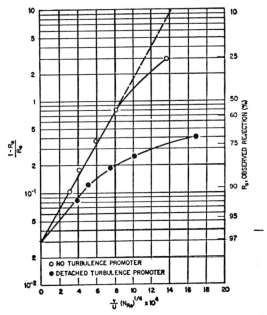

Industrial and Engineering Chemistry
Process Design & Development

Figure 26. Effect of detached spiral turbulence promoters on rejection of 0.01 MgCl₂ at 400 psi (9)

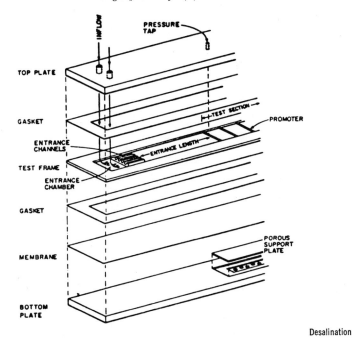

Desalination

Figure 27. Probstein's apparatus for investigating the effect of turbulence promoters in laminar-flow UF (10)

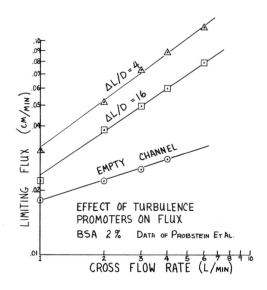

Figure 28.   Effect of turbulence promoters on flux in UF of BSA (10)

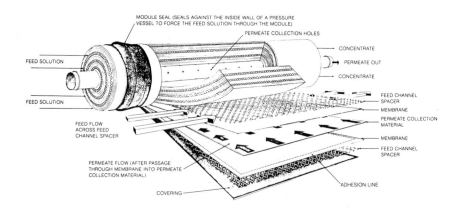

Figure 29.   Spiral-wound module construction (1)

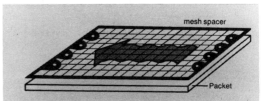

Figure 30.   Plate-and-frame cassette system using a screen spacer between membranes (11)

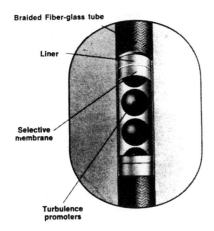

Figure 31.   Spherical turbulence promoters (1)

Static Mixers

A disadvantage of many of the inserts used for turbulence promotion is the high pressure-drop and/or stagnant regions associated with their obstructive nature. Middleman et al (13) (14) have studied the use of static mixers - a twisted tape insert (Figure 32) with alternating right and left-hand pitch which minimizes the two drawbacks noted above. Static mixers set up a helical flow-pattern, which establishes secondary flows (perpendicular to the main direction of flow). Further, the periodic alternation of the flow generates vortices which further enhance mass-transfer in the neighborhood of the tube wall.

The insertion of a static mixer in a 0.53 inch RO tubular membrane, for feed concentrations of 0.08 to 0.35m NaCl, showed an increase in flux of about 25 percent at N_{Re}=20 and of 266 percent at N_{Re}=1500.

The flux improvement was even more dramatic in the case of ultrafiltration. A one-inch tube was used to ultrafilter a 1 percent polymer latex emulsion. Figure 33 shows the improvement in flux at various Reynolds numbers with the static mixer and Figure 34 shows the ratio of fluxes (promoted/empty tube) as a function of Reynolds number.

The results are consistent with the expected behavior of the static mixer. At very low Reynolds numbers, the swirling flow generated by the mixer is insufficient to alter convection at the membrane surface to any appreciable degree. At very high Reynolds numbers, the level of turbulence in the unpromoted tube is so high that the addition of a swirling component of flow does not bring about a major reduction in the gel layer resistance. Hence, there is an intermediate Reynolds number where the flux ratio is maximized. Figure 34 shows a maximum flux ratio of 4.9 at a Reynolds number of 10^4.

Secondary Flow

One of the benefits of static mixers like those mentioned above are the secondary flow patterns set up by the swirling helical flow.

Secondary flow, i.e. flow perpendicular to the main direction of flow also occurs whenever fluid passes through a curved tube or channel. The phenomenon is caused by centrifugal forces, and can be readily understood by referring to Figure 35, the cross-section of a helically coiled tube. Near the tube's center the axial velocity is greatest, causing centrifugal forces to act most strongly. Fluid is thrown outward and replaced by recirculating fluid which flows inward along the walls. In both laminar and turbulent flow, two strong symmetrical patterns are normally established.

Figure 32.   Kenics Stype static mixer (12)

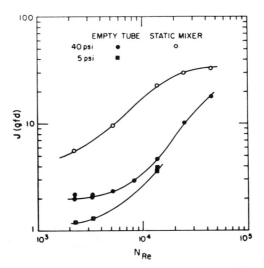

Industrial and Engineering Chemistry
Process Design & Development

Figure 33.   Improvement in UF flux on 1% polymer latex with static mixers (13)

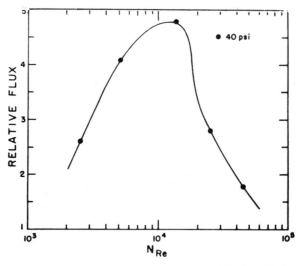

Industrial and Engineering Chemistry
Process Design & Development

*Figure 34.   Ratio of fluxes (with and without a static mixer) as a function of the
Reynolds number (1% polymer latex) (13)*

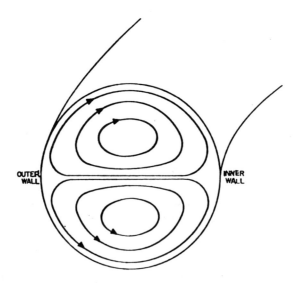

Figure 35.   Secondary flow patterns in the cross-section of a helically coiled tube

It is well known ($\underline{15}$, $\underline{16}$, $\underline{17}$) that coiled tube heat exchangers possess superior heat transfer characteristics because of secondary flow effects. At small curvatures, the Dean number, defined as $N_{De} = N_{Re}\sqrt{\frac{a}{R}}$ where a and R are tube and coil radii respectively, governs the transport processes in coiled tubes, higher Dean numbers causing higher transport rates. Dravid et al ($\underline{17}$) has shown experimentally that the heat transfer coefficient in a coiled tube varies as $N_{De}^{0.55}$ in the fully developed region of the boundary layer.

By analogy, the mass-transfer coefficient for laminar flow in spiral or coiled channels should vary as $N_{De}^{0.5}$ rather than as $N_{Re}^{0.33}$ as predicted in equation 4 (see reference $\underline{4}$). UF data (human albumin-laminar flow) taken by the author in a spiral thin-channel unit (Figure 36) confirm the 0.5 power dependence on the Reynolds number (Figure 37) rather than the usual 0.33 power dependence predicted by equation 4 and observed experimentally in linear thin-channel units (Figure 38).

Srinivasan and Tien ($\underline{18}$) have made an analytical study on the mass-transfer characteristics of reverse osmosis in curved tubular membranes. The increase in mass-transfer due to secondary flow resulted in a substantial reduction in the wall concentration (the polarization modulus) for $N_{De}=100$ and a/R=0.01 (see Figure 39). Further, the production capacity (permeation rate) was markedly increased (see Figure 40).

In the reverse osmosis field, only one commerical design has exploited the effect of secondary flow and it is no longer available (Figure 41).

Particulate Scouring

Davies ($\underline{20}$) used powdered activated carbon in conjunction with ultrafiltration of activated sludge to adsorb soluble organic constituents which might otherwise pass through the membrane until the biomass can metabolize them. The reduction in effluent COD is shown in Figure 42.

An additional benefit of the activated carbon was the scouring of the membrane surface to remove membrane foulants. Not only was the exponential decay in flux arrested, the flux was restored to its inital value as shown in Figure 43.

Bixler and Rappe ($\underline{21}$) also obtained UF data showing that increased flux values could be obtained by introducing solid particulate materials into the process stream (Figure 44). Bixler argued that these particles augmented the back diffusion from the membrane surface by mixing of higher concentration solutes near the membrane with lower concentration solutes more remote. He also recognized the scouring action of the beads in cleaning the membrane.

This author has previously suggested that the mechanism of flux enhancement might be due to the "tubular pinch effect" ($\underline{4}$). The lower density (0.94 g/cc) MMA beads show less tendency to

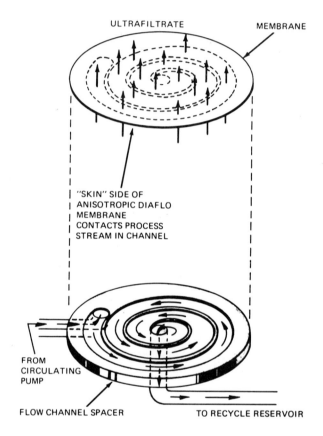

ULTRAFILTRATE   MEMBRANE

"SKIN" SIDE OF
ANISOTROPIC DIAFLO
MEMBRANE
CONTACTS PROCESS
STREAM IN CHANNEL

FROM
CIRCULATING
PUMP

FLOW CHANNEL SPACER   TO RECYCLE RESERVOIR

Industrial and Engineering Product
Research & Development

Figure 36.   Spiral thin-channel unit (4)

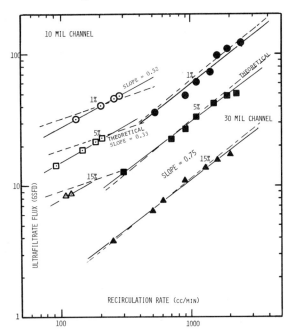

Industrial and Engineering Product
Research & Development

Figure 37.   UF flux as a function of recirculation rate for UF of HSA in a spiral thin-channel unit (4)

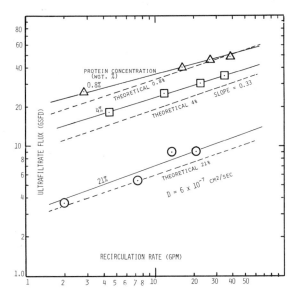

Industrial and Engineering Product
Research & Development

Figure 38.   UF flux as a function of recirculation rate for UF of HSA in a linear thin-channel unit (4)

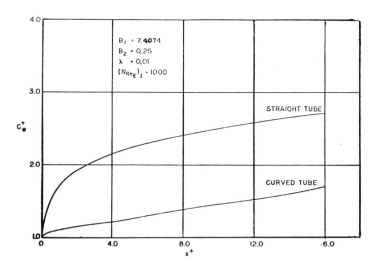

Figure 39. Wall concentration (dimensionless) vs. axial coordinate for straight and curved tubes (18)

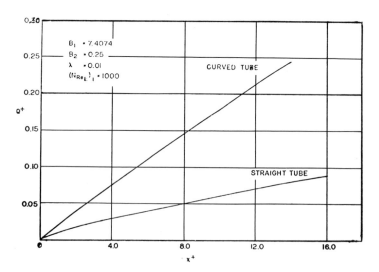

Figure 40. Production rate (dimensionless) vs. axial coordinate for straight and curved tubes (18)

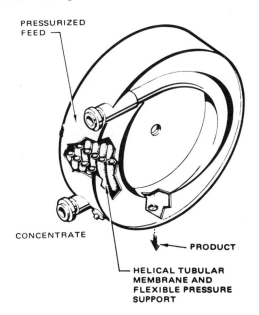

Figure 41.   Helical tubular membrane module (19)

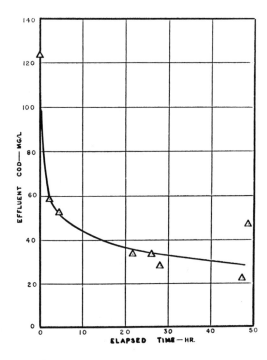

Figure 42.   Decline in effluent COD after addition of activated carbon

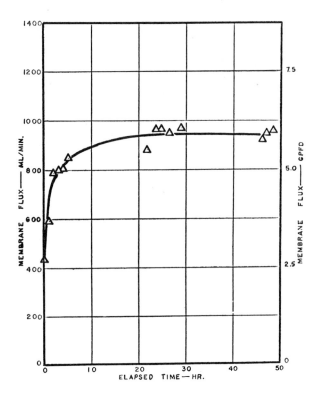

Figure 43. Restoration of flux by membrane scouring with activated carbon

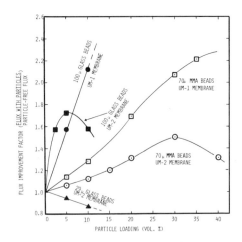

Figure 44. Flux improvement after introducing glass and MMA beads for UF of a 40,000 mol wt polysaccharide

settle on to the membrane surface and may never get there, resulting in a relatively inefficient use of the beads. The high-den-
sity (2.50g/cc) glass beads are more efficient provided the beads
are not too small. The "tubular pinch effect" predicts lower migration velocities away from the membrane for the smaller particles
and for higher concentrations. All of these mechanisms assume
that the particles pick up the solute by adsorption and provide
"facilitated transport" away from the membrane surface.

   Fluidized beds have also been used to promote mass-transfer
in both ultrafiltration and reverse osmosis. Smolders et al (22)
ran 18mm i.d. UF tubes and 12mm i.d. RO tubes with and without
fluidized beds (Ballotini glass spheres).

   In the case of RO, Smoulders saw very little change in the
flux, but the fluidized bed markedly improved the rejection for
NaCℓ (3000ppm)-see Figure 45. With the fluid bed, the axial velocity (pumping power) could be reduced significantly (80-95%) without sacrificing rejection. The maximum in the fluid bed rejection
curve is not unexpected considering the mechanics of fluidized
beds. As the axial velocity through a packed bed increases, the
bed expands-increasing the particle mobility and the mass-transfer
coefficient. At high velocities, particles begin to be entrained
out of the bed, and the concentration of particles begins to decrease enough to lower the nass-transfer coefficient.

   In Smolders ultrafiltration experiments, 4,000,000 mw polyethylene glycol was used as the solute (500ppm). Small particles
(0.5mm) in the fluidized bed failed to augment the flux to any
significant degree. Larger particles (2.0mm) resulted in a two-
fold increase in flux. Smolders concluded that the momentum of
the 0.5mm particles was insufficient to remove the gel-layer.

Cross-Flow Electrofiltration

   Many particles and/or macromolecules have a negative charge.
Consequently, a direct electric field can be used to cause these
species to migrate away from the membrane thereby augmenting the
mass-trnasfer coefficient obtained in normal cross-flow filtration
(see Figure 46).

   Henry et al (23) have collected experimental data on cross-
flow electro-filtration of Kaolin clay suspensious and oil-water
emulsions. Since both the Kaolin particles and the oil droplets
are negatively charged in aqueous suspensions, a direct electric
field will always give higher filtration rates than cross-flow
filtration alone. The level of improvement depends on the intensity of the fluid shear and the electric-field strength. Figures
47 and 48 present data for the increase in flux with electric
field strength for the oil-water emulsion and the clay suspension.

   One of the more curious phenomena associated with cross-flow
electrofiltration is that above some critical voltage (E_c), increases in the tangential velocity across the membrane may actually decrease the membrane flux (e.g. see Figures 49 and 50).

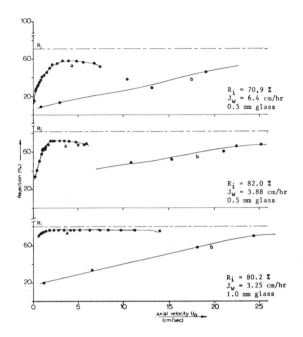

Figure 45.   Rejections for NaCl observed with (Curves a) and without (Curves b) a fluid-bed particulate scouring (22)

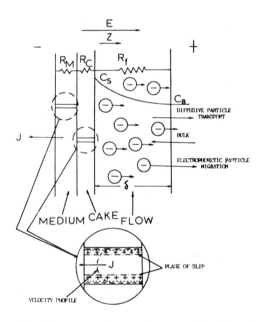

Figure 46.   Schematic of the crossflow electrofiltration concept

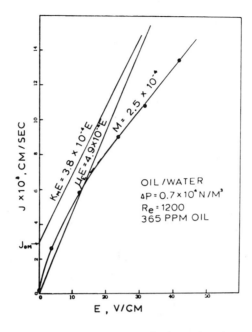

Figure 47. Increase in flux with electric field strength on oil–water emulsion (23)

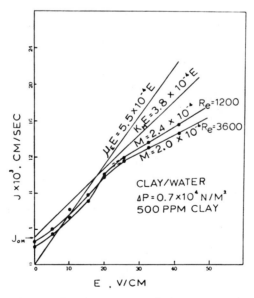

Figure 48. Increase in flux with electric field strength on clay suspension (23)

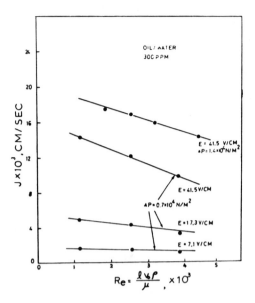

Figure 49.   Flux as a function of Reynolds number for crossflow electrofiltration of oil–water emulsions at several voltages (23)

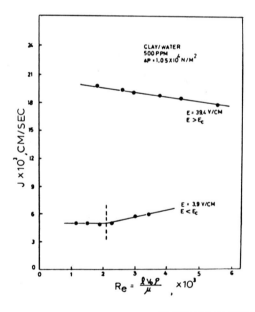

Figure 50.   Flux as a function of Reynolds number for crossflow electrofiltration of a clay suspension at two different voltages (23)

This can be explained by a model which is best understood by referring to Figure 51.

There are three operating regimes illustrated in Figure 51
where the applied voltage (E) is less than, equal to, or greater
than the critical voltage (E_c). The critical voltage is defined
as the voltage at which the net particle migration velocity toward
the membrane is zero, i.e. where the convective transport of particles toward the membrane is exactly equal to the electrophoretic
migration of particles away from the membrane.

Regime a) in Figure 51 exists when E is less than E_c. Concentration polarization still exists, but the electric field aug-
ments the back transport of particles away from the membrane
yielding higher flux values. In this regime, increases in the
tangential velocity will increase the flux (see Figure 50).

When the voltage is critical, regime b), there is no concentration polarization because the electrophoretic transport is
equal to the convective transport. Any build up of species on
the membrane will be dissipated due to diffusion driven by the
concentration difference. In this regime, increasing the tangential velocity is expected to have no influence on the flux because fluid shear can only improve the transport of particles
down a concentration gradient. In this case, there is no concentration gradient.

When the voltage is greater than the critical voltage, (regime c), the electrophoretic migration away from the membrane is
greater than the convective transport to the membrane. The concentration of particles at the membrane surface is depleted due
to removal by the electric field. In this case, increasing the
tangential velocity would be expected to decrease the flux because
the increased fluid shear improves the mass-transfer of particles
down the concentration gradient-in this case, toward the membrane
(see the data of Fitures 49 and 50).

In Figure 50, the lower curve for E=3.9 v/cm shows a transition in slope. The flux decreases with decreasing Reynolds numbers until a point is reached where the convective transport of
particles toward the membrane is just equal to the electrophoretic
migration away from the membrane-i.e. the voltage is now the critical voltage. Further decreases in the Reynolds number will not
decrease the flux as there is now no concentration polarization.

It should be noted that all of Henry's data were taken using
a 0.6 μm Nuclepore (capillary pore) membrane. Without the electric field, the oil droplets would not be retained by this pore
size. Indeed, this is why all of the data on oil-water emulsions
in Figure 49 were taken above the critical voltage-to avoid break
through. This suggests that many systems requiring ultrafiltration membranes at present can work with higher flow-rate microfiltration membranes. Since there is no gel layer at voltages
above the critical voltage, the membrane is the limiting resistance to flow and higher flow rate membranes are advantageous.

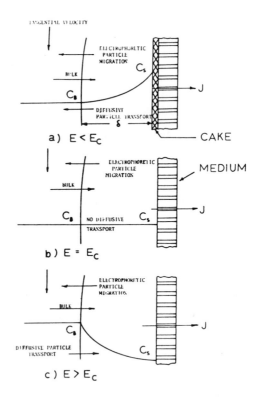

American Institute of Chemical Engineers Journal

Figure 51.   Three regimes of operation for crossflow electrofiltration (23)

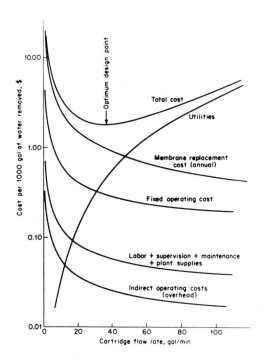

Figure 52.   Operating costs vs. recirculation rate for a crossflow UF plant

The cross-flow electrofilter has not been commercially exploited so far. However, it should find applications for suspensions or solutions of negatively charged species which have a low background ionic strength. Indeed, for shear sensitive particles, it may be advisable to dispense with cross-flow fluid management and to depend on eletrofiltration exclusively.

Conclusions For The Future

The choice of any of the fluid management techniques cited in this paper is largely a matter of economics. For example, the determination of optimum recircluation rate in a simple cross-flow tubular system must take into account the increased pumping power (utilities) required to produce higher flux values and reduced membrane replacement costs. Figure 52 shows the design point at the minimum in the total operating cost curve.

The increased energy costs of the future are expected to shift the design point of Figure 52 to the left-to lower recirculation rates.

Likewise, the increased pressure drop associated with some thin-channel systems, turbulence promoters, and static mixers must be weighed against the increased flux obtained.

It is the author's belief that systems utilizing low volumetric flow rates with minimized parasite drag, such as hollow fibers, will find increased use in the future.

In any event, it is also recognized that increased energy costs will dictate the use of membrane processes over competitive high energy processes such as distillation and evaporation. In this regard, we are indebted to Loeb and Sourirajan for a timely invention for the energy-scarce age we are now entering.

Symbols

a = tube radius
C = concentration of membrane-retained species
C_b = bulk stream concentration of membrane-retained species
C_g = gel concentration of retained species
C_p = concentration of solute in permeate
C_s = concentration of retained species at the surface of the membrane
C_w^+ = dimensionless wall concentration
D = diameter of wire used as turbulence promoter
d_h = equivalent hydraulic diameter
D_s = diffusivity or diffusion coefficient of retained species
E = electric field strength or voltage
E_c = critical voltage
J_s = solute flux to membrane surface ($=J_w C$)
J_w = water flux through membrane
k = mass-transfer coefficient
L = length of channel

ΔL = interpromoter spacing

N_{De} = Dean number = $N_{Re}\sqrt{\dfrac{a}{R}}$

N_{Re} = Reynolds number = $\dfrac{Ud_h}{\nu}$

ΔP = transmembrane pressure drop

Q^+ = dimensionless production rate

R = coil radius

R_c = resistance to permeation owing to cake or gel layer on membrane

R_m = resistance to permeation owing to membrane

R_o = observed rejection of membrane = $1-\dfrac{C_p}{C_b}$

U = fluid velocity down the channel or tube

v = permeation rate

x = distance from membrane surface

X^+ = dimensionless length

δ = boundary layer thickness

α = fluid shear rate at membrane surface = $\dfrac{U}{d_h}$

ν = kinematic vescosity = $\dfrac{\mu}{\rho}$

Π = osmotic pressure

$\Delta\Pi$ = osmotic pressure difference across membrane

Π_b = osmotic pressure with respect to bulk stream concentration (C_b)

Π_s = osmotic pressure with respect to concentration at membrane surface (C_s)

ρ = fluid density

Literature Cited

1. Abcor Product Literature
2. Porter, M.C., "What, When and Why of Membranes-MF, UF, and RO", A.I.Ch.E. Symp. Series No. 171, 1977, 73, 83-103
3. Parkin, M.F. and Marshall, K.R., "The Cleaning of Tubular Cellulose Acetate Ultrafiltration Membranes", N.Z. Journ. Dairy Sci. Technol., 1976, 11, 107-113
4. Porter, M.C., "Concentration Polarization with Membrane Ultra-filtration", Ind. Eng. Chem. Prod. Res. Develop.,1972, 11 (3), 234-248
5. DDS Product Literature
6. Dorr Oliver Product Literature
7. Porter, M.C., "Ultrafiltration of Coloidal Suspensions", A.I. Ch.E. Symp. Series No. 120, 1972, 68, 21-30
8. Kennedy, T.J.; Merson, R.L.; and McCoy, B.J.; "Improving PermeationFlux by Pulsed Reverse Osmosis", Chem. Eng. Science, 1974, 29, 1927-1931
9. Thomas, D.G. and Watson, J.S., "Reduction of Concentration Polarization of Dynamically Formed Hyperfiltration Membranes by Detached Turbulence Promoters", I & EC Process Design and Develop., 1968, 7, July, 397.

10. Probstein, R.F.; Shen, J.S.; and Leung, W.F.; "Ultrafiltra-
     tion of Macromolecular Solutions at High Polarization in
     Laminar Channel Flow", Desalination, 1978, 24, 1-16
11. Millipore Product Literature
12. Kenics Corp. Product Literature
13. Copas, A.L. and Middleman, S., "Use of Convection Promotion
     in the Ultrafiltration of Gel-Forming Solutes",Ind. Eng. Chem.
     Process Des. Develop., 1974, 13, 2, 143-145
14. Pitera, E.W. and Middleman, S., "Convection Promotion in Tub-
     ular Desalination Membranes", Ind. Eng. Chem. Process Des.
     Develop, 1973, 12, 52
15. Jeschke, D.; A Ver Deut Ing., 1925, 69, 1526
16. Kreith, F.; Trans. Am. Soc. Mech. Engrs., 1955, 77, 1247
17. Dravid, A.N.; Smith, K.A.; Merrill, E.W.; and Brian, P.L.T.;
     "The Effect of Secondary Fluid Motion on Laminar Flow Heat
     Transfer in Helically Coiled Tubes", paper presented at 68th
     National A.I.Ch.E. Meeting, Houston, Texas, 1971
18. Srinivasan, S., and Tien, C.; "Reverse Osmosis in a Curved
     Tubular Membrane Duct", Desalination, 1971, 9, 127-139
19. Philco-Ford Product Literature
20. Davies, D.S., "Carbon in Membrane Systems", U.S. Patent No.
     3,490,50, Jan. 20, 1970
21. Bixler, H.J. and Rappe, G.C., "Ultrafiltration Process", U.S.
     Patent No. 3,541,006, Nov. 17, 1970
22. Van der Waal, M.J.; Van der Velden, P.M.; Koning, J.; Smold-
     ers, C.A.; and Van Swaay, W.P.M.; "Use of Fluidized Beds as
     Turbulence Promoters in Tubular Membrane Systems", Desalina-
     tion, 1977, 22, 465-483
23. Henry, J.D.; Lawler, L.F.; and Kuo, C.H.A.; "A Solid/Liquid
     Separation Process Based on Cross Flow and Electrofiltration",
     A.I.Ch.E. Journal, 1977, 23, 6, 851-859

RECEIVED February 2, 1981.

INDEX

INDEX